Becoming Trauma Informed

Edited by
Nancy Poole
Lorraine Greaves

camh
Centre for Addiction and Mental Health

Library and Archives Canada Cataloguing in Publication

Becoming trauma informed / edited by Nancy Poole and Lorraine Greaves.

ISBN: 978-1-77114-058-4 (PRINT)
ISBN: 978-1-77114-059-1 (PDF)
ISBN: 978-1-77114-060-7 (HTML)
ISBN: 978-1-77114-061-4 (EPUB)

1. Psychic trauma—Patients—Care. 2. Psychic trauma—Patients—Mental health services.
3. Drug addiction—Treatment. 4. Mental illness—Treatment. I. Poole, Nancy. II. Greaves,
Lorraine. III. Centre for Addiction and Mental Health.

RC552.T7B42 2012   616.85'21   C2012-904264-1

Printed in Canada
Copyright © 2012 Centre for Addiction and Mental Health

This publication may be available in other formats. For information about alternative formats or
other CAMH publications, or to place an order, please contact Sales and Distribution:

Toll-free: 1 800 661-1111
Toronto: 416 595-6059
E-mail: publications@camh.ca
Online store: http://store.camh.net
Website: www.camh.ca

This book was produced by CAMH's Knowledge and Innovation Support Unit.

4566/09-2012/PG140

Contents

PART 1: WHAT IS "TRAUMA INFORMED" IN THEORY AND PRACTICE?

SECTION 1: THEORY

SECTION 2: PRACTICE

PART 2: TRAUMA-INFORMED PRACTICE FOR DIVERSE CLIENT GROUPS AND IN SPECIFIC SETTINGS

PART 3: CHANGING THE SYSTEM THROUGH EDUCATION AND INNOVATION

SECTION 1: EDUCATION

SECTION 2: INNOVATION

Acknowledgments

As with our previous collaboration on *Highs and Lows: Canadian Perspectives on Women and Substance Use*, developing this book has given us the opportunity to work with many wise and dedicated people across Canada and the United States. We wish to thank the contributors who were willing to share the lessons they were learning in the course of pioneering trauma-informed practices, and to devote many hours of their time to writing and responding to edits.

We profusely thank Julia Greenbaum, our publisher at the Centre for Addiction and Mental Health, for her wisdom, inspiration and trust. She has offered patient and important guidance and support throughout the development of this book. We will miss the warm Toronto gatherings where ideas were generated, debated and ultimately realized.

We also thank Diana Ballon and Hema Zbogar, who provided developmental and copy editing support respectively—not easy tasks with such complex subject matter. Diana patiently and expertly reviewed all of the submissions numerous times and asked many essential questions that led to more clarity and better reading. We appreciate all of these editing efforts.

We acknowledge the numerous projects and agencies that have nurtured and sustained our interests in trauma, violence, mental health and substance use; most important among these is the British Columbia Centre of Excellence for Women's Health, based in Vancouver.

We also thank the many reviewers who very generously volunteered their time to provide feedback on all or sections of this book: Christine Davis, Lynda Dechief, Suraya Faziluddin, Janine Gates, Colleen Kelly, Cheryl Peever, Elizabeth Poag, Wendy Reynolds, Laurie Robinson, Cheryl Rolin-Gilman, Lorrie Simunovic, Patti Socha and Graham Vardy.

We dedicate this book to the survivors of trauma who have experienced substance use and mental health concerns. We believe that increased understanding, services and support are directly needed to reduce trauma, violence and exploitation. We hope that this book will contribute to the development of a more comprehensive trauma-informed response in Canada and beyond.

Preface

Nancy Poole and Lorraine Greaves

Over the past few years, there has been growing recognition of the importance of considering trauma in the provision of mental health and substance use services.

Our experiences at the British Columbia Centre of Excellence for Women's Health (BCCEWH)—and with many partners across Canada interested in substance use and violence issues, particularly for women—have made us aware of how important it is for practitioners and services in different sectors to make the connections between the issues of trauma, violence, mental health and substance use. Only by making these connections can we deliver integrated or holistic care across health, social services, child welfare, justice and other sectors that responds to the many ways in which trauma influences people's lives.

In 2007/2008, BCCEWH was part of the Canadian National Treatment Strategy Working Group, sponsored by Health Canada and the Canadian Centre on Substance Abuse, which fostered discussion about tiered levels of support for people with substance use problems. It was clear that people with substance use issues were accessing a broad range of agencies and systems in services not identified as "treatment." At the same time, a key issue for many clients and practitioners was seeking support for trauma-related issues. Linking these often disparate services in the interests of serving people better became critical.

Our connections with the leaders of the Women, Co-occurring Disorders and Violence Study, sponsored by the Substance Abuse and Mental Health Services Administration in the United States, were important in shedding light on these complex issues. This key American study, which ran from 1998 to 2003, piloted integrated interventions across multiple sites for women with substance use and mental health concerns and histories of trauma and violence. The study found that comprehensive trauma-informed services could be effective without increased cost burden. These findings provoked us to think about how we might apply them to encourage similar improvements in service provision in Canada. This book is one part of our ongoing work in making some of those linkages and ideas come to life in the Canadian context.

Maxine Harris and Robert Fallot's book, *Using Trauma Theory to Design Service Systems* (2001), was also pivotal to our thinking. The authors articulated a systems-level approach to integrating responses to trauma into a range of systems: housing, mental health, anti-violence, primary care and addiction. Harris and Fallot introduced the idea of the importance of improvements at the systemic as well as individual service levels in providing effective support for people with experience of trauma, mental illness and addiction. We realized that a collective lack of understanding of trauma experiences rendered existing systems not very effective in providing services.

All of these resources and processes resonated with the situations we were encountering. But despite these books, studies and opportunities, it remained, and remains, a challenge to integrate trauma considerations into the range of mental health and substance use services in Canada. Nonetheless, there are numerous emerging examples of people and services working on the ground or thinking about these issues in their research and education. This book brings those voices together. Indeed, in editing it, we are intentionally sewing together some disparate activities and practices in substance use and mental health services and systems in Canada. In addition, we highlight some emerging trauma-informed practices in anti-violence and shelter services and increasingly understand how mental health and substance use issues are often the effects of abuse, violence and trauma.

Our goal is to encourage ourselves and others to move past simple cross-training between sectors or blending service provision in a "two-by-two" approach. Instead, we strive to initiate some higher-level considerations and examples of integrated design. We hope this book will serve as an impetus to further and ongoing development of trauma-informed service design and delivery in the Canadian context, especially, but not only, in substance use and mental health services.

Introduction

This guidebook is intended to support the work of practitioners in the substance use and mental health fields in Canada. It signals how a shift in the paradigm of our work in these fields is underway—a paradigm that recognizes how central the experience of trauma can be to those with whom we work, and that prompts us to be responsive to this reality at multiple levels. In this book, practitioners share their evolving approaches to shaping trauma-informed services for people with substance use and mental health concerns.

In Canadian mental health and addiction services, designing trauma-informed care, reflecting it in trauma-informed service and system design and developing research and evaluation to measure its impact are still an emergent practice. This book offers a range of examples of practitioner perspectives and organizational initiatives aimed at attaining these goals, and sets the stage for improving and developing design and practice in the coming years. The trauma-informed approaches described in this book will be relevant to a variety of readers, including practitioners working in community-based substance use and mental health programs, those employed in psychiatric settings and those who advocate and champion trauma-informed care through their work in program planning and organizational or staff development.

Why Trauma-Informed Care?

Trauma describes experiences that may overwhelm a person's capacity to cope. Traumatic events experienced early in life, such as abuse, neglect, witnessing violence and disrupted attachment, can be devastating. Equally challenging can be later life experiences that are out of one's control, such as violence, accidents, natural disaster, war, incarceration or sudden unexpected loss. These events can undermine or damage people's sense of safety, self and self-efficacy, as well as the ability to regulate emotions and navigate relationships. People who have experienced trauma often feel terror, shame, helplessness and powerlessness.

A substantial proportion of people who use mental health and substance use services have histories of trauma that contribute to their mental health and substance use problems, and affect their accessing of services and their recovery. A few examples of the connections:

The American Adverse Childhood Experiences study looked at the life histories of more than 17,000 people to determine the connections of adverse childhood experiences with health in adulthood (Anda et al., 2006). The researchers looked at eight categories of adverse childhood experiences relating to abuse and to growing up in dysfunctional households (including witnessing violence against the mother). They found that adverse childhood experiences were vastly more common than recognized and often involved multiple events and were directly linked to later life substance use and mental health problems and a range of chronic diseases (Anda et al., 2002; Anda et al., 2007). For example, the study found that women had a sixfold increased risk for recent depressive disorders when they reported five or more adverse childhood experiences (Chapman et al., 2004). The study also found that people who experienced five or more adverse childhood experiences were seven to 10 times more likely to report illicit drug use problems and addiction to illicit drugs (Dube et al., 2003). The authors note the profound implications for prevention but also for how we treat people for these conditions.

The links between women's experiences of violence and trauma and mental health and substance use problems are well documented in the literature (see, for example, Logan et al., 2002). A recent Canadian study involving six women's treatment centres from across the country found that 90 per cent of the women interviewed reported childhood or adult abuse histories in relation to their problematic use of alcohol (Brown, 2009). Data gathered at Canadian women's addiction treatment centres over the past decade confirm that a substantial proportion of women entering treatment for substance use problems have experienced violence and abuse as children and adults, underlining the need for an integrated response (Nicchols et al., 2009; Poole, 2007; Van Wyck & Bradley, 2007). Other Canadian studies have similarly identified a very high rate of sexual abuse among girls, and how, in turn, girls use substances to cope with trauma (Ballon et al., 2001). It is important to recognize the gendered, patterned and ongoing nature of these experiences.

Canadian substance use and mental health treatment providers are noting these connections and making service adaptations. In Chapter 15, Gloria Chaim, Susan Rosenkranz and Joanna Henderson note how the majority of youth accessing treatment at the Centre for Addiction and Mental Health's Youth Addictions and Concurrent Disorder Service have histories of traumatic stress (90 per cent of female clients and 62 per cent of males), as well as sexual abuse.

The prevalence of trauma experienced by men and its links to substance use and mental health problems is less well documented in Canada. In Chapter 13, Fallot and Bebout cite a 1995 source indicating that more than 50 per cent of men in the United States have been exposed to at least one traumatic event (Kessler et al., 1995). Service statistics from the Men's Trauma Centre in Victoria, B.C., indicate that among men seeking treatment and/or support for physical, sexual and emotional trauma in 2008, 32 per cent reported mental health problems and 50 per cent reported problems with alcohol and other drugs. Notably, 20 per cent of clients reported experiencing both mental health and substance use problems (Men's Trauma Centre, 2009).

For Aboriginal people, experiences of trauma are compounded by the inter-generational effects of trauma stemming from the legacy of Canada's residential schools. Unresolved historic trauma is reflected in high rates of complex posttraumatic stress disorder (PTSD), substance use, family disintegration, violence and suicide (Chansonneuve, 2005; Haskell & Randall, 2009; Wesley-Esquimaux & Smolewski, 2004). Research on the mental health outcomes of residential school survivors in British Columbia revealed that 64.2 per cent were diagnosed with PTSD, 26.3 per cent with substance abuse disorder and 21.1 per cent with major depression (Corrado & Cohen, 2003).

In short, there is compelling evidence that mental health and substance use problems are connected to people's experiences of violence, abuse and trauma. And as the chapters in this book illustrate, gender, race, class, culture, disability, immigration status and other forms of diversity interact to increase vulnerabilities related to trauma, and invite tailored responses.

Not only is trauma pervasive and connected to substance use and mental health problems; its impact can also be life-altering. In Chapter 1, Lori Haskell describes key neurobiological, psychological and psychosocial adaptations linked to the experience of developmental trauma. She identifies how early abuse can be a defining experience that shapes and distorts the core of a person's identity. She cautions that such adaptations to traumatic experiences —both early and in adulthood—can be missed or misdiagnosed when a trauma lens is not applied. Trauma affects people's sense of self and safety in the world, and greatly affects their confidence about accessing and continuing to receive assistance from service providers. Clients with trauma histories can be those most in need of support, yet most difficult to connect with.

Situating Trauma in Substance Use and Mental Health Practice

Early on, Judith Herman (1992) identified stages of trauma and healing in the context of understanding responses and recovery from sexual assault and violence against women, childhood physical and sexual abuse and neglect, witnessing violence, unexpected losses and many other life events, where previously the focus had centred on trauma arising from war and natural disasters. She articulated various stages of intense recovery, starting with safety, but including intense experiences of mourning and reconnection. Much of the current work on trauma-informed practice is grounded in Herman's insight regarding trauma survivors' needs to achieve a certain level of safety and stability before exploring the impact of their traumatic experiences in depth.

The mental health field has often identified trauma through a clinical diagnosis of PTSD—a diagnosis that often initiated treatment plans involving medication and other psychological or psychiatric interventions. For their part, early addiction treatment approaches often focused on intense, abstinence-oriented interventions, assuming that the route to recovery required a complete level of commitment and concomitant system design that accommodated and supported the single-focus approach.

Numerous shifts have occurred over the years, such as increased consumer engagement in mental health systems and the introduction of harm reduction principles within substance use treatment systems. Another shift has been to embrace recovery principles in treatment services that place clients at the centre of their treatment planning and care. For the substance use field, harm reduction–oriented practice has brought attention to how many people cannot or will not engage in abstinence-oriented treatment; yet these people deserve and benefit from less intensive and more accessible support to improve their health.

In the anti-violence field, a greater understanding of how violence, sexual assault and child sexual abuse produce short- and long-term effects on both women and men has slowly emerged in the past three decades. Anti-violence services recognized that existing approaches were not serving all women as well as they could, especially those with multiple issues such as substance use and mental health issues.

It has become evident that trauma is a useful concept for knitting together all of these experiences, services and systems. The important and ground-breaking Women, Co-occurring Disorders and Violence Study in the United States set out to explicitly address these intersections and to encourage or create system design improvements that could be evaluated.

The Need for Systemic Responses

Despite their importance, however, trauma-informed service and system design remain nascent in their definition and implementation within addiction and mental health settings. While there have been numerous important initiatives, the field remains in its early stages of development in Canada. Similarly, trauma- and substance-informed services in the anti-violence field are only slowly being built to respond to a wide range of needs emerging from trauma-related experiences (BC Society of Transition Houses, 2011).

The Centre for Addiction and Mental Health's (CAMH) practice model of care (Chan et al., n.d.) and the virtual National Center for Trauma-Informed Care, sponsored by the Substance Abuse and Mental Health Services Administration ([SAMHSA], 2011) in the United States, are two promising developments in emergent systemic approaches with the mental health and substance use systems of care. The CAMH practice model embeds trauma-informed care as one of the pillars of professional practice across the organization.

Interestingly, a parallel shift in responding to homelessness illustrates a similar evolution of understanding trauma-informed practice. An implicit and explicit recognition has emerged that trauma affects people who are homeless, and that their trauma-related issues should be considered in designing services to better meet their needs. The homelessness sector has pioneered trauma-informed practice in shelters; yet there is still much work to be done in implementing trauma-informed care within homeless services. As Hopper et al. (2010) comment:

> Strategies for implementation are obscure, few program models exist, and there is limited communication and collaboration among programs implementing trauma-informed care. The descriptive and research literature in this area is sparse, with only a handful of studies examining the nature and impact of trauma-informed care. More clarification is needed about what exactly defines trauma-informed care, what changes should be made within systems wishing to offer trauma-informed care, and how these changes should be implemented. (p. 81)

Defining Trauma-Informed and Trauma-Specific Practice

Various terms, such as *trauma-informed* and *trauma-specific practice,* describe the features of service and system responses used in Canada. A wide range of perspectives, disciplines and practices reflect different training, under-standing and purpose around trauma. The concept of trauma-informed practice can be a source of linkage in the support of trauma survivors across settings, disciplines and sectors.

Trauma-informed services recognize how the experience of trauma can affect the confidence, beliefs and behaviours of people coming for help for sub-stance use and mental health concerns. As identified by Maxine Harris and Roger Fallot in the early 1990s, trauma-informed services take into account an understanding of trauma in all aspects of service delivery and place priority on the trauma survivor's safety, choice and control.

In trauma-informed services, professionals are not required to treat trauma; rather, they approach their work with the understanding of how common trauma is among those they serve, how challenging it may be to establish a therapeutic connection and how critical pacing may be. As such, trauma-informed approaches are similar to harm reduction–oriented approaches.

Trauma-informed services consider issues around client safety and empowerment in their policies, practices and staff relational approaches. Trauma-informed services attend to creating a culture of non-violence, learning and collaboration (Bloom & Yanosy Sreedhar, 2008). Working in a trauma-informed way does not necessarily require disclosure of trauma; rather, services are provided in ways that recognize clients' likely need for physical and emotional safety, and for choice and control in decisions affecting their treatment. Practitioners consider safety in their every interaction with clients, and avoid confrontational approaches.

Trauma-specific services more directly address the need for healing from traumatic life experiences and facilitate trauma recovery through counselling and other clinical interventions. Psychological treatments such as cognitive-behavioural treatments, exposure therapy and sensorimotor psychotherapy are examples of therapeutic models used in trauma-specific services (Hien et al., 2009). While not the focus of this book, trauma-specific services are an essential part of a continuum of care.

A continuum view, with an equity orientation, is embedded in many service designs. For example, skills training to help trauma survivors build coping strategies to manage overwhelming emotions and enhance self-care can be included in both trauma-informed and trauma-specific practice. This is not surprising, given that safety is the core of first-stage trauma treatment (Haskell, 2003) and is central to trauma-informed practice. As such, many trauma interventions, such as Seeking Safety (Najavits, 2002) and the Sanctuary model (Bloom et al., 2003), include both trauma-informed and trauma-specific elements.

The successful integration of trauma-informed and trauma-specific practice within services and across systems of care remains an important challenge. Achieving this integrated continuum of responsiveness to trauma is rendered even more difficult by the need to take into account how social determinants of health such as gender, race and class affect the experience of trauma, the stigmatization of those affected and their capacity to access care.

Principles of Trauma-Informed Practice

In the invitation to submit chapters, we invited contributors to reflect on principles of trauma-informed practice. As such, you will see attention to principles as a common thread throughout this book.

Two presentations of principles greatly affected our early thinking on trauma-informed practice. First, we were influenced by primary care practitioners in Saskatoon, Sask., who articulated nine principles of sensitive practice, built on patient-centred care, but that are "so critical to survivors' feeling of safety" that they term them principles of "Sensitive Practice" (Schachter et al., 2008). The principles include respect (to be sensitive to how diminished survivors may feel), taking time (to address feelings of depersonalization and devaluing), rapport (to increase people's sense of safety), sharing information (to decrease anxiety and support involvement), respecting boundaries (to avoid retraumatization), fostering mutual learning, understanding non-linear healing and demonstrating awareness and knowledge of interpersonal violence.

We were also influenced by an article entitled "Trauma-informed or trauma-denied" (Elliot et al., 2005), in which clinicians and researchers involved in the U.S. Women, Co-occurring Disorders and Violence Study presented 10 principles of trauma-informed services for women, beginning with a principle related to recognition of the impact of violence and victimization on development and coping strategies. The second principle stresses how important it is for recovery from trauma to be integrated as a primary concern in this work, not delivered in sequential or parallel services: this is critical whether one is providing trauma-informed or trauma-specific services. The authors discuss at length aspects of employing an empowerment model and striving to maximize a woman's choices and control over her recovery, as it applies to survivors. The fifth principle situates healing in the context of relational collaboration built on safety, trust and (as much as possible) a flattening of the hierarchy of power inherent in a helping relationship. The sixth principle concerns changing the service atmosphere to modify staff approaches, procedures and even the physical setting to create a place perceived as safe and welcoming for survivors. The authors make "strengths-based" a principle, and make it specific to trauma by noting how important it is to highlight adaptations over symptoms and resilience over pathology. Minimizing the possibilities of retraumatization is another principle: the authors point out how often survivors can be retraumatized by the services they receive, especially when they are pushed to uncover memories when they are already overwhelmed. Cultural competence is also considered a key principle, for both understanding each woman in the context of her life experiences and cultural background and supporting unique cultural resources that may support healing. Finally the authors stress, as with harm reduction, how critical it is to solicit consumer input and involve consumers in designing and evaluating services as a core principle of trauma-informed practice.

These principles of trauma-informed practice surface and resurface throughout this book as authors align their work with these values.

Perspectives on Trauma-Informed Practice

In this book, the authors provide varied interpretations of trauma and its features. The concept of trauma is described according to disciplinary perspectives, or in the context of the determinants of health, anti-oppression frameworks or medical diagnostic practices. Not surprisingly, each of these understandings of trauma implies different responses—from changing social structures, to various therapeutic approaches, to medication. Different interpretations also imply different breadths of response, often involving multiple perspectives and systems of care.

It is this most expansive experience and broadest systems approach that inspires this book, building on the assumption that trauma, whether diagnosed or not, recognized or not, can determine life course and engagement with and outcome of health services. Further, all three systems —mental health, addiction and substance use treatment and violence services—have encountered challenges to understanding one another, and to moulding their services for clients of the other systems.

So what might trauma-informed systems of care look like? Harris and Fallot (2001) suggest that experiences of trauma be taken into account in all aspects of service delivery and design. It is not necessary to disclose or be diagnosed with trauma to experience and benefit from these services—a universal approach recommended by several contributors. Trauma-informed systems also avoid retraumatizing people through authoritarian or "power over" relationships, or by challenging clients to change in daunting or demanding ways. Harris and Fallot also suggest that in a wholly trauma-informed system, there would be no need to link to other care systems in order to get trauma-informed care. In other words, people could turn up at any service and experience trauma-informed care.

Fallot and Harris (2009) later included trustworthiness of providers and choice for clients as additional key elements of trauma-informed care. More recently, SAMHSA has added nuance to these elements from the client and provider perspectives and identified the need to foster environments that are physically welcoming and that encourage the building of community (SAMHSA, 2011). Within these more nuanced and evolving versions of trauma-informed care, a range of emotions are both validated and tolerated, allowing space for distress to be enacted without restrictive responses. These, then, are the rudimentary features of trauma-informed services and systems. Numerous evolutions are occurring to reflect these concepts. Practitioners are being encouraged to provide more open environments in a range of settings that assume and tolerate trauma-related behaviours, without forcing clients into diagnostic or treatment moulds.

At the same time, a system of trauma-specific treatment responses exists, where people with diagnoses linked with trauma receive counselling and interventions such as eye movement desensitization and reprocessing (EMDR) or medication. There are integrated therapeutic approaches, such as the Seeking Safety model, that aim to promote healing and the development of coping skills, as well as the SAMHSA approaches that meld trauma and addiction treatment responses. These trauma-specific approaches can coexist in trauma-informed systems. This book provides examples of trauma-informed approaches that have been applied with trauma-specific settings.

What does equity have to do with being trauma informed? As in other health issues, the distribution of trauma may reflect particular inequities and may contribute to the production of ongoing inequities. For example, experiences of trauma are mediated by individual and group characteristics such as gender, age, ethnocultural identity or context. Consequently, trauma-informed systems must be designed to respond to these differences, identities and contexts as a key part of their approach.

While not all diverse experiences can be represented in this book, it remains clear that a consistent gender and equity lens must be applied to fully understand trauma-informed principles and practices. Each chapter in this book pays some attention to gender and equity and to designing systems and services with these factors and goals in mind. In particular, applying an equity lens to responses to trauma reveals a variety of needs and issues. Robust trauma-informed responses are not neutral; there is no "one size fits all"; rather, trauma-informed responses reflect the different needs and features of various groups and sub-populations.

References

Anda, R.F., Brown, D.W., Felitti, V.J., Bremner, J.D., Dube, S.R. & Giles, W.H. (2007). Adverse childhood experiences and prescribed psychotropic medications in adults. *American Journal of Preventive Medicine, 32,* 389–394.

Anda, R.F., Felitti, V.J., Bremner, J.D., Walker, J.D., Whitfield, C., Perry, B.D. et al. (2006). The enduring effects of abuse and related adverse experiences in childhood: A convergence of evidence from neurobiology and epidemiology. *European Archives of Psychiatry and Clinical Neuroscience, 256,* 174–186.

Anda, R.F., Whitfield, C.L., Felitti, V.J., Chapman, D., Edwards, V.J., Dube, S.R. et al. (2002). Adverse childhood experiences, alcoholic parents, and later risk of alcoholism and depression. *Psychiatric Services, 53,* 1001–1009.

Ballon, B.C., Courbasson, C.M.A. & Smith, P.D. (2001). Physical and sexual abuse issues among youths with substance use problems. *Canadian Journal of Psychiatry, 46,* 617–621.

BC Society of Transition Houses. (2011). *Reducing Barriers to Support for Women Fleeing Violence: A Toolkit for Supporting Women with Varying Levels of Mental Wellness and Substance Use.* Vancouver: Author.

Bloom, S.L., Bennington-Davis, M., Farragher, B., McCorkle, D., Nice-Martin, K. & Wellbank, K. (2003). Multiple opportunities for creating sanctuary. *Psychiatric Quarterly, 74,* 173–190.

Bloom, S.L. & Yanosy Sreedhar, S. (2008). The Sanctuary model of trauma-informed organizational change. *Reclaiming Children and Youth, 17*(3), 48–53.

Brown, C. (2009, March). *The pervasiveness of trauma among Canadian women in treatment for alcohol use.* Paper presented at the Looking Back, Thinking Ahead: Using Research to Improve Policy and Practice in Women's Health Conference, Halifax, NS.

Chan, H., Abela-Dimech, F., Chambers, J., Herie, M., Kelly, C., Mawhinney, J. et al. (n.d.). *CAMH Practice Model: Partners in Care.* Toronto: Professional Practice Office, Centre for Addiction and Mental Health.

Chansonneuve, D. (2005). *Reclaiming Connections: Understanding Residential School Trauma among Aboriginal People.* Ottawa: Aboriginal Healing Foundation.

Chapman, D., Whitfield, C., Felitti, V.J., Dube, S., Edwards, V. & Anda, R. (2004). Adverse childhood experiences and the risk of depressive disorders in adulthood. *Journal of Affective Disorders, 82,* 217–225.

Corrado, R.R. & Cohen, I.M. (2003). *Mental Health Profiles for a Sample of British Columbia's Aboriginal Survivors of the Canadian Residential School System.* Ottawa: Aboriginal Healing Foundation.

Dube, S., Felitti, V.J., Dong, M., Chapman, D., Giles, W. & Anda, R. (2003). Childhood abuse, neglect, and household dysfunction and the risk of illicit drug use: The Adverse Child Experiences Study. *Pediatrics, 111,* 564–572.

Elliott, D.E., Bjelajac, P., Fallot, R., Markoff, L.S. & Glover Reed, B. (2005). Trauma-informed or trauma-denied: Principles and implementation of trauma-informed services for women. *Journal of Community Psychology, 33,* 461–477.

Fallot, R. & Harris, M. (July 2009). *Creating Cultures of Trauma-Informed Care (CCTIC): A Self-Assessment and Planning Protocol.* Washington, DC: Community Connections

Harris, M. & Fallot, R.D. (2001). *Using Trauma Theory to Design Service Systems.* San Francisco, CA: Jossey Bass.

Haskell, L. (2003). *First Stage Trauma Treatment: A Guide for Mental Health Professionals Working with Women.* Toronto: Centre for Addiction and Mental Health.

Haskell, L. & Randall, M. (2009). Disrupted attachments: A social context complex trauma framework and the lives of Aboriginal Peoples in Canada. *Journal of Aboriginal Health, 5*(3), 48–99.

Herman, J. (1992). *Trauma and Recovery: The Aftermath of Violence—From Domestic Abuse to Political Terror.* New York: Basic Books.

Hien, D., Litt, L.C., Cohen, L.R., Meile, G.M. & Campbell, A. (2009). *Trauma Services for Women in Substance Abuse Treatment: An Integrated Approach.* Washington, DC: American Psychological Association.

Hopper, E.K., Bassuk, E.L. & Olivet, J. (2010). Shelter from the storm: Trauma-informed care in homelessness services settings. *Open Health Services and Policy Journal, 3,* 80–100.

Kessler, R.C., Sonnega, A., Bromet, E. & Hughes, M. (1995). Posttraumatic stress disorder in the National Comorbidity Survey. *Archives of General Psychiatry, 52,* 1048–1060.

Logan, T., Walker, R., Cole, J. & Leukefeld, C. (2002). Victimization and substance abuse among women: Contributing factors, interventions and implications. *Review of General Psychology, 6,* 325–397.

Men's Trauma Centre (2009). *Annual Report.* Retrieved from www.menstrauma.com/?page_id=16

Najavits, L.M. (2002). *Seeking Safety: A Treatment Manual for PSTD and Substance Abuse.* New York: Guilford Press.

Niccols, A., Dell, C.A. & Clarke, S. (2009). Treatment issues for Aboriginal mothers with substance use problems and their children. *International Journal of Mental Health and Addiction, 8,* 320–335.

Poole, N. (2007). Interconnections among women's health, violence and substance use: Findings from the Aurora Centre. In N. Poole & L. Greaves (Eds.), *Highs and Lows: Canadian Perspectives on Women and Substance Use* (pp. 211–212). Toronto: Centre for Addiction and Mental Health.

Schachter, C., Stalker, C.A., Teram, E., Lasiuk, G.C. & Danilkewich, A. (2008). *Handbook on Sensitive Practice for Health Care Practitioners: Lessons from Adult Survivors of Childhood Sexual Abuse.* Ottawa: National Clearinghouse on Family Violence.

Substance Abuse and Mental Health Services Administration. (2011). National Center for Trauma-Informed Care. Retrieved from www.samhsa.gov/nctic/

Van Wyck, L. & Bradley, N. (2007). A braided recovery: Integrating trauma programming at a women's substance use treatment centre. In N. Poole & L. Greaves (Eds.), *Highs and Lows: Canadian Perspectives on Women and Substance Use* (pp. 365–372). Toronto: Centre for Addiction and Mental Health.

Wesley-Esquimaux, C. & Smolewski, M. (2004). *Historic Trauma and Aboriginal Healing.* Ottawa: Aboriginal Healing Foundation.

PART 1

WHAT IS "TRAUMA INFORMED" IN THEORY AND PRACTICE?

Introduction

Section 1: Theory

This first section describes the landscape of trauma-informed thinking and sets out the terrain of this book. Four authors trace the evolution of trauma-related concepts, ask key questions about trauma and trauma-informed practice, describe some approaches to therapy and name critical issues connected to disclosure.

What is trauma and how is it conceptualized? What does it mean to be trauma informed? What are some examples of trauma-informed practice? How does disclosing trauma affect both individuals and service providers? What can be learned from trauma? Raising these questions is critical to understanding the field of trauma-informed practice and the challenges faced by service providers in various segments of the system.

The range of questions and disciplines engaged in thinking about trauma-informed and trauma-specific practice is potentially wide. In Chapter 1, Haskell outlines essential elements to understanding the bio-psychosocial implications of trauma. She describes complex, developmental trauma and how chronic stress affects the brain and body. She provides a succinct and compelling overview of the importance of attachment to developing the capacity to regulate physiological arousal and form a sense of identity and agency. Haskell describes how understanding the impact of trauma on emotional development and reactivity is essential for anyone working with people who have been traumatized: this understanding enables the practitioner to respond to survivors with the message that their lives are understandable and that their behaviours (including alcohol and other drug use) make sense when they are interpreted through a trauma-informed framework.

There are many forms of trauma—simple, complex, developmental, inter-generational—and many variations in how trauma is experienced. While it is beyond the scope of this book to provide detail on the mechanisms underlying all trauma responses, Haskell's discussion of the impact of developmental trauma is intended to promote understanding of the basis for the trauma-informed work and to invite the interested reader to seek in-depth exploration of trauma responses beyond these pages. Haskell and other contributors advocate the use of a trauma lens to help practitioners better understand the trajectories, coping strategies and strengths of the people seeking help for mental health and substance use concerns.

In Chapter 2, Zingaro addresses a fundamental but often overlooked set of questions about the effects of trauma disclosure on practitioners as well as clients, and what we can learn from trauma. She provides a nuanced commentary about the processes and dynamics of disclosure. Zingaro's provocative piece makes us see the complex aspects of disclosure, a key element in discussions of trauma-informed practice. Asking certain questions to evoke disclosure, she argues, is not necessary to trauma-informed work; in fact, it can complicate the recovery process. Rather, Zingaro suggests that some assumptions can be made about the universal aspects of trauma experiences and that practices be based on a "universal precautions philosophy." Instead of demanding disclosure at intake, for example, building strong relationships between survivors and service providers will enable disclosure to take place, possibly, in a more controlled and safe manner.

Toner and Akman, in Chapter 3, draw parallels between trauma-informed practices and feminist understandings of helping work. They argue that feminist therapy is inherently trauma informed; it was feminists who set the stage for understanding and diagnosing posttraumatic stress disorder. Toner and Akman suggest that trauma-informed work embodies many components of feminist paradigms. They describe the dimensions of their Gender Role Socialization Scale, which measures the effects of general oppressive practices on women's mental health. They also present their Enhancing Women's Well-Being group intervention that encourages women to examine the effects of gender-role messages on their mental health. While not solely focused on trauma, both the scale and the intervention they have developed address the overarching oppressive circumstances that result in trauma in women's lives.

In Chapter 4, Timothy describes anti-oppression psychotherapy as a form of trauma-informed practice. She, too, links trauma to other forms of oppression and suggests that the treatment of trauma and oppression be carried out recognizing the intersectional nature of violence—the fact that violence derives from multiple sources at once. Not only is anti-oppression psychiatry helpful to clients; it also engages change processes in therapists and communities by encouraging them to "actively resist oppressive practices." Timothy describes the steps involved in engaging with anti-oppression psychotherapy with clients, emphasizing the fluidity of the processes and the change opportunities for both the client and the practitioner, given continuous reflexivity.

Taken together, these four chapters engage critically with trauma-informed principles and ask deep questions about the links between societal practices and oppressive structures and trauma. They also probe the links between trauma and practice, arguing for overarching, universalist approaches, as well as continued reflexivity for practitioners and systems as they set the stage—or not—for disclosure of trauma.

Section 2: Practice

Contributors to Section 2 illustrate various practices or approaches to doing healing work, describing how they can be, or become, trauma informed. Three examples are outlined, with trauma-informed questions forming the basis of these descriptions. These direct applications, or adaptations, of practice represent hopeful opportunities for modifying practice and evolving current approaches into more trauma-informed responses.

For example, Urquhart and Jasiura in Chapter 5 discuss motivational interviewing and how it coincides with trauma-informed practice. They illustrate some fundamental principles of motivational interviewing that support and enliven trauma-informed practices, such as collaborating with clients, strengthening relational ties, building on strengths, avoiding direct confrontation with clients and not limiting their options or using negative labels. Instead, motivational interviewing is consistent with Haskell's trauma-informed recommendation for reframing problems as coping behaviours and symptoms as adaptations. Further, motivational interviewing calls on service providers to rein in their natural inclinations to "fix" the client or her or his problems and to give advice.

In Chapter 6, Haarmans discusses cognitive-behavioural therapy (CBT) for psychosis and links it to trauma-informed practices. She illustrates how closely tied are the experiences of trauma and psychosis and how many typical responses to psychosis, such as forced hospitalization, restraints or medications, are retraumatizing and may cause posttraumatic stress disorder.

Haarmans argues that psychosis can be viewed as a possible response to trauma. She also points out the importance of sex/gender in understanding psychosis in relation to trauma and laments the lack of attention to these factors. Haarmans suggests that an empowerment model can be integrated into CBT as trauma-informed practice by normalizing symptoms, collaborating with clients and teaching coping strategies.

Hughes and Hyman discuss bodywork and trauma and how bodywork can be trauma informed. In Chapter 7, they argue that trauma often creates a mind/body separation and that bodywork is a practical way to create reconnections. Hughes and Hyman link laughter yoga and Brain Gym to stress management and healing for people with substance use and mental health issues who may also have trauma histories. In part, bodywork encourages "mindfulness" and reinforces agency in those with trauma histories who are trying to heal and recover, without requiring disclosure. These techniques are part of positive psychology and encourage the development of supportive social environments for people experiencing trauma.

These three wide-ranging examples of responsive approaches to working with clients with trauma histories illustrate the adaptability of old forms of therapy, as well as introducing newer forms into existing therapeutic milieus. These examples incorporate elements of trauma-informed care, offering innovative, positive ways for practitioners and clients to deal with symptoms without necessarily requiring disclosure of past trauma.

PART 1

SECTION 1: THEORY

Chapter 1

A Developmental Understanding of Complex Trauma

Lori Haskell

Traumatic experiences shape many aspects of the lives of survivors of abuse. The changes or alterations in abuse survivors' cognitions and emotional regulation are often complicated and varied. When not seen through a trauma lens, these alterations or changes can be inappropriately labelled as pathological by service providers instead of being viewed as understandable adaptations a person has had to make in order to cope with life's circumstances. It is not a coincidence that many people struggling with substance use problems have abuse and trauma histories that have not been addressed. It is critical that mental health and substance use service providers understand the dynamic interplay between the traumatic stressors and the complex and often diverse adaptations that people develop in order to survive.

A trauma lens allows us to appreciate that early abuse and neglect are not discrete events; instead, they often become defining life experiences that can shape and even distort core aspects of a person's identity. These early adverse experiences are often formative and people respond by constructing a sense of self, a sense of others and a belief about the world that is profoundly influenced by these horrific life experiences (Harris & Fallot, 2001). It is important that people working in the helping professions understand that abuse survivors are often not able to recall these early adverse experiences; rather, they are evoked or triggered. A trauma-informed perspective recognizes that people who have been chronically abused or neglected may have many possible triggers. These triggers often include situations where clients experience a lack of respect and safety and an absence of control and choice—experiences that often mimic and resonate with past traumatic experiences.

Working in a trauma-informed way involves more than adhering to a set of general principles. It requires service providers to work from a thorough understanding of the complex and diverse alternations in the many domains of a traumatized person's development. This chapter outlines some of the fundamental ways in which chronic abuse and neglect in childhood lead to traumatic responses, which can reverberate through many aspects of a person's life. These traumatic experiences have developmental impacts on both mind and body, and can sometimes lead to substance use problems as a way of coping with overwhelming experiences and intolerable feelings. This chapter's goal, therefore, is to inform the practice of service providers in the mental health and substance use fields about the importance of a trauma-informed approach when working with trauma survivors.

Understanding Complex Trauma through a Biopsychosocial Lens

Complex Trauma

People who are abused and neglected in childhood often experience a range of long-term effects, both psychological and physical. It is well established in the literature and from clinical experience that survivors of abuse tend to experience significantly more mental health difficulties, such as depression, sexual dysfunction, dissociation, anger, suicidality, self-harm and substance use problems, than people who do not have histories of abuse (Briere & Jordan, 2004). Prolonged childhood abuse can also be associated with harmful long-term physical health effects. Recent research shows that the more adverse childhood experiences a person reports, the more likely he or she is to develop life-threatening illnesses such as heart disease, cancer and stroke (Van der Kolk, 2005).

Traumatic effects are especially acute when the abuse or neglect is ongoing, when it begins in childhood and when the perpetrator is someone the person should have been able to trust. A child's earliest experiences, even those beyond conscious recall, play a crucial role in his or her behaviours, attitude development, relationships and sense of self in later life. Adverse childhood experiences can alter the young child's social, emotional, neurological, physical and sensory development.

Understandably, children who have been abused often have problems with attachment and forming intimate relationships. They are often unable to regulate their emotions and impulses and can experience cognitive impairment and attention deficits, as well as somatic (bodily) disorders like chronic pain.

In many cases, people who endured childhood abuse and neglect develop what might seem like a bewildering array of problems throughout their lives. These difficulties can appear to be incomprehensible to those who do not understand how abuse and trauma can impair a person's capacities and, in turn, limit his or her life opportunities. Many service providers, and in many cases the survivors themselves, can misunderstand these difficulties as self-inflicted because they do not understand how abuse, trauma and their effects reverberate throughout a person's life.

The Potential for Misdiagnosis

Without a clear understanding of how trauma affects people developmentally, misdiagnosis can be an issue in working with people with substance use and mental health problems. For example, without applying a trauma lens, coping mechanisms, such as self-harming, may be given diagnoses such as bipolar disorder and treated exclusively with drugs and behaviour management (Van der Kolk, 2005). Borderline personality disorder is another diagnosis that can be inaccurately applied, especially to women who have experienced trauma. Trauma experts underline that it is important to understand that people with complex posttraumatic stress disorder (PTSD) do not have symptoms that constitute separate, "dual" or comorbid diagnoses, but rather, that these symptoms represent the complex somatic, cognitive, affective and behavioural effects of trauma. A single diagnosis of complex PTSD presents an empirically based, conceptually coherent and unified set of symptoms as a basis for compassionate treatment planning (Cloitre et al., 2009).

Because the study of traumatic stress is still an emerging field, psychiatrists, social workers and psychologists trained in traditional frameworks may underestimate the role that abuse and neglect play in both mental health and substance use problems. We now know, however, that early abuse and neglect can have diverse and far-reaching effects on attachment, brain development, emotion regulation and cognition, and that early abuse can disrupt development at different stages, even when the abuse has stopped.

There have been dramatic developments in our understanding of the nature and impact of trauma, including the distinction between simple and complex trauma, in the fields of psychology, psychiatry and neuroscience in recent years.

How Stress Affects the Brain and the Body

When faced by threat or danger, the mind and body protect us by preparing us to fight or flee. These responses are controlled by the autonomic nervous system (ANS) and are automatic and unconscious. The ANS has two complementary divisions: the sympathetic nervous system, which activates our nerves, organs and muscles into a heightened state of arousal and regulates the "fight or flight" mechanism, and the parasympathetic nervous system, which controls the body's calming mechanisms (as well as the "freeze" response) and is designed to shut down body systems or return the body to baseline arousal levels.

The standard physiological model of the ANS is of reciprocal tension between the sympathetic and parasympathetic systems, with the two parts keeping each other in check. When the sympathetic response goes up, the parasympathetic response goes down. A good example of optimal autonomic balance can be seen in cats, which become alert to certain sounds or movements, but return immediately to a relaxed state as soon as the situation is assessed as safe.

The parasympathetic nervous system comes into operation after the threat has been responded to and action has been taken. It has the opposite effect of sympathetic activity, allowing the body to wind down and rebalance. The activation of the parasympathetic nervous system encourages relaxation of muscles, slowing the heart rate and lowering blood pressure. It helps breathing to return to its normal rate; digestive juices flow; bladder and bowels are ready to function again; the pupils constrict; and immune functions, such as the production of white blood cells, recommence. The para-sympathetic mode supports rest and sleep.

The fight or flight response is activated by the amygdala, which is located in the limbic system and is the defensive centre in the brain. (The amygdala can be seen as having a similar function to a smoke detector.) Sensory threat cues (sights, sounds, body sensation and smells) are encoded in the amygdala, and this database of threat cues allows the amygdala to respond to danger quickly and without thought.

Once a threat is detected, a cascade of neurochemicals from the adrenal glands is released into the bloodstream and initiates the adrenaline stress response. These patterns of nerve cell firing and chemical release prepare the body for action: heart rate and respiration increase; oxygen flow to muscle tissue increases; and other non-essential organ systems, including the frontal cortex, are turned off.

When the Threat of Danger Becomes Chronic

Survivors of trauma and abuse often live in environments where they constantly face the threat of danger. This danger can be in the form of emotional or physical abuse, neglect, abandonment or sexual violation. Living with constant fear results in a state of constant alertness or hyperarousal, which is extremely taxing on the nervous system.

People who live in conditions of constant danger eventually experience a breakdown in the amygdala's ability to discriminate threat cues. As a result, survivors of abuse begin to have persistent, recurring, overly defensive reactions, even to harmless stimuli.

Simply said, when danger is ever-present, the alarm (amygdala) goes off too frequently, and the brain becomes conditioned to treat all potential threats as actual threats. When this happens, past and present danger become confused, and the brain is hyperaroused and reactive to any number of triggers, without being able to differentiate between real and perceived threats. This state of alert causes people to be on the lookout for every possible danger. Fear becomes the lens through which they see the world.

As a result, trauma survivors, who feel chronically on high alert, are easily triggered to take flight or fight. The thinking brain (prefrontal regions) automatically shuts down in the face of triggers. In this state, people are unable to reflect or cognitively assess their reactions; instead, they experience states of anxiety, panic or dissociation.

Complicating this hyperaroused brain state even more is the fact that traumatic memory is stored and processed differently than normal memory (Van der Kolk, 1994). Psychiatrist Bessel van der Kolk (1994) explains that traumatic memories are stored as dissociated sensory and perceptual fragments that may be triggered by current unrelated life events, like a tone of voice or a facial expression we notice in someone else. When people are triggered, the present feels like the past. Survivors are not remembering their traumatic experiences; they are re-experiencing them.

The physiological adaptations that abuse survivors develop in response to ongoing threat produces a chronic, underlying state of "dysregulation" or imbalance in the body, which often results in hyperarousal and hypervigilance (in which a person seems to overreact to every situation) or listlessness and dissociation (in which a person seems numb and disconnected in stressful or dangerous situations). This dysregulation of the brain and body systems perpetuates mental, emotional and physical distress.

Loss of Optimal Autonomic Balance

Children living in households where they are unsafe, neglected or abused must learn and grow despite the pervasive experience of threat. Children are able to do this by adapting to the ongoing state of fear they are experiencing, but they do so at a great cost to their development. The developing brain is exquisitely sensitive to stress. Infancy and childhood are the most critical developmental periods; the human brain completes 75 per cent of its total development within the first six years of life (Eliot, 2000).

The cumulative effect of the body undergoing the excessive stress of being in a hyperaroused state, in which the person is constantly prepared to take fight or flight, eventually takes a toll on physical health. Parasympathetic nervous system processes are suppressed by overactive sympathetic arousal. As a result of this imbalance, problems with digestion and sexual dysfunction can develop. Excessive stress does not always show up as the "feeling" of being stressed. Many stresses go directly into one's physical body and may only be recognized by the physical symptoms the person manifests.

For example, disorders of the autonomic nervous system, such as headaches, irritable bowel syndrome and high blood pressure, are common in people with trauma histories. As well, prolonged stress responses may result in chronic suppression of the immune system, creating susceptibility to infection, chronic fatigue, depression and autoimmune diseases such as rheumatoid arthritis, lupus and allergies (Van der Kolk et al., 1996). Traumatic experiences alter the functioning of the central nervous system, as well as general physiological functioning. In this way, trauma has both emotional and physical effects.

As overwhelming and complex as these changes appear, they are only a part of the overall picture. Children who experience ongoing neglect and abuse by their own parents or caretakers are often not soothed or comforted when they are frightened or overwhelmed. Instead, in an attempt to manage these overwhelming dysregulated states and chronic stress, abuse survivors often develop what may appear to be extreme coping strategies.

Abuse survivors frequently engage in self-harm in an attempt to reduce tension or downgrade high levels of arousal. Neurobiological attempts to cope with the trauma include self-harm (which may be invasive and involve cutting), suicidality, eating disorders and addictive behaviour. These signify different ways of modulating or managing a dysregulated nervous system. For example, trauma survivors who feel dead inside or chronically numb may use self-injury and suicidal ideation to induce adrenaline and endorphin responses. For others who feel too much, self-starvation and overeating may create feelings of numbness. Subsequently, addictive behaviours can be tailored to induce either numbing or increased arousal or a combination of both (Fisher, 2003).

People who have been traumatized become focused on short-term survival and are not able to consider long-term consequences of their coping strategies. They will do whatever they can to keep themselves out of pain. They learn to disconnect from their bodies in order to avoid feeling the overwhelming pain and stress.

The accumulation of years of prolonged stress and the extreme adaptations developed to manage these chronic states (e.g., self-harm, substance abuse) result in greater morbidity and higher mortality from all causes, including accidents and homicide (Vaccaro & Lavick, 2008).

Attachment, Attunement and the Development of Core Self-Capacities

A comprehensive overview of a child's psychological development, attachment system and social context is required to understand the depth and complexity of prolonged childhood abuse and neglect. This is because complicating and amplifying the intense difficulties with chronic physiological arousal is the added problem of not developing the capacity to regulate and manage physiological arousal.

Regulating emotions is fundamental to the development of the self. Attachment relationships are the primary context within which we learn to regulate affect and to access, modulate and use our emotions (Fonagy et al., 2002; Schore, 2003). A child requires secure attachment for healthy psychobiological development. Learning to soothe and calm intense emotional states is a developmental lesson that is often adversely affected as a result of childhood abuse and neglect.

Parents are required to keep children safe and to teach them how to handle adversity and emotional upset. When parents are able to provide safety and predictability and to teach skills to manage different psychological experiences, children develop important self-capacities. Self-capacities are the inner abilities that allow individuals to manage their intrapersonal worlds and allow them to maintain a coherent and cohesive sense of self (McCann & Pearlman, 1990).

The three self-capacities that are thought to be especially important to the individual's response to averse events are identity, boundary awareness and affect regulation (Briere, 1996). The child's developing capacity to regulate emotions and develop a coherent sense of self requires sensitive and responsive parenting; otherwise the child will develop dysregulated affect (meaning that he or she cannot regulate the intensity of feelings or problem-solve ways to manage them).

Maté (2008) explains:

> A child's capacity to handle psychological and physiological stress is
> completely dependent on the relationship with her parent. Infants
> have no ability to regulate their own stress apparatus. We acquire this
> capacity gradually as we mature—or we don't, depending on our
> childhood relationships with our caregivers. (p. 191)

Children who are neglected and abused experience overwhelming emotional
pain without anyone to comfort them. As a result, they do not implicitly learn
problem-solving strategies or means to comfort themselves or self-soothe. The
emotional pain they carry exceeds their capacity to handle pain. This means that
a person who is traumatized early in life not only has higher levels of anxiety, agitation and general physiological arousal; he or she also has a diminished ability
to regulate or deal with these intense states. In other words, the trauma survivor
has increased emotional distress and decreased capacities to cope with it.

The Importance of Parental Attunement

In order for children to develop an authentic, foundational sense of who they
are in the world, they require a secure attachment relationship where they
experience a caregiver who is emotionally attuned to them. To "attune" to a
child means having a caregiver who responds to the child's needs, particularly
emotionally. This results in the child developing a sense of being understood,
cared for and valued. It is often assumed that infants first learn to identify
their emotional states from internal cues. On the contrary, infants learn to
differentiate their internal states on the basis of external cues (parents' empathic
emotional responses).

Children develop secure attachment as a result of experiencing a parent who
is predictably and consistently responsive to their basic needs, for feeding
and caring for them, as well as for protection and play. Attachment theory
suggests that the care an infant receives becomes a model around which the
child's developing brain learns to organize his or her behaviour. Sensitive,
responsive care will result in a secure attachment; inconsistent, rejecting,
neglectful or abusive care—when the child's emotions are ignored, discounted,

humiliated or punished—will produce a child who is insecurely attached or has other attachment difficulties.

The inability to be safely and securely attached to others undermines the person's capacity to develop and rely on relationships to establish a feeling of security. These experiences can lead to long-standing anxiety and stress, feelings of rejection and abandonment and continual dissatisfaction with and distrust of close, intimate relationships. People who have these experiences can enter similar states as adults without any explicit memory of this experience (Maté, 2008). They often will describe these feelings as coming out of nowhere. These implicit memories of shame, degradation and neglect often get triggered in relationships throughout life.

Early attachment patterns strongly predict how a person will deal with other relationships throughout the lifespan. Abuse that happens in a primary attachment relationship undermines the development of the core self, including the capacity for self-regulation.

The Effect of Abuse and Neglect on Identity and Agency

Children who have experienced ongoing abuse, parental misattunement and neglect develop a view of the world that incorporates their betrayal and hurt. An expectation that they will be harmed permeates their relationships. This expectation is expressed as negative self-attributions, loss of trust in caretakers and loss of the belief that someone will look after them and make them feel safe. These children tend to lose the expectation that they will be protected, and act accordingly. While these defensive mechanisms may work for a child who is trying to protect himself or herself from external threats or internal pain, these coping mechanisms also set up the child for a lifetime of emptiness, loneliness and emotional isolation. People who have been neglected and traumatized often do not develop an internal sense of self. Instead, they defensively withdraw, and this self-protective retreat impairs their ability to be self-reflective. This results in their lacking the language to refer to internal states and in a diminished interpretive ability (Siegel, 1999). They tend to dissociate from both their inner and outer worlds, without knowing what they are feeling, and they often lack even a basic knowledge of their emotional states.

Dissociating precludes the need to develop other, more complex affect regulation skills. At the same time, individuals who have been traumatized become hypervigilant. This constant external focus pulls attention away from internal developmental tasks, such as building self-awareness and affect-modulation skills. As a result, trauma survivors do not have the ability to predict their own reactions in different situations, so they are unable to anticipate what they may feel and prepare coping strategies. People require access to their feelings in order to guide their behaviour. For example, being fearful of walking on a secluded, dark street usually motivates people to take extra precautions or avoid the dangerous situation altogether.

One of the most important components of affect regulation is the ability to correctly perceive and label emotions as they are experienced. Without knowing what we are feeling, we are at a loss as to how to develop a strategy to modulate that feeling state. This combination of processes undermines the individual's ability to develop affect regulation skills.

The combination of having a deficit in skills or strategies to manage and tolerate affect and a dysregulated nervous system stemming from early abuse and neglect results in heightened reactivity. The implication of these coalescing processes is that people who have been traumatized have a diminished ability to deal with the stress and challenges of everyday life. They develop a lower set for their internal stress system and are often anxious, distressed and triggered easily.

One of the most detrimental effects of early abuse and neglect is the development of an implicit schema that people are not to be trusted. After years of feeling hurt and abandoned by their caretakers, traumatized people often feel separate from others. They often lack the ability to have healthy and reciprocal relationships, because they have never developed an internal template for what a healthy relationship is like.

Many people do not understand that individuals who have been traumatized fear not only being physically or sexually harmed; they also fear being emotion-ally overwhelmed by what others may trigger in them. They experience people as threats to emotional well-being and learn to avoid close emotional connection. Unfortunately, this often means that they do not have others to draw on as a source of comfort.

Neglect and abuse impinge on a sense of self-agency and promote a defensive withdrawal from the mental and emotional world. Many difficulties that people who have been traumatized experience relate to these two factors—emotional vulnerability plus deficits in the skills needed to regulate and manage these vulnerabilities. This dual process of an easily dsyregulated response to stress and daily emotional challenges and the deficits in core self-capacities leaves the individual vulnerable to developing substance use problems.

Trauma-Informed Practice

This chapter has outlined the many different domains of individual functioning that are affected by prolonged abuse and neglect. It has explained how different areas of a person's functioning have been shaped and altered by early experiences of abuse, neglect, misattuned parenting, insecure attachment and, often, maladaptive coping. The physiological adaptations resulting from traumatic stress, as well as the effects of this stress on identity and agency, have implications for how mental health and substance use services should be delivered.

Understanding the impact of trauma on emotional development and reactivity is essential for anyone working with traumatized individuals. This is particularly the case because situations involving control and choice are bound to occur in the helping relationship.

The most useful interventions are collaborative, meaning that the therapist or other service provider and the client work together to help the client learn about his or her interpersonal schemas and triggers. Clients need this information so they can work actively to create strategies and approaches for dealing with their triggers, rather than using the information to avoid situations or interpersonal interactions that resonate and trigger them.

One of the most important components of providing services for people who have experienced trauma is to respond to survivors with the message that their lives are understandable and that their behaviours make sense when interpreted through a trauma-informed framework. Clients feel understood and validated, especially when the adaptations they have developed are recognized as being their best attempts at coping. Many of these coping strategies helped survivors to endure the abuse while it was occurring. The use of alcohol and other substances is a common coping strategy to numb emotional pain.

Many of the adaptations that people who have experienced trauma develop to survive their abuse may be perceived as pathological conditions in intake and assessment processes that are not trauma informed. For example, clients who chronically dissociate and imagine a protective spirit whisking them away from danger may be misunderstood (or incorrectly diagnosed) as having a psychotic condition. Herman (1992) explains that women who are highly dissociative as a result of early trauma may be diagnosed with depression and in some cases schizophrenia. When this happens, clients may be offered medications to treat their "delusions," instead of being given a framework within which to understand the development of their dissociative response.

The importance of the biopsychosocial trauma framework and the insights it provides mental health and front-line workers is crucial for working from a trauma-informed approach. Understanding clients with abuse and neglect histories and substance use problems from a neurobiological perspective allows treatment to focus on helping them increase their self-capacities. Specifically, it orients the clinical work toward enhancing clients' abilities to self-regulate their emotional states and calm their nervous systems. Rather than focusing on clients' narratives of the past, the focus is on their physical self-experience and self-awareness.

Helping people make necessary therapeutic changes in their lives can be extraordinarily difficult. In addressing people's maladaptive coping (such as drinking), Marsha Linehan (1993) explains the therapeutic challenge in striking a delicate balance between supporting and reassuring the client and focusing on the client's need to make positive and concrete life changes. Trauma interventions require considerable therapeutic focus on accepting and validating the client's current coping, while simultaneously teaching a broad range of behavioural skills. The therapeutic stance that Linehan promotes is a focus on acceptance with a corresponding focus on change (Linehan, 1993).

Although the ultimate goal is to help clients develop more effective coping strategies, this cannot be effectively done if clients feel that what they have been attempting to do is invalidated and harshly assessed. Clients with abuse histories often develop extreme coping to adapt to life demands, even when these adaptations (e.g., self-harm, dissociation, substance use) create their own sets of problems. When trauma survivors feel validated and understood, they are able to start feeling less threatened.

It is important for people who have been traumatized to learn that their adaptations were developed as responses to overwhelming stressors. It is also important for them to recognize that the coping strategies they have developed have a function and purpose. Most important, perhaps, it is reassuring for survivors to learn more effective ways of coping.

Working with substance use problems using a trauma-informed framework means assessing the function of the substance use as it relates to the individual's abuse history and adaptations. How does this adaptation (substance use) help this person? What difficulty is being addressed by using substances? What would this person need in order to cope without this adaptation? For example, when examining a client's substance use problem, the therapist, rather than considering "How do I understand this problem or this symptom?" would, in keeping with a trauma-informed approach, consider, "How do I understand this person?" This approach shifts the focus onto the individual and away from some limited aspect of his or her functioning (Harris & Fallot, 2001).

As Harris and Fallot (2001) explain, it is rarely effective to eliminate the coping strategy of intoxication without providing alternative solutions that target specific trauma-related problems. We must understand the specific function of the substance use problem (e.g., alcohol helps me be social) in order to offer alternatives. For example, a person who has a schema of unworthiness and self-loathing may feel a great deal of fear about being social with others and feel shame about exposing who he or she is to others. However, when the person drinks alcohol, these fears are obliterated and he or she feels more comfortable being social.

Linking Trauma-Informed Approaches with Trauma-Specific Therapies

There is often a necessary overlap between trauma-informed approaches and first-stage trauma treatment. State-of-the-art trauma therapies are strongly influenced by increasing clinical awareness that affect intolerance and dys-regulation, rooted in our biology and bodies, contribute to ongoing distress in traumatized clients. Neurobiological research and theory strongly suggest the need to develop new approaches to treatment to incorporate these insights. Increasingly, trauma therapists are using treatments that focus on somatic (body) processing and that teach clients how to calm their nervous system.

The core tasks of these types of therapies are to provide clients with psycho-education so they better understand their experiences of having overaroused nervous systems and their automatic trauma reactions or triggers. As well, clients learn to disrupt their habitual trauma responses by recognizing them in the moment. In sessions with the clinician, clients are taught mindfulness instead of reactivity; with carefully paced therapies, clients are typically able to experience a more regulated nervous system.

Insight and understanding are not enough to keep traumatized clients from regularly feeling and acting as if they are experiencing trauma all over again. They need to learn to manage affect intensity and to regulate emotions. The role of the mental health professional is to facilitate self-awareness and self-regulation. Clinicians need techniques and approaches that help traumatized clients become aware of their internal sensations and that help clients know that it is safe to experience their feelings.

Trauma-Specific Therapies

Some of the current trauma-focused clinical treatments found to be most effective in reducing the symptoms of trauma tend to link sensorimotor responses (body movements and sensations) to thoughts and feelings. These treatments, outlined below, are based on the theory that focusing attention on the traumatic responses of the body and mind will encourage and facilitate a client's inherent self-regulatory abilities. Clients who are interested in additional stages of support can benefit by being referred to clinicians who deliver these trauma-specific therapies.

Clinical research has demonstrated the efficacy of these trauma-specific treatment approaches, provided they are offered by practitioners with advanced training and a sophisticated clinical skill set. Some of the main trauma therapy techniques that are currently used include somatic experiencing and other somatic therapies, mindfulness training, mentalization-based treatment, eye movement desensitization and reprocessing (EMDR) and neurofeedback. None of these techniques asks the client to relive or re-experience trauma in order to heal it (in contrast with prolonged exposure therapy).

Developed by Francine Shapiro (2001), EMDR is a well-researched intervention for the treatment of trauma. Traditionally, the goal of EMDR is to reprocess and reintegrate traumatic experiences in order to change the negative interpretations and reduce the distressing physiological arousal associated with traumatic memories. For somatic processing, specific EMDR techniques and approaches can help clients learn that they can shift from an anxious state to a relaxed state through different protocols and strategies.

Somatic experiencing, developed by Peter Levine (1997), is a therapy based on "restoring the wisdom of the body" as a way to gain access to an individual's inner resources, restore the autonomic nervous system's ability to self-regulate and repair the damage caused by trauma.

Sensorimotor psychotherapy, developed by Pat Ogden (Ogden et al., 2006), combines verbal therapy techniques with body-centred interventions that directly address the neurobiological effects of trauma.

Mindfulness-based stress reduction (MBSR), developed by Jon Kabat-Zinn (1990, 2005), is a form of mental training involving a series of exercises that encourages "living in the present." In his book, *Mindsight,* Daniel Siegel (2010) explains that mindful awareness may lead to enhanced well-being by changing our view of our own mental processes. Siegel explains that figuring out what the mind is up to helps us control our responses to traumatic events, painful memories and physical symptoms of trauma.

Mentalization-based treatment, developed by Fonagy et al. (2002), is a form of psychodynamic therapy that strives to enhance clients' capacities to "mentalize" or understand their thoughts, feelings, wishes and beliefs, as well as those of others, in the context of a safe, secure relationship between client and therapist.

Neurofeedback training is based on neuroscientific findings that people can change perceptions and attention by altering the electrical rhythms inside the brain. Clients treated with this approach are able to alter their own brainwaves by increasing certain frequencies and decreasing others through feedback from a computerized program. During neurofeedback, a sensor placed on the head detects electrical brain activity, and these brain signals are then transmitted onto a computer screen. The brain is rewarded for making specific brainwaves; as a result, clients are able to change dysregulated responses.

Conclusion

There are clear links between childhood neglect and abuse and later psychological, emotional, behavioural, physiological and interpersonal problems. Cognitive, affective and psychosocial development are shaped and affected by a combination of chronic abuse; lack of emotionally connected parenting; and/or the deprivation of basic childhood needs, such as safety, parental constancy and emotional validation. In order to survive these overwhelming experiences, people are compelled to make complex adaptations.

The coalescing of chronic dysregulated emotional responses to traumatic reminders—such as hyperarousal, hypervigilance and emotional numbing, along with an inadequately developed capacity to regulate emotional distress —results in a heightened need to find some form of relief. It is not surprising that many people will turn to substances and other coping behaviours in an attempt to deal with their overwhelming traumatic responses.

People who have untreated complex trauma often face what can feel like insurmountable obstacles to receiving effective treatment and support. Historically, addiction and mental health treatment have been provided separately. Addiction clients with both substance use problems and trauma were not provided treatment and support for their related mental health concerns, such as depression, that could be driving their substance use. They typically have also not received treatment for their related physical health concerns, such as gastrointestinal problems. The clients themselves often do not recognize that these problems are linked to attempts to cope with dysregulated nervous systems.

Understanding how trauma leads to disturbances in self-regulatory capacities is useful, as it creates conceptual coherence around the multiple, diffuse and often contradictory symptoms of complex trauma. Whether in a psychiatric hospital or a community clinic, service providers working with people with mental health and substance use problems need to understand client behaviours, including violent ones, as trauma responses and learn about their clients' triggers. It is hoped that increased understanding of the pervasive role of psychological trauma in the lives of clients with histories of abuse and neglect will lead to more compassionate and effective treatment and support approaches in helping them rebuild their lives.

References

Briere, J. (1996). *Therapy for Adults Molested as Children: Beyond Survival* (2nd ed.). New York: Springer.

Briere, J. & Jordan, C.E. (2004). Violence against women: Outcome complexity and implications for treatment. *Journal of Interpersonal Violence, 19*, 1252–1276.

Cloitre, M., Stolbach, B., Herman, J., van der Kolk, B., Pynoos, R., Wang, J. & Petkova, E. (2009). A developmental approach to complex PTSD: Childhood and adult cumulative trauma as predictors of symptom complexity. *Journal of Traumatic Stress, 22*, 399–408.

Eliot, L. (2000). *What's Going On in There? How the Brain and Mind Develop in the First Five Years of Life.* New York: Bantam.

Fisher, J. (2003, July). *Working with the neurobiological legacy of trauma.* Paper presented at the Annual Conference of the American Mental Health Counselors Association, Seattle, WA.

Fonagy, P., Gergely, G., Jurist, E.L. & Target, M. (2002). *Affect Regulation, Mentalization, and the Development of Self.* New York: Other Press.

Harris, M. & Fallot, R.D. (Eds.). (2001). Using Trauma Theory to Design Service Systems [Special issue]. *New Directions for Mental Health Services, 89.*

Herman, J. (1992) *Trauma and Recovery: The Aftermath of Violence—From Domestic Abuse to Political Terror.* New York: Basic Books.

Kabat-Zinn, J. (1990). *Full Catastrophe Living: Using the Wisdom of Your Body and Mind to Face Stress, Pain, and Illness.* New York: Delacorte Press.

Kabat-Zinn, J. (2005). *Wherever You Go, There You Are: Mindfulness Meditation in Everyday Life.* New York: Hyperion.

Levine, P. (1997). *Waking the Tiger: Healing Trauma—The Innate Capacity to Transform Overwhelming Experiences.* Berkeley, CA: North Atlantic Books.

Linehan, M. (1993). *Cognitive-Behavioral Treatment of Borderline Personality Disorder.* New York: Guilford Press.

Maté, G. (2008). *In the Realm of Hungry Ghosts: Close Encounters with Addictions.* Toronto: Alfred A. Knopf.

McCann I.L. & Pearlman, L.A. (1990). *Psychological Trauma and the Adult Survivor: Theory, Therapy and Transformation.* New York: Brunner/Mazel.

Ogden, P., Minton, K. & Pain, C. (2006). *Trauma and the Body: A Sensorimotor Approach to Psychotherapy.* New York: W.W. Norton.

Schore, A. (2003). *Affect Dysregulation and Disorders of the Self.* New York: W.W. Norton.

Shapiro, F. (2001). *Eye Movement Desensitization and Reprocessing (EMDR): Basic Principles, Protocols, and Procedures* (2nd ed.). New York: Guilford Press.

Siegel, D.J. (1999). *The Developing Mind: Toward a Neurobiology of Interpersonal Experience.* New York: Guilford Press.

Siegel, D.J. (2010). *Mindsight: The New Science of Personal Transformation.* New York: Bantam Books.

Vaccaro, G. & Lavick, J. (2008). Trauma: Frozen moments, frozen lives. *BETA, 20*(4), 31–41.

Van der Kolk, B.A. (1994). The body keeps the score: Memory and the emerging psychobiology of post traumatic stress. *Harvard Review of Psychiatry, 1*, 253–265.

Van der Kolk, B.A. (2005). Developmental trauma disorder: Toward a rational diagnosis for children with complex trauma histories. *Psychiatric Annals, 35*, 401–408.

Van der Kolk, B.A., McFarlane, A.C. & Weisaeth, L. (Eds.). (1996). *Traumatic Stress: The Effects of Overwhelming Experience on Mind, Body, and Society.* New York: Guilford Press.

Chapter 2

Traumatic Learning

Linde Zingaro

What does it mean to be trauma informed? One morning as I was driving to work, I was listening to a "trauma expert" on the radio. He was talking about the hundreds of children orphaned and traumatized by a tsunami, a hurricane or some brutal conflict. The interviewer asked this psychologist what could be done to help these children. His answer was, essentially, that we need to work to help them realize that the world is a safe place. Of course the psychologist was speaking in compassionate tones and conveyed a sense of responsibility and a commitment to providing the kind of care (impossible, in most of those circumstances) that would give that reassurance. But for me, he was only partly "trauma informed." My question to anybody I talked to in the next few days was "Where does he live that he thinks the world is a safe place?"

One of the main problems for anyone working in health care, social work or addiction treatment is the struggle to hold on to some version of a safe world for ourselves when we are seeing the evidence and hearing the stories of trauma that offer other important and disturbing information: that the world, for very many people, is not a safe place. Sometimes, in programs that provide services to people experiencing the most destructive responses to trauma, even the workplace is unsafe. A trauma-informed program must recognize that many helpers who provide community-based addiction, mental health and family violence programs may have their own experiences of trauma or may be unsafe in their private lives, even while they are offering safety and support to others.

Being trauma informed must go further than believing that traumatic events occur and knowing what happens to the minds and bodies of those who experience trauma. Trauma-informed care must go beyond diagnosis and medication, beyond the application of our therapeutic tools and techniques. Being trauma informed must include respecting and honouring the fact that what is learned from the experience of trauma is a kind of knowledge, in the same way that what we learn about trauma is knowledge. In both cases, what is known is contextual and deeply nuanced. It is overlaid with historical and sometimes colonized cultural and personal differences, and is always embodied. In our most helpful exchanges, both client and service provider are involved in a relationship of learning about strength and resilience from each other's experiences of safety or lack of safety. So maybe the question for trauma-informed service should be, "How can we create and support the space for this kind of learning?"

This chapter discusses what survivors learn from traumatic experiences and how disclosure can amplify the painful consequences. It uses the theory of "threshold concepts of learning" to help us understand the processes involved for survivors to shift their learned responses to trauma and how service providers may pressure survivors in ways that makes this new learning more difficult. Finally, considerations for practice and policy are discussed, where the negative effects of forcing a disclosure are understood and a trauma-informed "universal precautions" approach is advocated.

Learning from Trauma

One of the important practical outcomes of recent work on brain functioning and traumatic experience has been greater sensitivity to how, for many survivors, the trauma experience welds an enduring link or association between the particular sensations, emotions and cognitions coincident with the event. Some of the most difficult interactions with clients or patients result from what, in clinical language, we have learned to call "triggers": external drivers of certain behaviours based in a previous traumatic experience. What might be seen by others as an innocuous and unrelated interaction can activate thoughts and feelings associated with the overwhelming sense of threat experienced in the original traumatic context. The behaviours that accompany these triggers are often charged with an urgency and self-protective panic that seem completely out of proportion to the present context, or that might be appropriate only in a desperate struggle for survival.

This is one way of thinking about traumatic learning: that the person has learned, through some extreme life experience, certain ways to handle (or avoid) the stress of life-threatening or identity-threatening situations. These trauma-tailored management skills may not be useful in a setting where trauma is reduced (or in a "safe world") and are in themselves sometimes dangerous and self-damaging. Taking trauma into account, it makes sense for service providers to view a substance use issue as "self-medication" or compulsive behaviour as "self-soothing," or to assume that a specific triggering event in the moment may represent something not actually present in the environment at the time of the reaction. This connection, however, may not be apparent to the client.

For the trauma survivor, the emotions of the original event are present in the exchange, particularly when she or he is questioned about the trauma experience. With the emotions come the physical sensations and the cognitive or perceptual evaluations of the environment as dangerous. Clients sometimes say, "I felt like I was dying," or "I couldn't breathe in there" in situations where service providers feel that they have been acting in completely non-threatening ways. The sense of being overwhelmed with negative emotion can be stimulated by "talking about it." If people have not yet developed alternative skills and strategies for handling the feelings and the physical overstimulation generated by this association, they will often default to the automatic avoidance, self-numbing or self-damaging behaviour that may have brought them into the helping relationship in the first place.

In a long practice of caring for vulnerable people, I have often observed a version of this "triggered" behaviour that also needs to be incorporated into our understanding of this concept of trauma-based learning as a component of trauma-informed care. I have called this constellation of learned reactions and emotions "disclosure consequences." I became painfully aware of it as a significant dynamic in the late 1970s as the result of an incident in the emergency group home for street youth that I was operating at the time.

In those years, increasing social awareness of the extent and consequences of family violence contributed to many changes in welfare policy, including the introduction of extensive training for child protection workers in the specifics of child sexual abuse. Our staff had identified a young woman in the emergency shelter as needing to be taken into care, as we believed that she was unsafe at home. A newly trained social worker came to the house to interview her in order to support the decision to ask for a court-ordered intervention. After about an hour with the 15-year-old, the worker came out of the interview and went to another room to phone her office to make arrangements for the child, satisfied that her investigation had uncovered enough evidence to justify a child protection apprehension. The child followed her out of the office, went directly into the kitchen and—right in front of me as I was cooking—grabbed a large chopping knife and smashed the blade down onto the back of her hand, attempting to cut off her fingers.

From observing this immediate demonstration of the pain of disclosure, and many others where the self-punishment process has taken longer to come into effect after a disclosure, I came to believe that for some people, "telling" a story of their experience of trauma, shame or helplessness holds the potential for this kind of response. I saw how the apparently impulsive and sometimes inexplicable behaviours that follow this kind of disclosure often function as demonstrations of an emotional logic based on traumatic learning, which creates the need to do three things:

- to provide some external evidence to match the internal experience of crisis and/or helplessness that is the consequence of certain kinds of trauma
- to deflect attention from the person as vulnerable
- to create a diversion that will remove the person from the intimacy of the present interpersonal situation.

For many people, the pain of a trauma disclosure triggers an urgent need for them to retract the story—demonstrating their own self-hate, creating in their own behaviour the proof that they are worthless, that what they are saying cannot be believed. For some, this self-discrediting impulse involves abusing alcohol or other drugs, gambling, fighting or sabotaging their work or important relationships. For others, the punishment system requires more active self-harm, self-mutilation or even suicide. It is these internal processes of self-blame and self-punishment that impose a limit on the person's ability to make use of our interventions, even with the best intentions. Being trauma-informed service providers means that our commitment to providing safety must take this process into account. We have to work toward protecting all the people in our care from the specific risks of their own limits, even while we try to help them learn to protect themselves (Zingaro, 2009).

The Trauma of Learning

Recent research in the area of adult education may offer another explanation for the prevalence in some settings of disclosure consequences. It suggests that we attain mastery of any field of endeavour, including developing the skills for surviving and thriving, by moving through a series of increasingly complex "threshold concepts," each of which requires a profound shift in world view. Cousin (2006) describes the threshold concept as being:

- *transformative*—we are changed by learning: new understandings become part of what we know, who we are, how we see and how we feel
- *irreversible*—once knowledge has been integrated, the learner is unlikely to forget it and finds it very difficult to think of ever not knowing it
- *integrative*—it allows the learner to make connections that were previously hidden
- *bounded*—there is a potential for the learning to become rigid: it is important to maintain a position of continued questioning (difficult in trauma)
- *"troublesome"*—concepts or information that challenges our "common sense" or previous learning is emotionally disturbing.

Implicit in these conceptual elements is the idea that any significant change in circumstance or world view implies a loss for the learner, who must give up some part of her or his previously mastered, familiar world—no matter how dysfunctional or dangerous that world may be. For any of us, moving into the unstable space required for the identity shifts that are needed for significant behavioural change feels threatening and creates in us a need to construct our own conditions of safety (Cousin, 2006). In fact, for some, the familiar conditions of safety depend on the behaviours that our programs are intended to change.

Even after a person has learned to identify possible "triggers," even after she or he may have processed and integrated the concept of the dynamic of traumatic associations, the potential is still there for some part of the response. Some new experience or unexpected external condition may once again stimulate the automatic responses of traumatic learning because the deepest learning in some kinds of trauma is the experiential knowledge that the world is not safe.

This conception of traumatic learning suggests that, in situations such as treatment for addiction or mental distress, where there is a potential (indeed a hope) for important changes in behaviour or cognition, we are actually increasing the pressure on the person's capacity to cope, thus increasing the likelihood of "triggered" responses. If we add that pressure to a pre-established tendency for the automatic self-punishment strategies that often emerge as disclosure consequences, we must expect that, even with our best intentions, the necessary structures and systems of control in our programs sometimes contribute to the lack of safety for our clients. Especially with clients who display the self-punishing or self-defeating behaviours that can result from trauma, we, as service providers, must be able to tolerate the painful possibility that, for any traumatized person, we often start out as just another representative of an unsafe world.

Trauma-Informed Practice

A trauma-informed position for policy and practice in service delivery requires some very practical considerations that will affect our everyday actions. One of the first of these relates to the process of gathering information. Eliciting and recording the present circumstances and the relevant history of the client is not a simple housekeeping task; it is actually an obvious place where the whole definition of trauma-informed care resides. Before we begin, we need to ask some questions of ourselves and of our programs and listen to the answers with an awareness of the original lessons of trauma.

If we believe that trauma may be part of the experience of any clients in our care, and if we understand that trauma has certain predictable if not inevitable consequences for the person, then what kind of questions do we need to ask? What do we do with the answers and what can we take for granted in the lives of people in need of care? What difference will the answers (or lack of them) make to our practice, to our policies, perhaps to the research that may also be ongoing as a part of service delivery or advocacy in the therapeutic setting? Except for the exploration process involved in helping the person understand her or his own triggers, does knowing or not knowing the particulars of the trauma change our practice? Do we really need an explicit description of what we understand as trauma in order to respond to an obvious need for service?

In the context of trauma-informed care, we need to ask ourselves, "What difference will the questions and the answers, or the lack of them, make to the client?" Even the simple forms of interrogation for intake and the inevitable translation of individual experience into generalized clinical language can have a huge impact on the person seeking help. Being trauma informed does not mean that we ask no questions. But perhaps instead of requiring a routine set of questions on intake, we could make use of a "universal precautions" philosophy, intentionally operating "as if" anyone who comes into our care is likely to be a trauma survivor. Being attentive to these forms of traumatic learning in this way will help us to develop policies and practices that will prevent the automatic behavioural re-enactments that continue to undermine the best intentions of both the helper and the client—those that in the process endanger the relationships, the dignity and sometimes the very lives of people who have been traumatized.

Service providers who are truly informed about traumatic learning commit to consciously participate in creating greater safety for their clients and for themselves. The focus of the work then involves building relationships that take trauma into account as a part of a complex and contexted life experience that may exist on both sides of the helper/helped divide and providing support, information and understanding and as much experience of safety as we can manage. If, in the process, we open a space to hear the story of trauma in a context of connection, where the person can have some control over the disclosure experience, then we must be prepared to really hear and respect-fully attend to the layers of meaning in every unique story of trauma and to the vulnerability of the telling.

In the same way that universal precautions became standard best practice in early health care service for populations who were thought to be at risk for HIV, today's trauma-informed care should be structured to be safe and appropriate, even for those living with the most devastating consequences of trauma— even if we don't know what the particular trauma is or was. An immediate effect of this practice would be to reduce the number of program failures and dramatic reactions that arises from over-disclosure or from some common screening procedures. A trauma-informed approach with universal precautions might recognize the existence of trauma in our culture, while dignifying the particular and personal experience of traumatic learning.

Using this kind of trauma-informed approach can help us fulfil our commit-ment to support the strength and courage of survivors. Otherwise we risk finding ourselves engaged in the reductive process of decontextualizing violence, renaming human tragedy as trauma and attempting to contain social, economic or historical despair and desperation within the language of a limited symptom-based treatment paradigm, simply because we have learned some tools for managing individual behaviour.

References

Cousin, G. (2006). Threshold concepts, troublesome knowledge and emotional capital: An exploration into learning about others. In J.H.F. Meyer & R. Land (Eds.), *Overcoming Barriers to Student Understanding: Threshold Concepts and Troublesome Knowledge* (pp. 134–147). Oxford, U.K.: Routledge.

Zingaro, L. (2009). *Speaking Out: Storytelling for Social Change.* Walnut Creek, CA: Left Coast Press.

Chapter 3

Using a Feminist- and Trauma-Informed Approach in Therapy with Women

Brenda Toner and Donna Akman

This chapter aims to contextualize trauma-informed care within the larger framework of feminist psychotherapy theory and practice and describe how we have integrated feminist theory into our clinical initiatives in the field of women's mental health.

Feminist Therapy *Is* Trauma-Informed Care

Feminist ideologists have been proponents of trauma-informed care from their earliest writings. As Brown (2004) writes, the diagnosis of posttraumatic stress disorder owes its existence at least in part to feminist therapists, who identified gender-based violence as a source of trauma and described the wide range of consequences for its victims. Brown suggests that, given the influence of feminist thinkers on the diagnosis and treatment of posttraumatic experiences, trauma treatment implicitly embodies many feminist paradigms.

Feminist theorists and clinicians have consistently maintained a focus on violence against women as a major source of women's problems, while at the same time drawing attention to other factors that they considered to be oppressive and unhealthy for women. These factors include women's experiences of economic and political disadvantage, body oppression, gender role expectations, ageism, racism and other systemic disadvantages (Worell & Remer, 2003).

Feminism has sensitized us to the potential consequences of experiencing these oppressive circumstances, not only when they occur in overt and distinct ways, such as when a person is subjected to physical or sexual abuse, but also when they occur in a more subtle, insidious fashion, such as when a person is subjected to acts of exclusion, dismissal, diminishment and disempowerment based on race, gender, sexual orientation, age and other personal and social identities.

From a feminist perspective, these types of oppressive experiences can have long-standing and far-reaching consequences that can be perceived as traumatizing. A trauma-informed approach to therapy assumes that social, economic and political disadvantages can have a negative effect on women's health and well-being and can contribute to or account for some of the mental health difficulties they experience. In fact, studies suggest that women's experiences of sexist events are related to their psychological symptomatology (e.g., Klonoff et al., 2000; Landrine et al., 1995; Moradi & Subich, 2002, 2003, 2004; Swim et al., 2001).

Thus, using a trauma-informed lens, attention must be paid to reducing the oppressive circumstances of women's lives in order to improve their lives. A trauma-informed approach considers a wide range of oppressive circumstances and social structures, including but not limited to violence and abuse, in conceptualizing, investigating and developing clinical interventions for women's mental health concerns. Within this framework, trauma-informed care considers the many influences on women's health and well-being and helps women effect change in those areas of their lives that may be oppressive and/or unhealthy.

Using a wide scope includes assessing how social and political factors shape the experience and naming of trauma and the ways in which trauma is treated at both the individual and societal levels. This kind of assessment can help promote a more nuanced understanding of trauma-related difficulties and ways to effectively intervene (Brown, 2004). By considering the socio-political circumstances of women's lives, theorists, researchers, clinicians and consumers can learn to develop and use strategies for change that promote both personal and political empowerment. The next section will describe how we have integrated feminist theory into our own research and clinical initiatives with women.

Gender Role Socialization and Women's Mental Health

The literature on gender and mental health has discussed the detrimental impact of adherence to some traditional feminine gender roles on women's health and well-being (Worell & Remer, 2003). These discussions have focused on associations between mental health problems in girls and women and gender-related expectations, such as societal standards for attractiveness (Tolman et al., 2006); social norms regarding women's caretaking role in relationships, which can involve the expectation that women suppress their own needs in favour of preserving their relationships and/or promoting the well-being of others (Jack, 1991); and sanctions against anger expression in women (Norwood et al., 2011; Van Daalen-Smith, 2008). These discussions suggest a need to develop research and clinical tools to assess the degree to which women have internalized these societal messages and the effects of this internalization process on women's mental health. We believe that the onslaught of messages women receive about gender-related expectations, as well as the societal consequences of not measuring up to these expectations, can be oppressive and have mental health consequences. To address some of these concerns, we have developed the Gender Role Socialization Scale for Women ([GRSS], Toner et al., 2011) as presented in Figure 1.

Identifying Gender Role Oppression

Because many societal standards for women are restrictive and oppressive, efforts to live up to them can sometimes lead to personal and political disempowerment and contribute to mental health problems. In our clinical experience, we have found that there is a lack of measurement tools that address societal prescriptions for women. To address this gap, we have developed a scale that measures the internalization of gender role messages for women. Our interest in developing this tool grew out of our belief that traditional care providers were framing women's mental health problems as arising from internal deficits, and that the focus was on individual pathology rather than on understanding the contributions of oppressive circumstances to women's problems. Further, we were interested in contributing to the knowledge base regarding women's mental health by developing a tool to identify salient gender role messages for women, explore these messages in clinical practice and further the understanding of the association between gender role socialization and other aspects of women's personal, interpersonal and social functioning.

In keeping with our feminist-informed framework, the GRSS moves the focus of attention from the individual to the environment. The GRSS is a 30-item self-report scale specifically designed to measure women's internalization of prescribed gender role messages that can be oppressive and that can affect women's mental health and well-being. Examples of items that are rated on a seven-point scale from strongly disagree to strongly agree include: If I take time for myself, I feel selfish; If I do not like my body, I am to blame; If I ever feel overwhelmed, it must mean that I am incompetent; I feel that the needs of others are more important than my own needs; No matter how I feel I must always try to look my best; If a relationship fails, I usually feel that it is my fault. I can't feel good about myself unless I feel physically attractive. The GRSS can be used for both clinical and research purposes as an assessment tool and as a predictive and/or outcome measure in psychotherapy research.

Although the GRSS measures the degree to which women internalize gender role messages, the aim is to use the scale to help women learn that their beliefs and behaviours have been influenced by external forces and that their struggles may be less about personal pathology and more about detrimental social structures. To the degree that the scale can help women generate a multifaceted perspective on their problems, it can then help generate a multi-faceted perspective on solutions. Challenging social dictates regarding gender, identifying and/or developing different expectations for oneself that are not restricted by gender rules, and finding role models or like-minded individuals who can support attempts to challenge the systemic discrimination embedded in gender role messages are all possible outcomes of exploring these messages.

Figure 1: Gender Role Socialization Scale for Women

Please read the following statements and indicate how each one applies to you at this time in your life. *Please circle only one number for each item.* There are no right or wrong answers to these statements.

1) Strongly disagree
2) Disagree
3) Slightly disagree
4) Neutral
5) Slightly agree
6) Agree
7) Strongly agree

1. If I don't accomplish everything I should, then I must be a failure.

   1   2   3   4   5   6   7

2. I am to blame if I have low self-esteem.

   1   2   3   4   5   6   7

3. If I don't get what I need, it is because I ask for too much.

   1   2   3   4   5   6   7

4. What I look like is more important than how I feel.

   1   2   3   4   5   6   7

5. I feel embarrassed by my own sexual desires.

   1   2   3   4   5   6   7

6. I feel that I must always make room in my life to take care of others.

   1   2   3   4   5   6   7

7. I will never be happy if I am not in a romantic relationship.

   1   2   3   4   5   6   7

8. Compared to men, I am less able to handle stress.

   1   2   3   4   5   6   7

9. If I am unhappy, it is because I am too hard to please.

   1   2   3   4   5   6   7

10. If I take time for myself, I feel selfish.

| 1 | 2 | 3 | 4 | 5 | 6 | 7 |

11. If I do not like my body, I am to blame.

| 1 | 2 | 3 | 4 | 5 | 6 | 7 |

12. If other people let me down, it is because I expect too much.

| 1 | 2 | 3 | 4 | 5 | 6 | 7 |

13. I have only myself to blame for my problems.

| 1 | 2 | 3 | 4 | 5 | 6 | 7 |

14. I can't feel good about myself unless I feel physically attractive.

| 1 | 2 | 3 | 4 | 5 | 6 | 7 |

15. If I ever feel overwhelmed, it must mean that I am incompetent.

| 1 | 2 | 3 | 4 | 5 | 6 | 7 |

16. I feel that I must look good on the outside even if I don't feel good on the inside.

| 1 | 2 | 3 | 4 | 5 | 6 | 7 |

17. I feel that the needs of others are more important than my own needs.

| 1 | 2 | 3 | 4 | 5 | 6 | 7 |

18. No matter how I feel I must always try to look my best.

| 1 | 2 | 3 | 4 | 5 | 6 | 7 |

19. I don't feel that I can leave a relationship even when I know that it is not satisfying.

| 1 | 2 | 3 | 4 | 5 | 6 | 7 |

20. I feel that I am not allowed to ask that my own needs be met.

| 1 | 2 | 3 | 4 | 5 | 6 | 7 |

21. I don't like to say nice things about myself.

| 1 | 2 | 3 | 4 | 5 | 6 | 7 |

22. Whenever I see media images of women, I feel dissatisfied with my body.

| 1 | 2 | 3 | 4 | 5 | 6 | 7 |

23. I feel that I must always put my family's emotional needs before my own.

| 1 | 2 | 3 | 4 | 5 | 6 | 7 |

24. I feel as though I should be less sexually forward than men.

        1   2   3   4   5   6   7

25. If a relationship fails, I usually feel that it is my fault.

        1   2   3   4   5   6   7

26. If I take time for myself, I feel guilty.

        1   2   3   4   5   6   7

27. Whenever I am eating, I am always thinking about how it will affect my body size.

        1   2   3   4   5   6   7

28. I often give up my own wishes in order to make other people happy.

        1   2   3   4   5   6   7

29. I feel as though I can't reveal the struggles in my life.

        1   2   3   4   5   6   7

30. In a relationship, I feel I must always put my partner's needs before my own.

        1   2   3   4   5   6   7

From "Developing a gender role socialization scale," edited by John L. Oliffe and Lorraine Greaves, 2012, *Designing and Conducting Gender, Sex and Health Research.* Los Angeles: Sage. Reprinted with permission.

Enhancing Women's Well-Being: A Group Intervention

The Enhancing Women's Well-Being group is an intervention that was developed to create a space for women to explore the relationship between gender role messages and their mental health and well-being. It has been offered in both inpatient and outpatient settings with women who present with a variety of mental health concerns. The group aims to create a supportive and validating space for women to share their experiences and, in doing so, learn from other women. The group also includes psychoeducation based on the book *Too Good for Her Own Good* (Bepko & Krestan, 1990), about gender role messages and their impact on women's well-being.

This feminist-informed, trauma-informed intervention offers women a space to examine the often rigid and conflicting gender role messages they have received throughout their lives, share common experiences, explore factors that may be associated with mental health problems and consider a multifaceted approach to both problems and resolutions. With an enhanced awareness of social factors that affect women, a wider range of strategies for change can be identified and used. In this sense, it is an empowerment model, encouraging women to take more control over their own situations and address those that may be oppressive, traumatic and silencing.

Using our experience in developing and implementing this intervention, we are now creating a clinical manual with suggested content for sessions based on issues or themes that have been identified in the theoretical research literature and in our clinical and research work in women's mental health. However, these issues are meant to serve as guidelines and should be tailored to the individual goals of clients in partnership with therapists. This manual will have broad application potential in that its emphasis on the gender role socialization construct will increase awareness among treatment providers and the larger community about factors that contribute to women's health and well-being. Given that this therapeutic approach aims to cut across diagnostic categories within women's mental health, such an intervention can be implemented, adapted and used in a variety of settings with different client groups. In addition, because the intervention contains a large component of education and consciousness-raising, it has the potential to be adapted for health promotion.

Conclusion

This chapter has positioned trauma-informed care within a larger framework of feminist theory and psychotherapy. Within this framework, several writers have argued that various oppressive circumstances and social structures in the lives of women are traumatizing, including violence, abuse, economic and political disadvantage, body oppression, gender role socialization, sexism, ageism and racism. We have highlighted the construct of gender role socialization to illustrate the development and implementation of a feminist-informed, trauma-informed assessment tool and group intervention in our work with women. Our goal is to use these assessment and intervention strategies to empower women to examine and challenge social structures and situations that may be oppressive and traumatic.

References

Bepko, C. & Krestan, J. (1990). *Too Good for Her Own Good: Searching for Self and Intimacy in Important Relationships.* New York: HarperCollins.

Brown, L. (2004). Feminist paradigms of trauma treatment. *Psychotherapy: Theory, Research, Practice, Training, 41,* 464–471.

Jack, D. (1991). *Silencing the Self: Women and Depression.* Cambridge: Harvard University Press.

Klonoff, E.A., Landrine, H. & Campbell, R. (2000). Sexist discrimination may account for well-known gender differences in psychiatric symptoms. *Psychology of Women Quarterly, 24,* 93–99.

Landrine, H., Klonoff, E.A., Gibbs, J., Manning, V. & Lund, M. (1995). Physical and psychiatric correlates of gender discrimination: An application of the Schedule of Sexist Events. *Psychology of Women Quarterly, 19,* 473–492.

Moradi, B. & Subich, L.M. (2002). Perceived sexist events and feminist identity development attitudes: Link to women's psychological distress. *Counseling Psychologist, 30,* 44–65.

Moradi, B. & Subich, L.M. (2003). A concomitant examination of the relations of perceived racist and sexist events to psychological distress for African American women. *Counseling Psychologist, 31,* 451–469.

Moradi, B. & Subich, L.M. (2004). Examining the moderating role of self-esteem in the link between experiences of perceived sexist events and psychological distress. *Journal of Counseling Psychology, 51,* 50–56.

Norwood, S., Bowker, A., Buchholz, A., Henderson, K., Goldfield, G. & Flament, M. (2011). Self-silencing and anger regulation as predictors of disordered eating among adolescent females. *Eating Behaviors, 12,* 112–118.

Swim, J., Hyers, L., Cohen, L. & Ferguson, M. (2001). Everyday sexism: Evidence for its incidence, natures, and psychological impact from three daily diary studies. *Journal of Social Issues, 57,* 31–53.

Tolman, D., Impett, E., Tracy, A. & Michael, A. (2006). Looking good, sounding good: Femininity ideology and adolescent girls' mental health. *Psychology of Women Quarterly, 30,* 85–95.

Toner, B., Tang, T., Ali, A., Akman, D., Stuckless, N., Esplen, N.J. et al. (2011). Developing a gender role socialization scale. In J.L. Oliffe & L. Greaves (Eds.), *Designing and Conducting Gender, Sex, and Health Research* (pp. 189–200). Thousand Oaks, CA: Sage.

Van Daalen-Smith, C. (2008). Living as a chameleon: Girls, anger and mental health. *Journal of School Nursing, 24,* 116–123.

Worell, J. & Remer, P. (2003). *Feminist Perspectives in Therapy: Empowering Diverse Women* (2nd ed.). New York: Wiley.

Chapter 4

Anti-oppression Psychotherapy as Trauma-Informed Practice

Roberta K. Timothy

Anti-oppression psychotherapy (AOP) is a therapeutic approach that clinicians can use to support clients as they cope with the effects of oppression, trauma and intersectional violence in their lives. This chapter is based on the anti-oppression psychotherapy model created by Continuing Healing Consultants,[1] which looks at concrete ways to work with clients around intersectional violence and trauma.

In AOP, an expanded notion of trauma recognizes that systemic and/or social problems can present in many different forms, such as racism, sexism, classism, colonialism, ageism, homophobia/heterosexism, transphobia, ableism, discrimination, and violence based on religion or spiritual affiliation. AOP incorporates both anti-oppression theories and practices and psychotherapy to understand and work with individuals and groups who may have experienced intersectional forms of trauma and violence. This AOP approach involves the therapist first examining his or her own identities (or "locations") before working with clients around these same issues. The therapist explores with the client how his or her relationships transnationally (connections to people and places in different countries) and transgenerationally (influenced by past and present familial generations) affect the client's experiences of intersectional violence. By examining these experiences, AOP can provide clients, therapists and their communities with a catalyst for "empowerment-centred" change.

---

1. For more information about the anti-oppression psychotherapy model, contact the author at info@healingconsultants.org.

Figure 1: Intersectional Violence and Trauma

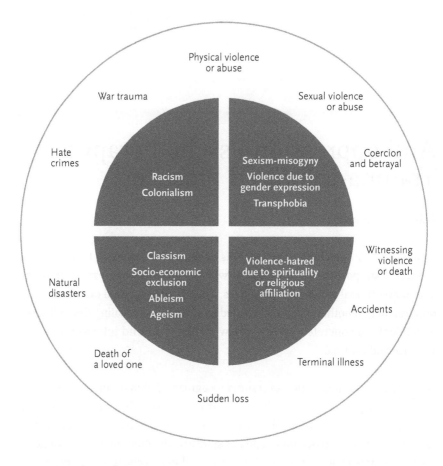

Adapted from Timothy & Umaña, 2009.

Critical to AOP is helping clients to actively resist oppression and to become resilient in the face of their experiences so that they do not simply survive or cope with adversity—but actually thrive (Timothy & Umaña, 2009).

Over the last decades, trauma models have expanded to address the complexities of the human experience, particularly in relation to intersectionality (Cole, 2009) —to the interrelationship or connection between factors of identity, including race, indigeneity, class or socio-economic status, gender/gender identity, sexual orientation, (dis)ability, age and spirituality. In relation to trauma, intersectionality speaks to the connection between these factors and different types of traumas resulting from discrimination and violence against particular individuals and communities based on their "assumed" or perceived identities.

The trauma of daily experiences of intersectional violence and the potential for clients to be retraumatized in clinical settings has been documented extensively (Aponte et al., 1995; Ibrahim & Ohnishi, 2001; Sue et al., 2007). The following sections introduce ways to work from a trauma-informed intersectional AOP perspective.

An Expanded Notion of Trauma

Within a trauma-informed approach to violence, AOP therapists recognize the complexity in their clients' lives and experiences. Consider the case of Asha, a sexual assault survivor of African descent. Using an AOP approach, the therapist facilitates a discussion with Asha about the various influences of violence in her life—from her being not only a woman, but a black woman, and middle class. The therapist explores with Asha how a history of African enslavement, inhumane rape laws and current racist stereotypes of black women as "easy," "hypersexual" and "provoking rape" intensify and add complexity to her traumatic experiences.

Practitioners of AOP must expand their frames of reference not only to understand how factors of identity and intersectional violence influence the therapeutic interactions, but also to understand how these factors are influenced by time and place. For instance, rather than seeing only the here and now as important, an AOP approach recognizes that the past—and what is not here—also influences clients' traumatic experiences and resources. Asha's story, for example, must be understood in the context of her legacy as a sixth-generation African-Canadian, and in light of historical and contemporary practices of racism and colonialism.

Being trauma informed from an AOP lens enables the "whole picture" of clients' distress (trauma) to be known. Using this wider lens, the therapist can better support the client from an anti-violence praxis and lessen the chance of her being retraumatized. Using an anti-oppression framework, the therapist encourages the client to explore who she is holistically—recognizing or including all aspects of her experiences—so she can feel greater safety. At the same time, the therapist is aware of how her own personal experiences and social locations may facilitate or strain the therapeutic interaction with her clients.

Working with Survivors of Intersectional Violence and Trauma

Within an AOP model, identity trichotomy (Timothy & Umana, 2009) is a tool to help clients and therapists examine the impact of intersectional violence in their own lives and in their communities. This tool consists of three tenets or stages that look at the impact of fixed notions of identity and intersectional violence in clients' lives. The tool helps therapists to deconstruct their own and other people's biases and assumptions about their clients' social locations, and to look at ways clients can make changes through acts of resilience and resistance.

Clients do not necessarily progress through these tenets in a linear fashion. Rather, the progression is fluid, with clients and therapist addressing different tenets at different times, depending on the issue. From the onset, resistance occurs at different levels—resistance to fixed notions of the self, to a changing self-concept and to integrating these changes into clients' lives and community.

Tenet 1: Fixed notions of identity and trauma—the "box"
This first tenet requires therapists and clients to explicitly examine the impact in clients' lives of fixed notions of identity. Fixed notions are essentialized (categorized or stereotyped), discriminatory and prejudiced views prescribed by individuals, groups or institutions that sanction systems of oppression and practices of exclusion. For example, the stereotype of an Asian woman as smart, while seemingly positive, is—like all stereotypes—oppressive because it creates stress and anxiety for the person to live up to this image. Fixed notions of identity become "boxes" that limit our understanding of the complexities of human experience. These static notions of identity are frequently promoted and re-inscribed in covert ways (e.g., through media stereotypes) and in overt ways (e.g., by physical, verbal and emotional attacks that are not always publicly recognized as violent).

Fixed notions of identity are usually created to limit the access of certain people or groups to various mainstream services and/or resources (e.g., to health care, education, social supports). They produce "fabrications of otherness"—where people are separated as "outside of" and "non-deserving" —or as "uncivil" and "worthless." These fixed notions generate misleading explanations for physical, sexual or emotional abuse. For example, a fixed notion of identity can lead someone to believe that Aboriginal women experience more abuse within their communities or that Israeli women are pushy or overly aggressive—both perspectives that are insulting to people within these communities and that oversimplify a perspective as pertaining to all individuals within a community. Another common fixed notion about trauma is the erroneous belief that experiencing racism does not affect or exacerbate mental health issues.

Consider the example of a therapist working with a practising Muslim woman of Arab descent named Fatima, who comes to therapy in a state of extreme anxiety after being physically abused by her partner. The therapist working with Fatima has to explore and challenge his or her own fixed notions of what being a Muslim woman is in order to provide a safe and less retraumatizing mental health environment for the client. Part of working with Fatima may involve addressing other forms of violence she may also have experienced, such as Islamophobia from the workers at the hostel where she had been seeking support. But the therapist must first work on his or her own Islamophobia.

Therapists and clients must address their own fixed notions of identity and trauma both in their own lives and in their clinical settings. Only then can the therapeutic alliance foster empowerment.

- Some key questions the therapist can reflect on in Fatima's example are:
- What are my fixed ideas about trauma?
- What are my fixed ideas about Muslim women and abuse?
- Where did I get these messages about Muslim women from (e.g., family, media, religion, school)?
- How comfortable am I exploring Fatima's mental health issues related to Islamophobia as trauma?
- How do I challenge my own fixed notions of her identity and trauma experiences?
- How do I make her feel safe and empowered and lessen retraumatization?

Tenet 2: Different notions of intersecting identities and trauma

After deconstructing and challenging fixed notions of identity, therapists and clients examine their intersecting identities and experiences of intersectional trauma. Tenet 2 invites therapists to talk to clients about their experiences or stories over time without interpreting them and judging how the clients might feel or act. The therapeutic interaction acknowledges how clients may experience multiple oppressions and violence, as well as their own specific experiences with others based on their intersectional identities: race, indigeneity, gender/gender identity, class or socio-economic status, sexual orientation, (dis)ability, age and spirituality. It provides a framework that accommodates the particularities of the individual's unique and collective experiences.

The therapeutic interaction becomes a space where clients and therapists discuss and gain insight into their own identities. This insight is crucial to understanding clients' "lived experiences" of trauma and ways they have actively resisted or shown resilience in the face of this trauma. From exploring intersecting identities emerges a stronger therapeutic alliance based on trust. When therapists look at clients' identities as fluid and intersecting, their concepts of mental health supports expand to include both their intersectional experiences of trauma and their resiliency and resistance.

This dialogue can be done using various tools and exercises to facilitate a new change-oriented narrative over time. Consider a therapist working with Sean, a gay (two-spirited) man of Ojibwe descent who is severely depressed after being "outed" at work. The therapist begins by exploring with the client not just his experience of being exposed as being gay, but also examining the homophobia he confronted at work and people's prejudices around his being Aboriginal and two-spirited. The therapist then explores Sean's depression as it relates to his race, gender and sexual orientation and how these and other important aspects of Sean's identity are interrelated. The therapist encourages Sean to discuss how he has been resilient in the past and how he can actively resist the oppression he has experienced at work; for example, by honouring his spiritual connection to Ojibwe people by becoming more involved with his community and its elders. Sean eventually decides to leave his job and return to school to study Aboriginal identity and social justice and to speak out about being two-spirited in an Aboriginal community and about homophobia in and outside of the community.

Some key questions the therapist can reflect on are:

- What do I know and not know about Sean's identities?
- What do I know and not know about his experiences of trauma?
- How does he identify in relation to intersectional identities and intersectional trauma?
- What is the impact of his intersectional identities on his experiences of trauma?
- What is the impact of his indigeneity on his experiences of intersectional trauma? What transgenerational connections relate to his experiences of trauma?
- What role does intersectional violence play in relation to his mental health concerns? Do colonialism, racism, sexism, homophobia and other forms of intersectional violence intersect, amplifying the client's experience of trauma?

Tenet 3: Strengthening the therapeutic alliance through negotiating understanding and using identities for change

When therapists engage clients in an active dialogue, the process helps clients to reject fixed notions of identity, create their own notions of community and consider how they can make changes in their lives by reconfiguring notions of who they are to reflect more fluid and reaffirming aspects of their identities. This process is particularly important, as it interrupts clients' prescribed notions of being "hopeless," "isolated" and "victimized." Instead, they form new understandings of their belonging to different communities that have resisted intersectional trauma historically and transnationally.

By this stage, the strength of the therapeutic alliance and the coping skills clients have cultivated can help them resist intersectional forms of trauma and violence in their lives.

Case study

Consider the case of Sarah, a white Jewish woman of European descent who has a hearing impairment and has been sexually and verbally abused both as a child and young adult. Sarah is phobic of people and places and is quite isolated. She has been having difficulty sleeping since the recent death of her grandmother.

Applying tenet 1, the therapist assists Sarah to examine and dismantle any fixed notions of identity and trauma. The therapist explores with Sarah how she has isolated herself from society, believing that she does not deserve to be treated well and is not worthy of getting support. Together, Sarah and the therapist challenge this notion of being "unworthy" and look at ways Sarah can reach out, find support and actively resist these views of herself as undeserving.

Using tenet 2, the therapist supports Sarah to generate a holistic understanding of her complex experiences—of anxiety, sleep disturbances, bereavement, as a survivor of sexual and ableist violence, and of her transgenerational and transnational experiences of anti-Semitism. With her therapist, Sarah explores the interconnectedness between her intersectional trauma and identities. For example, they look at various ways Sarah had been victimized—for being hearing impaired, as a survivor of sexual abuse, from the legacy of having a grandmother who had gone through the Holocaust and through current expressions of anti-Semitism in her community. Exploring these different forms of violence helps Sarah to understand and frame her experience differently. She can see various connections with her own experiences of silencing her trauma, and ways that her unique experiences have influenced her will to survive.

The therapist also explores the relationship between Sarah's sleep disturbances and phobias and her experiences of abuse, loss, ableism and transgenerational trauma.[2] A closer examination of her transnational and transgenerational connections brings up information about her grandmother with whom she lived and who was a Holocaust survivor. Sarah recalls the nightmares and flashbacks her grandmother would have of the atrocities that she experienced and witnessed in the concentration camps. The therapy addresses how these experiences, along with the family's silence around the grandmother's experiences and Sarah's own experiences of sexual violence, result in Sarah growing up feeling that the world is unsafe and hostile.

Using tenet 3 as a therapeutic strategy, the therapist supports Sarah to focus on building resistance and resilience personally, and with her community.

Sarah and the therapist examine her coping strategies and various options available to her to make empowering changes in her life. The therapist supports Sarah to connect with various aspects of her identity more holistically.

2. All case examples in this chapter involve transgenerational trauma.

Sarah decides to get involved with the disability community as well as her synagogue, where she asks for ASL (American Sign Language) so she can participate more fully. Sarah talks with her therapist about her shame in asking for ASL; this dialogue begins to help her feel more deserving by having the "full picture" of who she is included in the therapeutic space.

Some key questions the therapist can reflect on are:

- How can I strengthen the therapeutic alliance with clients?
- What is the relevance of intersectional identity, trauma and transnational and transgenerational connections in providing supportive mental health care?
- How can I incorporate transnational and transgenerational connections into the case conceptualizations of my clients?
- Is this client's mental health issue impacted by transgenerational trauma?
- How can a client's intersectional identities and experiences of trauma provide Clues about resistance/resilience resources needed to deal with present-day mental health crises?

Conclusion

This chapter highlighted how a trauma-informed AOP approach can support mental health practitioners with differently located client populations. Exploring the intersectionality between different forms of trauma and how they affect the mental health of these populations provides practitioners with a more informed lens so they can provide supports that better match their clients' needs.

Exploring clients' identities, along with experiences of intersectional trauma, transnational and trangenerational connections and resistance and resilience, lessens the potential for retraumatization and increases the opportunity for empowerment-centred, safer mental health practices. Understanding intersectionality is critical to gaining holistic insight into the lived experiences of clients and to lessen the biases and stigma that often occur when clients are looked at from a single or monoculturalistic lens. This encourages clients to engage in a collaborative change process with the therapist, which strengthens the therapeutic alliance.

To implement the trauma-informed AOP approach effectively, it is highly recommended that therapists and clinical providers continuously examine the AOP principles, particularly the identity trichotomy, in their own personal therapeutic work and in clinical supervision.

References

Aponte, J.E., Rivers, R.Y. & Wohl, J. (1995). *Psychological Interventions and Cultural Diversity.* Boston: Allyn & Bacon.

Cole, R. (2009). Intersectionality and research in psychology. *American Psychologist, 64,* 170–180.

Ibrahim, F. & Ohnishi, H. (2001). Posttraumatic stress disorder and the minority experience. In D. Pope-Davis & H. Coleman (Eds.), *The Intersection of Race, Class, and Gender in Multicultural Counseling.* Thousand Oaks, CA: Sage.

Sue, D.W., Capolidupo, C., Torino, G., Bucceri, J., Holder, A., Nadal, K. et al. (2007). Racial microaggressions in everyday life: Implications for clinical practice. *American Psychologist, 62,* 271–286.

Timothy, R. & Umana, M. (2009). *Anti-oppression Psychotherapy Training Guide.* Toronto: Continuing Healing Consultants.

PART 1

SECTION 2: PRACTICE

Chapter 5

Collaborative Change Conversations
Integrating Trauma-Informed Care and Motivational Interviewing with Women

Cristine Urquhart and Frances Jasiura

> *I still don't know how you [cocaine] got full control of me. It pisses*
> *me off. I wasn't supposed to go through that. That wasn't the road*
> *I was supposed to go down. It makes me angry that I allowed myself*
> *to do those things I did to myself and my son. I am the strong one.*
> *I am not a fall down. I am NOT a FALL DOWN. Never again*
> *will you take me DOWN.*
> —*Written by a participant in a women's day treatment program*

As service providers, we can only imagine the full story behind this woman's statement. We hear her passionately reclaiming her identity as someone who wants and is capable of a better life for herself. Through a motivational interviewing lens, we also pay close attention to what she is hearing herself say. By responding empathically and strategically, we encourage her to keep talking herself into, and committing to, the change she sees as possible.

With greater awareness of the interconnections between trauma, substance use and mental health, service providers are broadening their understanding of the pivotal role of violence in women's lives. Trauma-informed care recognizes the larger socio-political-historical influences on women's lives, and reframes the question from "What is wrong with her?" to "What has happened to her?" (Williams & Paul, 2008). Motivational interviewing is one approach that can guide service providers through these sensitive conversations to support positive changes in women's lives. Combining relational, principle-based work with key skills and strategies, motivational interviewing offers service providers a language and communication style that is collaborative and strives to understand the woman's world view, strengthen her sense of self, accept her as she is and encourage her to move at her own pace in the direction of the change she has identified as possible.

Miller and Rollnick define motivational interviewing as "a collaborative, person-centred form of guiding to elicit and strengthen motivation for change" (2009, p. 137). With more than 200 published clinical trials to date, this approach is well documented as measurable and learnable (Miller & Moyers, 2006; Miller & Rose, 2009). It is found to improve engagement, retention and treatment outcomes across many areas, including substance use and mental health (Hettema et al., 2005; Rollnick et al., 2008; Rubak et al., 2005). Research indicates that motivational interviewing is particularly effective with minority populations, and that it has a synergistic effect when combined with other methods (Hettema et al., 2005). Evidence supports the use of this approach to improve the health of women with substance use problems and related health concerns in both individual and group contexts (Floyd et al., 2007; Ingersoll et al., 2005; LaBrie et al., 2009; Yahne et al., 2002). Recently, motivational interviewing was found to be effective in a group program for young homeless women with multiple risk factors, including substance use, violence and trauma (Wenzel et al., 2009).

The key components of motivational interviewing, listed in Figure 1, include spirit, principles, change talk and OARS communication skills.

Figure 1: Key Components of Motivational Interviewing

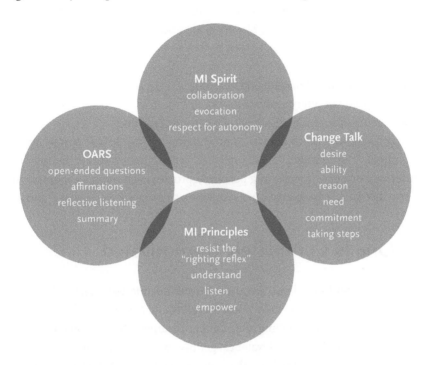

Adapted from Miller & Rollnick (2002); Rollnick et al. (2008); and Rosengren (2009).

Working in the Spirit of Motivational Interviewing

Similar to the trauma-informed view that women "grow in connection" (Harris & Fallot, 2001, p. 65), motivational interviewing indicates that motivation for change is cultivated within the collaborative relationship between the service provider and the person seeking help (Rollnick et al., 2008). Central to the spirit of both motivational interviewing and trauma-informed approaches is the perspective that women are experts on their own lives. The focus is on understanding what each woman values while evoking her own reasons for change. Thus, autonomy is encouraged while building therapeutic alliance and evoking her own desire to change.

Research has identified a number of service provider behaviours that compromise the spirit of motivational interviewing and adversely affect outcomes (Gaume et al., 2009; Moyers et al., 2007; Moyers et al., 2010). These include:

- advising without permission and warning
- directing and not offering choice
- confronting by arguing, disagreeing, shaming, labelling
- using labels such as "in denial," "non-compliant," "borderline personality," "alcoholic," "drug addict." Avoiding labels is congruent with the trauma-informed practice of reframing perceived problem behaviour as attempts to cope, disorders as responses and symptoms as adaptations (Haskell, 2003).

No One Is Completely Unmotivated

In both trauma-informed practice and motivational interviewing, service providers seek to strengthen the woman's safety and sense of self by moving at her pace and avoiding getting ahead of her readiness. Motivational interviewing understands that ambivalence, getting stuck between the costs and benefits of change, is normal and that motivation fluctuates. It is one thing for a woman to know change is important, another to believe she can do it (as with the writer of the letter to cocaine that opens this chapter) and still another to be resourced well enough to follow through on her commitment to change. From the perspective of motivational interviewing, no one is completely unmotivated (Rollnick et al., 2008), and the service provider remains curious to discover what—to the person—is relevant, important, possible and consistent with her world view, personal values, present capacities and priorities.

Research indicates that individual levels of motivation are significantly influenced by the communication style of the service provider. This is a particularly important premise when working with women with trauma/ violence, substance use and mental health concerns. Individual responses (or lack thereof) and behaviour can often be misinterpreted as not caring or lacking motivation: "You would think the threat of violence and losing your children would be enough to leave an abusive relationship/stop using substances." That understanding can leave service providers feeling stuck, frustrated, even helpless. Just as the trauma-informed approach reminds service providers to honour the complexities of the woman's situation, motivational interviewing helps them consciously move away from dismissive, categorical thinking with the subtle shift from "Why isn't this person motivated?" to "For what is this person motivated?" (Miller & Rollnick, 2002, p. 18).

Change Talk: What People Say about Change Matters

People talk themselves into and out of change. One of the key components of motivational interviewing is its strategic emphasis on recognizing, drawing out and reinforcing a specific type of speech identified as change talk. Listening to what people say about change indicates how likely they are to change (Rollnick et al., 2008). Change talk, expressed in statements of desire, ability, reasons and need, forms the building blocks of readiness. Commitment statements (i.e., I will, I promise) and taking steps have been shown to predict change (Amrhein et al., 2003). As an example, in the quote that begins this chapter, change talk is recognized in "I am the strong one" (expressing ability). Using OARS (as depicted in Figure 1), the service provider guides the conversation toward change by carefully drawing out and strengthening those moments when the person expresses confidence and commitment to change.

Understanding the mechanism of change talk is crucial when working with someone who is ambivalent and asking herself "Should I or shouldn't I change? Can I/Can't I? Will I/Won't I?" The service provider who falls into persuasion, for example, by offering all the reasons why the woman should leave her abusive partner, unwittingly elicits her reasons not to change (sustain talk). These exchanges lead to "Yes . . . but" conversations, such as when the woman responds to persuasion with "Yes, but he's a good father . . . ." The service provider is on the wrong side of the conversation; as the woman hears herself argue against change, she consequently becomes more committed to the status quo.

Resisting the "Righting Reflex"

In motivational interviewing, resisting the righting reflex—the natural desire to fix, give advice, make better or even prevent harm from happening (Miller & Rollnick, 2002)—aligns with the trauma-informed emphasis on minimizing potential revictimization and focusing instead on creating safety in the relationship (Elliot et al., 2005). Rather than telling the woman what to do, and why she should do it, the service provider effectively draws out the woman's own reasons, motivations and possibilities for change.

Instead of acting as the authority or trying to persuade the woman, the service provider offers a response consistent with motivational interviewing that respects her autonomy and decisions. Working collaboratively, they together are curious about the areas in the woman's life where she does have influence, such as self-care and safety planning (Motivational Interviewing and Intimate Partner Violence Workgroup, 2009; Wahab, 2006). Sharing power and collaborative decision-making are benchmarks in both trauma-informed care and motivational interviewing. At the same time, it is important to note that motivational interviewing is not an approach for every situation. Service providers use their clinical judgment and ethical guidelines to assess situations and shift to appropriate interventions. For example, they may move to a more directive style when issues of safety (risk of harm to self or others) arise.

Strategies for Getting Started

Motivational interviewing involves a combination of relational (empathy and spirit) and technical skills (differential eliciting and strengthening of change talk) (Miller & Rose, 2009). Complex reflections are a necessary skill in motivational interviewing conversations and are used strategically to engage, understand and guide change. Two strategies that integrate well with trauma-informed approaches are collaborative agenda setting and providing information in a way that is consistent with motivational interviewing, known as elicit-provide-elicit (Rollnick et al., 2008). Although several strategies are practised within motivational interviewing, if they are used in isolation of the spirit and principles, it is not a motivational interviewing conversation (Miller & Rollnick, 2009).

The following dialogue captures segments of a conversation that is consistent with motivational interviewing between a social worker, nurse, physician or therapist and a woman who is coming to a substance use or mental health outpatient clinic for the first time. In this scenario, the woman is 30 years old, lives by herself and works as a cashier. She has many health and social concerns, including alcohol and tobacco use, depression, anxiety, financial struggles, social isolation and a history of trauma. This section is drawn mid-conversation, without obvious beginnings or endings.

Service provider: Thanks, Sarah, for sharing that information with me. It isn't always easy talking to someone you don't know. . . . Many of the women I talk with, as we get started, have identified several topics helpful to talk about, such as nutrition, self-care, substance use, safety. And maybe there is something else on your mind today that you want to talk about?

Approach: affirmation; collaborative agenda setting; identifying topics and parameters for the conversation in a non-threatening way. The service provider makes no assumptions about what is most important to the woman or where the conversation might start, and instead invites her to substantially influence the direction of their time together.

Woman: Well, I did want to talk a bit about my sleep. I guess that could fit under self-care. And I know I should look at exercise.

Service provider: So you have a couple of things coming up—sleep, exercise. What else?

Approach: reflection; open question

Woman: No, that's it.

Service provider: So, sounds like this a good place for us to start.

Approach: reflection; collaborative agenda setting

Woman: Yeah, my sleep is really bothering me. That's part of the reason going on and he's on me about my smoking and drinking.

Service provider: Things have changed and you're not feeling yourself.

Approach: complex reflection; avoids the trap of focusing on one topic too quickly

Woman: I have been stressing about money big time! My shifts are getting cut at work. And when I don't work, I end up staying at home—sometimes for days at a time. Just too depressed to get off the couch. So I sit and smoke all day, and in the evenings my neighbour comes by and we have a couple of drinks.

Service provider: The stress is paralyzing you.

Approach: complex reflection

Woman: Yeah! I need to keep busy or things just fall apart.

Service provider: This has happened before . . . and you have some ideas about what to do.

Approach: complex reflection; strengthening autonomy and self-efficacy

Woman: Nothing is worse than being in your head all the time.

Service provider: There are things you don't want to think about, and the cigarettes and alcohol seem to be helping, and you're here today trying to figure this all out.

Approach: complex reflection; working in a trauma-informed way, without judgment and recognizing attempts to cope

Woman: Yeah, I never thought of it that way. I just need to get some more sleep. The alcohol helps a bit to get to sleep, but not stay asleep.

Service provider: It doesn't last. I wonder what you have heard about how alcohol, depression and sleep relate to one another?

Approach: complex reflection of change talk; open question, moving toward providing information (eliciting what she already knows)

Woman: I know that sometimes if I drink too much wine, I feel even more depressed than usual. I always figured alcohol helps you to sleep though.

Service provider: It can be confusing. Would you be interested in hearing a little bit more about the connection?

Approach: complex reflection; closed question, eliciting permission to share information

Woman: Sure.

Service provider: [provides information on connections between alcohol, depression and sleep] . . . I appreciate some of this may be new information to you, Sarah, and I'm wondering how it might fit for you, if at all?

Approach: open-ended question; eliciting woman's understanding in her own words; strengthening autonomy and choice with "if at all"

Woman: Makes sense, I guess. Sounds like I might be doing myself more harm than good.

REFLECTION EXERCISE

Reflecting on this conversation, the following questions may help you consider when and how motivational interviewing can support your work with women:

1. What stands out for you, if anything, about how the agenda was set?
2. What might have happened if the service provider had focused on the smoking and drinking immediately after the woman mentioned it?
3. Where might you go next with this conversation?
4. Identify examples of the motivational interviewing spirit (autonomy, collaboration, evocation).
5. What trauma-informed and motivational interviewing principles were demonstrated in this dialogue?

Conclusion

There are many parallels between working in a trauma-informed way and motivational interviewing. Both identify a collaborative rather than power- or expert-based approach. The woman sets the pace and the service provider avoids getting ahead of her readiness. Both are strengths-based approaches that aim to amplify the woman's self-efficacy by guiding the conversation toward those changes she identifies as possible and important. Motivational interviewing brings a fresh understanding to change conversations by evoking and strengthening the woman's own natural change talk. Strategic use of specific communication skills and motivational-interviewing strategies equip service providers to work in a trauma-informed way. The combination of the technical and relational components of motivational interviewing constitutes the guiding framework for practice that is consistent with this approach, making it possible to integrate trauma-informed concepts into collaborative conversations for change. As a communication style to support change, motivational interviewing can help to increase service providers' confidence and skill when working with women with complex health and social concerns. A breadth of research supports the success of motivational interviewing in engaging and retaining people in care and encouraging healthier outcomes in their lives.

References

Amrhein, P.C., Miller, W.R., Yahne, C.E., Palmer, M. & Fulcher, L. (2003). Client commitment language during motivational interviewing predicts drug use outcomes. *Journal of Consulting and Clinical Psychology, 71*, 862–876.

Elliott, D.E., Bjelajac, P., Fallot, R., Markoff, L.S. & Glover Reed, B. (2005). Trauma-informed or trauma-denied: Principles and implementation of trauma-informed services for women. *Journal of Community Psychology, 33,* 461–477.

Floyd, R.L., Sobell, M., Velasquez, M.M., Ingersoll, K., Nettleman, M., Sobell, L. et al. (2007). Preventing alcohol exposed pregnancies: A randomized control trial. *American Journal of Preventive Medicine, 32,* 1–10.

Gaume, J., Gmel, G., Faouzi, M., & Daeppen, J.B. (2009). Counselor skill influences outcomes of brief motivational interventions. *Journal of Substance Abuse Treatment, 37,* 151–159.

Harris, M. & Fallot, R.D. (Eds.). (2001). Using Trauma Theory to Design Service Systems [Special issue]. *New Directions for Mental Health Services, 89.*

Haskell, L. (2003). *First Stage Trauma Treatment: A Guide for Mental Health Professionals Working with Women.* Toronto: Centre for Addiction and Mental Health.

Hettema, J., Steele, J. & Miller, W.R. (2005). Motivational interviewing. *Annual Review of Clinical Psychology, 1,* 91–111.

Ingersoll, K.S., Ceperich, S.D., Nettleman, M.D., Karanda, K., Brocksen, S. & Johnson, B.A. (2005). Reducing alcohol-exposed pregnancy risk in college women: Initial outcomes of a clinical trial of a motivational intervention. *Journal of Substance Abuse Treatment, 29,* 173–180.

LaBrie, J.W., Huchting, K., Lac, A., Tawalbeh, S., Thompson, A.D. & Larimer, M. (2009). Preventing risky drinking in first-year college women: Further validation of a female-specific motivational-enhancement group intervention. *Journal of Studies on Alcohol and Drugs, 16,* 77–85.

Miller, W.R. & Moyers, T.B. (2006). Eight stages in learning motivational interviewing. *Journal of Teaching in the Addictions, 5*(1), 3–17.

Miller, W.R. & Rollnick, S. (2002). *Motivational Interviewing: Preparing People for Change* (2nd ed.). New York: Guilford Press.

Miller, W.R. & Rollnick, S. (2009). Ten things that motivational interviewing is not. *Behavioural and Cognitive Psychotherapy, 37,* 129–140.

Miller, W.R. & Rose, G.S. (2009). Toward a theory of motivational interviewing. *American Psychologist, 64,* 527–537.

Motivational Interviewing and Intimate Partner Violence Workgroup. (2009). Guiding as practice: Motivational interviewing and trauma-informed work with survivors of intimate partner violence. *Partner Abuse, 1,* 92–104.

Moyers, T.B., Martin, T., Christopher, P.J., Houck, J.M., Tonigan, J.S. & Amrhein, P.C. (2007). Client language as a mediator of motivational interviewing efficacy: Where is the evidence? *Alcoholism: Clinical and Experimental Research, 31* (Suppl. 3), 40–47.

Moyers, T.B., Martin, J.K., Miller, W.R. & Ernst, D. (2010). *Revised Global Scales: Motivational Interviewing Treatment Integrity 3.1.1.* Retrieved from http://casaa.unm.edu/download/ MITI3_1.pdf

Rollnick, S., Miller, W.R. & Butler, C.C. (2008). *Motivational Interviewing in Health Care: Helping Patients Change Behavior.* New York: Guilford Press.

Rosengren, D.B. (2009). *Building Motivational Interviewing Skills.* New York: Guilford Press.

Rubak, S., Sandbæk, A., Lauritzen, T. & Christensen, B. (2005). Motivational interviewing: A systematic review and meta-analysis. *British Journal of General Practice, 55,* 305–312.

Wahab, S. (2006). Motivational interviewing: A client centred and directive counseling style for work with victims of domestic violence. *Areté, 29*(2), 11–22.

Wenzel, S.L. D'Amico, E.J., Barnes, D. & Gilbert, M.L. (2009). A pilot of a tripartite prevention program for homeless young women in the transition to adulthood. *Women's Health Issues, 19,* 193–201.

Williams, J. & Paul, J. (2008). *Informed Gender Practice: Mental Health Acute Care That Works for Women.* London, UK: National Institute for Mental Health in England.

Yahne, C.E., Miller, W.R., Irvin-Vitela, L. & Tonigan, J.S. (2002). Magdalena pilot project: Motivational outreach to substance abusing women street sex workers. *Journal of Substance Abuse Treatment, 23,* 49–53.

Chapter 6

Cognitive-Behavioural Therapy for Psychosis

A Trauma-Informed Praxis*

Maria Haarmans

> *But the word is more than just an instrument which makes dialogue possible. . . . Within the word we find two dimensions, reflection and action, in such radical interaction that if one is sacrificed—even in part—the other immediately suffers. There is no true word that is not at the same time a praxis. Thus, to speak a true word is to transform the world.*
>
> *—Paulo Freire,* Pedagogy of the Oppressed

Emerging research is demonstrating clear links between psychosis and trauma, particularly childhood trauma. Yet trauma within psychosis is often undiagnosed or untreated (Callcott et al., 2004). Cognitive-behavioural therapy for psychosis (CBTp) has been gaining considerable attention as an effective treatment approach. It has advantages over other psychosocial approaches, such as supportive therapy, in that it is evidence-based and, unlike biochemical treatments alone, addresses the trauma element in psychosis. Due to an expanding empirical base for the effectiveness of CBTp, clinical guidelines recommend its use in several countries, including the United States, and in the United Kingdom, where the National Health Service

---

* I have deliberately chosen the term "praxis" to emphasize the importance of collaboration and reflection and action (or integrating theory with practice). It is important for the therapist and client, through a process of mutual dialogue, shared reflection and action, to be conscious of and acknowledge how socio-political conditions affect human experience. Adopting an anti-oppressive practice, or praxis, is a critical part of a trauma-informed approach.

mandates its use for anyone with a psychosis diagnosis (Addington et al., 2005; Dixon et al., 2010; Lehman et al., 2004; McGorry, 2005; National Institute for Clinical Excellence, 2002; National Institute for Health and Clinical Excellence, 2009).

This chapter focuses on two principles of trauma-informed mental health care that are integral to CBTp: adopting an empowerment model and linking current difficulties or symptoms to past trauma. The chapter reviews the literature on trauma and psychosis and outlines how CBTp is consistent with a trauma-informed approach. A trauma-informed approach to mental health care in general has been growing in popularity, not only with service providers, who may have been frustrated with the limitations of other models to help their clients, but with clients themselves.

Empirical Support for the Link between Trauma and Psychosis

Experiences of trauma are increasingly being recognized as common in the lives of people with psychosis. Mueser et al. (1998) noted that 98 per cent of people diagnosed with a serious mental illness had a history of trauma and 48 per cent met criteria for posttraumatic stress disorder (PTSD). Romme and Escher (1989) found that 70 per cent of people who hear voices developed their hallucinations following a traumatic event. More recent studies are also finding a high prevalence of trauma histories in people with psychosis (Bentall & Fernyhough, 2008; Morgan & Fisher, 2007; Read et al., 2008); in groups at "ultra-high risk" for psychosis (Bechdolf et al., 2010); in people with psychotic experiences from large epidemiological samples (Bebbington et al., 2004; Bebbington et al., 2011; Janssen et al., 2004; Shevlin et al., 2007); and in studies using a case-control design (Cutajar et al., 2010). In fact, a recent meta-analysis found a strong association between childhood adversity and psychosis (Varese et al., 2012).

The literature reveals three main possible relationships between trauma and psychosis:

- an increased understanding of the subjective experience of psychotic phenomena and their sequelae (e.g., forced hospitalization, medication, restraints and seclusion after entering the mental health system and subsequent victimization in the community or in hospital [sexual assaults on wards]) as traumas associated with PTSD (Bentall et al., 2006; Jackson & Birchwood, 2006; Jankowski et al., 2006)

- psychosis and PTSD as part of a spectrum of possible responses to trauma (e.g., hallucinations as decontextualized trauma flashbacks) (Morrison et al., 2003; Read, Van Os et al., 2005). Interestingly, Morrison (2001) suggests that it is the cultural unacceptability of the person's interpretation of psychotic phenomena (such as hallucinations) that is related to the person being diagnosed with psychosis as opposed to being diagnosed with PTSD symptoms.
- trauma as an etiological pathway of psychosis, particularly the association of hallucinated voices and childhood sexual abuse (Brabban & Callcott, 2010; Elklit & Shevlin, 2011; Larkin & Morrison, 2006a; Read et al., 2008).

Severe and Prolonged Abuse Raises Risk

In a comprehensive review of the literature on trauma and psychosis, Read et al. (2008) found that child maltreatment (i.e., emotional, physical and sexual abuse, neglect and bullying) was significantly related to psychosis in 10 out of 11 recent general population studies, even after controlling for other variables such as family history. Eight of these studies found a dose-response, meaning that the more severe and prolonged the abuse, the more likely the person was to develop psychosis. In a study examining the effects of cumulative traumas, people who had experienced three types of trauma (sexual abuse, bullying, violence in the home) were 18 times more likely to have psychosis than people who were not abused. People who had experienced five types of trauma were 193 times more likely to have psychosis (Shevlin et al., 2008). Another study, which followed more than 4,000 Dutch people for three years, revealed that people abused as children (of which women represented more than half of the sample) were nine times more likely to develop psychosis and that people who experienced the most severe level of abuse were 48 times more likely to develop psychosis (Janssen et al., 2004). The meta-analysis by Varese et al. (2012) found this 50-fold increased risk in people who had severe and multiple traumas consistent across the different studies they analyzed.

Lack of Sex- and Gender-Based Analysis

Unfortunately, most studies on schizophrenia do not provide information on sex separately or examine gender (the sociocultural construct) (Nasser et al., 2002). In some of the few studies that have recruited large numbers of women, researchers have "controlled for sex" rather than treating women and gender as important areas to explore (Read et al., 2008; Taylor & Bragado-Jemenz, 2009). An exception to this is Shevlin et al.'s (2007) analysis of non-institutionalized samples in the United States: they found that childhood physical abuse predicted psychosis in both sexes, with rape being more predictive for males than females. In a critical review of trauma and childhood abuse in schizophrenia, Morgan and Fisher (2007) report that females experienced more sexual abuse than males. Another study that examined the association of childhood abuse and psychosis by sex found that reports of severe childhood physical and sexual abuse were associated with psychosis in women but not in men and that women were 2.6 times more likely to have been either sexually or physically abused than men (Fisher et al., 2009).

In a study examining the association between trauma history and development of psychosis in individuals assessed to be at "ultra-high risk," investigators found that a history of sexual trauma predicted eventual diagnosis of a psychotic disorder (Bechdolf et al., 2010), and rates of trauma, especially sexual traumas —rape and sexual molestation—were significantly higher for females (Thompson et al., 2010). Another recent study from Denmark found that females who experienced sexual abuse were 10 times more likely to later receive a diagnosis of psychosis than those who were not sexually abused (Elklit & Shevlin, 2011). A more recent study using data from the 2007 Adult Psychiatric Morbidity Survey in England has revealed in this community sample that the link between sexual abuse and psychosis was stronger in women than men (Bebbington et al., 2011). Reviews of inpatient and outpatient samples revealed that family members were perpetrators in more than half of childhood sexual abuse cases among girls and in about a quarter of cases among boys (Read et al., 2008). Read et al.'s (2008) review of 59 studies of inpatients and outpatients revealed different rates of childhood sexual abuse for males and females, with a weighted average of 46.9 per cent for females and 28.7 per cent for males. Cutajar et al. (2010) reported a significantly higher rate of abuse involving penetration for females than for males. In this study, involving 2,759 children who had experienced sexual abuse, 79.8 per cent were female. When males and females with histories of childhood sexual abuse were examined separately, rates for psychosis were significantly higher for both males and females compared to controls, and rates of schizophrenic disorders remained significantly higher for females. However, when cases with penetration only were analyzed, the difference in rate of schizophrenic disorders between females and males disappeared. The combination of experiencing penetrative abuse, being over age 12 and having more than one abuser resulted in a 15-fold increase in risk of psychosis.

Such studies that have used a sex- and gender-based analysis reveal differential rates and impacts of trauma, underlining the importance of this approach to analysis, as well as the need for gender-specific models of CBTp.

Why Don't More Clinicians in the Psychosis Field Use a Trauma-Informed Approach?

While research is advancing our understanding of the complex and multiple relationships between trauma and psychosis, adapting services to reflect this link has been much slower (Morrissey et al., 2005; Read, 2005). By privileging a biogenetic model to explain the etiology of psychosis, many clinicians ignore trauma-informed approaches that acknowledge the social determinants of mental health (Larkin & Read, 2008) and are unlikely to assess for abuse in the first place (Bentall, 2009; Read et al., 2007; Read, Van Os et al., 2005; Young et al., 2001). Clinicians may also minimize or ignore the significance of trauma because they lack training in how to ask about and respond to childhood abuse (Read et al., 2007) or because they assume that the client's report of trauma is part of the psychosis and therefore unreliable (Mueser et al., 2002). However, research demonstrates that such reports are as reliable as those of the general population (Darves-Bornoz et al., 1995; Goodman et al., 1997).

One of the major implications of this research is recognition that we need to ask service users about traumatic events in their life history. CBTp experts assert that failing to do so will "'impede installation of appropriate treatment strategies' and therefore prolong distress unnecessarily" (Read, Morrison et al.,

2005, p. 327).[1] Failing to assess and treat the trauma element in psychosis can contribute to vicious cycles that maintain the problem.

CBTp as a Trauma-Informed Practice

According to Denby et al. (2008), "It is not the event that determines whether something is traumatic, but the individual's experience of the event" (p. 17). This is consistent with the underlying philosophy of CBT that it is not the event (e.g., hallucinated voices) that causes distress, but rather the person's interpretation of the event or the meaning he or she ascribes to it; for example, "This means I am going crazy" or "It is an evil spirit punishing me" (Morrison et al., 2004). While various clinical research centres around the world have developed different "brands" of CBTp with varying emphasis and practice (Tarrier, 2007), all share this underlying philosophy.

The literature identifies several important principles guiding trauma-informed practice (Burke et al., 2010; Denby et al., 2008; Elliot et al., 2005; Harris & Fallot, 2001). Two principles of trauma-informed mental health care—using an empowerment model of practice and linking current difficulties or "symptoms" to trauma/life experiences—are fundamental to CBTp and are discussed here, focusing on models from the United Kingdom, where CBTp has advanced considerably in the last 30 years (Chadwick, 2006; Chadwick et al, 1996; French & Morrison, 2004; Gumley & Schwannauer, 2006; Larkin & Morrison, 2006b; Morrison et al., 2004).

Applying these principles is essential in order to prevent retraumatization and/or premature dropout among clients with trauma histories. Harris and Fallot (2001) recommend "universal precautions": "since providers have no way of distinguishing survivors from non-survivors, best practices are those that treat all [women] as if they might be trauma survivors. . ." (Elliot et al., 2005, p. 463). This practice is especially important when working with individuals with a psychosis diagnosis. One study revealed that the average length of time for girls to disclose childhood sexual abuse was 16 years (Read et al., 2006).

---

1. See Read et al. (2007) for an in-depth discussion of trauma assessment.

An Empowerment Model

In trauma-informed practice, an empowerment model is critical for recovery from the sense of powerlessness and fear related to a history of victimization. It encompasses the following overlapping principles, with a shared aim of "increasing the client's power in personal, interpersonal and political spheres" (Elliot et al., 2005, p. 465). Empowerment involves:

- collaboration—maximizing the client's choices and control over the treatment process in order to provide a corrective to the experience as a powerless victim (e.g., goals of the work are established collaboratively)
- sharing information, educating and teaching coping strategies
- normalizing responses typically defined as "symptoms" within the medical model
- expanding the client's resources and support networks and decreasing reliance on professional services
- understanding the client's issues as created or shaped by his or her socio-political and cultural context.

Collaboration

A trauma-informed approach recognizes that the experience of collaboration provides both the client and service provider with increased self-worth, competence and comfort in taking action on personal goals (Elliott et al., 2005). The following are some of the key processes in CBTp, as outlined by CBT founder Aaron Beck, which aim to achieve this increased sense of self-efficacy, ensure choice and promote collaboration (Morrison et al., 2004):

- The client decides the problems from his or her problem list with which to get help. These problems are then prioritized and transformed into short- and long-term goals for therapy.
- An agenda for what will be covered during the session is decided on collaboratively at the start of each session.
- The therapist seeks specific feedback from the client about key points and insights and any negative reactions to both the previous and current sessions. (One of the aims of this process is to promote mutual understanding with the meta-message that the client's perceptions and feelings are important and respected. Another purpose is to provide continuity and reinforce important skills and/or knowledge learned.)

- Homework or coping strategies the client has tried in the previous week are reviewed to assess how well they worked and any conclusions the client made afterward are discussed.
- Regular capsule summaries and feedback by the therapist to check for understanding on the part of both therapist and client can be especially helpful for individuals whose psychotic experiences, such as hearing voices, may influence communication and information-processing. This process also helps to acknowledge the client's viewpoint, allowing him or her to feel listened to and understood (French & Morrison, 2004).
- The therapist seeks the client's ideas about what might be helpful to do between sessions for new homework as opposed to "assigning" a task.

Psychoeducation and teaching coping strategies

According to Schachter et al. (2008), sharing information involves "a mutual process of information exchange in which both parties feel heard and understood" (p. 20). CBTp therapists educate clients about the psychological processes involved in experiences of distress (e.g., anxiety and depression) and the cognitive model of anomalous experiences. This model explains how hallucinations and unusual beliefs or delusions influence our thoughts, behaviours, physiological responses and mood and how these interactions generate or maintain psychotic experiences. However, clients are considered experts on their experience, and a guided discovery or "Socratic questioning" approach is used to increase understanding of these interactions (Padesky, 1993).

Helping clients to build skills and develop coping strategies is also important in order for clients to manage distressing psychotic experiences, such as hallucinated voices, recognizing that the goal is not necessarily to eliminate these experiences (Morrison et al., 2004).

Coping strategies that the client has been using and found effective are reinforced as demonstrating his or her strength in dealing with the voices. In addition, coping strategies that other "voice hearers" have found helpful are shared and presented as options to try. Identifying idiosyncratic triggers or cues for voice hearing is also empowering, as some people who hear voices do not recognize that there are triggers for their voices (Chadwick et al., 1996). This is similar to helping abuse survivors identify emotional triggers to their trauma, challenging their belief that internal responses arise out of nowhere, which results in feeling fearful and powerless (Harris & Fallot, 2001).

Triggers can assume various forms, such as internal bodily sensations; emotional states; thoughts and memories; interpersonal dynamics, such as being criticized or judged; or sensory experiences, such as sights, sounds and smells. By identifying these triggers, the person can feel more in control and less vulnerable. Sometimes these triggers are directly related to abuse; other times they may be less obviously connected to the trauma survivor's history (Harris & Fallot, 2001). For example, one client's hallucinations were triggered by the colour red; only after some time did she realize that this was the colour of her abuser's shirt. Triggers may also be settings perceived as psychologically or interpersonally threatening, such as crowded buses or formal situations (Chadwick et al., 1996).

Learning to use coping strategies such as voice diaries and evaluating the content of critical hallucinations can increase clients' sense of control over the experience and lessen their depression (Morrison et al., 2005). This approach is consistent with Harris and Fallot's (2001) emphasis on helping clients to build skills, rather than simply reduce "symptoms." Education about abuse and trauma are provided according to the individual formulation. Individuals often do not define their experiences as abuse, nor do they have an under-standing of PTSD. Clients can learn grounding and self-soothing techniques, such as breathing exercises, to help themselves cope with PTSD symptoms.

Normalizing responses

It is important for clients to learn that their responses are normal, given their experiences (Harris & Fallot, 2001). In CBTp, helping clients to identify links between their traumatic experiences and current psychotic phenomena via the individual formulation also helps to normalize these experiences, reduce distress and increase perceived control (Morrison et al., 2005).

Normalizing these experiences involves depathologizing unusual perceptual experiences and beliefs as part of the continuum of normal experience by presenting information about their prevalence in the general population. For example, 10 to 25 per cent of the general population has a lifetime incidence for hearing voices; and up to 70 per cent describe delusional beliefs (Morrison et al.,

2004). High incidences of hallucinations among the general population are known to occur following trauma, bereavement, sleep deprivation, solitary confinement, hostage situations, sensory deprivation and upon falling asleep or waking (Morrison et al., 2004). Presenting this information helps to improve clients' self-esteem and reduce their "fear of going mad." These kinds of facts are destigmatizing and deshaming and enable clients to feel less isolated and better understand these experiences as psychological phenomena (Kingdon & Turkington, 2005). The deshaming process is often twofold for people with a psychosis diagnosis: they may have internalized stigma of the diagnosis and shame from the childhood trauma, particularly childhood sexual abuse.

Expanding the client's resources and support networks
Expanding the client's sense of support includes helping clients "become their own therapist" and use the skills they have learned on their own (Chadwick, 2006; Morrison et al., 2004) without relying on professionals. Introducing clients to peer support groups such as the Hearing Voices Network or INTERVOICE, an international online forum for voice hearers, will also help them to become less reliant on the mental health system.

Making Sense of Psychotic Experiences: Connecting Trauma to Current "Symptoms"

One of the fundamental principles of CBTp is that the therapy is based on an ever-evolving formulation of the client's difficulties or a "working hypothesis" of why a problem developed, how it is maintained and how problems are related to the person's life history and core beliefs about self, others/world and future and the experiences that have shaped these beliefs (Bentall & Fernyhough 2008; Larkin & Morrison, 2006a; Read, 2005). This formulation involves an ongoing collaborative process of collecting data to develop a shared understanding of the client's difficulties, incorporating personal life history and context (Gumley & Schwannauer, 2006) and should include the impact of socio-political issues such as culture, race, class and gender. Such an analysis is part of "conscientization" or critical consciousness-raising (Freire, 1993, p. 25), which is particularly important for addressing the self-blame and sense of powerlessness that many trauma survivors experience and is consistent with a culturally responsive approach (Ivey, 1995). Traumatic or adverse life events are linked to current psychotic experiences such as hallucinations and/or delusions, which helps to make sense of and demystify these phenomena.

Making sense of psychotic experiences may also involve understanding the meaning in the themes and content of voices and delusions (Bebbington et al., 2004). While highly personal and idiosyncratic, psychotic phenomena are not "un-understandable," as has been supposed since Karl Jaspers in the early 1900s made the distinction between the understandable symptoms of anxiety and depressive disorders and "un-understandable" symptoms of psychosis, asserting that the content of delusions and hallucinations were meaningless (Bentall, 2003). The content is often based, directly or symbolically, on memories of childhood trauma (Morrison et al., 2003; Read et al., 2008) and may express the client's core beliefs about self, others/world and/or future (Bentall & Fernyhough, 2008; Brabban & Callcott, 2010).

Though many times the difficulties a client experiences may seem quite unrelated to the trauma, the content of hallucinations or delusions may be metaphorical or symbolic of the abuse (Shulman, 1996). In studies examining content of psychotic phenomena, investigators found relationships between sexual trauma and content of both attenuated and full-blown psychotic symptoms, such as delusions of being watched in the shower, hallucinations of sexual content, content of trauma directly corresponding to the content of hallucinations, and/or themes of trauma corresponding to themes of hallucinations (Hardy et al., 2005; Thompson et al., 2010). By making these links and understanding behaviours in context, what are traditionally labelled as psychotic "symptoms" are reframed as functional "survival strategies," especially at the time they developed, though they may not have changed to reflect the person's current environment and have outlived their usefulness (Morrison et al., 2004). Harris & Fallot (2001) write:

> This way of looking at behaviours allows trauma survivors to reclaim the positive coping aspects of their symptoms. . . . As women come to see the power in their defences and coping strategies, they also come to believe that they have the strength and the wisdom to make changes in their lives. (p. 15)

Elliott et al. (2005) point out:

> The medical model highlights pathology and inadvertently gives the impression that there is something wrong with a person *rather than that something wrong was done to that person* [italics added]. . . . Understanding a symptom as an adaptation reduces the client's guilt and shame, increases her self-esteem, and provides a guideline for developing new skills and resources to allow new and better adaptations to the current situation. (p. 467)

Conclusion

A growing body of empirical evidence supports the link between trauma and psychosis. Regardless of clinicians' beliefs about the etiology of psychosis, a trauma-informed approach to CBTp benefits clients. An integral part of assessment and developing the CBTp individual formulation is considering the possible role of trauma in the development and maintenance of distressing psychotic experiences and asking about it. The role of trauma is not limited to adverse life experiences, but may also include the traumatic reaction to the subjective experience of psychosis and traumatization or retraumatization from forced hospitalization via police; from the use of physical and/or chemical restraints; or from subsequent victimization in the community. Read et al. (2007) point out that while not everyone is convinced that childhood abuse is a risk factor for psychosis and schizophrenia, "psychiatrists do not have to be convinced of a causal relationship to each and every diagnostic category to understand the importance of asking the people they are trying to help what has happened in their lives" (p. 102). And as Bentall (2009) has poignantly described when advocating complaints-based research and practice:

> By focusing on symptoms rather than diagnoses, we can see how the experiences of patients arise understandably from their misfortunes. Far from assuming that abnormal cerebral functioning is the primary cause of illness, complaints-orientated research shows that the troubled brain cannot be considered in isolation from the social universe. Clinically, it leads us to recognize that the stories patients

tell us are important, and that there is a very thin dividing line between the "them" who are ill and the "us" who are sane. (p. 182)

References

Addington, D., Bouchard, R., Goldberg, J.O., Honer, B., Malla, A., Norman, R. et al. (2005). Canadian clinical practice guidelines for the treatment of schizophrenia. *Canadian Journal of Psychiatry, 50* (Suppl. 1), 29–36.

Bebbington, P., Bhugra, D., Brugha, T., Singleton, N., Farrell, M., Jenkins, R. et al. (2004). Psychosis, victimization, and childhood disadvantage: Evidence from the second British national survey of psychiatric morbidity. *British Journal of Psychiatry, 185,* 220–226.

Bebbington, P., Jonas, S., Kuipers, E., King, M., Cooper, C., Bhugra, T. et al. (2011). Childhood sexual abuse and psychosis: Data from a cross-sectional national psychiatric survey in England. *British Journal of Psychiatry, 199,* 29–37.

Bechdolf, A., Thompson, A., Nelson, B., Cotton, S., Simmons, M.B., Amminger, G.P. et al. (2010). Experience of trauma and conversion to psychosis in an ultra-high-risk (prodromal) group. *Acta Psychiatrica Scandinavica, 121,* 377–384.

Bentall, R.P. (2003). *Madness Explained: Psychosis and Human Nature.* London, UK: Penguin.

Bentall, R.P. (2009). *Doctoring the Mind: Is Our Current Treatment of Mental Illness Really Any Good?* New York: New York University Press.

Bentall, R.P. & Fernyhough, C. (2008). Social predictors of psychotic experiences: Specificity and psychological mechanisms. *Schizophrenia Bulletin, 34,* 1012–1020.

Bentall, S., McGorry, P. & Krstev, H. (2006). The trauma of being psychotic: An analysis of posttraumatic stress disorder in response to acute psychosis. In W. Larkin & A.P. Morrison (Eds.), *Trauma and Psychosis: New Directions for Theory and Therapy* (pp. 239–258). East Sussex, UK: Routledge.

Brabban, A. & Callcott, P. (2010, May 20–21). *CBT and the Treatment of Psychosis, Trauma and Dissociation.* Workshop at the Royal Ottawa Mental Health Centre, Ottawa, ON.

Burke, P., Chapman, C., Hohman, M., Manthey, T., Slack, K., Stout, D. et al. (2010). Guiding as practice: Motivational interviewing and trauma-informed work with survivors of intimate partner violence. *Partner Abuse, 1,* 92–104.

Callcott, P., Standart, S. & Turkington, D. (2004). Trauma within psychosis: Using a CBT model for PTSD in psychosis. *Behavioural and Cognitive Psychotherapy, 32,* 239–244.

Chadwick, P. (2006). *Person-Based Cognitive Therapy for Distressing Psychosis.* Chichester, UK: John Wiley & Sons.

Chadwick, P.D.J., Birchwood, M.J. & Trower, P. (1996). *Cognitive Therapy for Delusions, Voices and Paranoia.* Chichester, UK: John Wiley & Sons.

Cutajar, M.C., Mullen, P.E., Ogloff, J.R.P., Thomas, S.D., Wells, D.L. & Spataro, J. (2010). Schizophrenia and other psychotic disorders in a cohort of sexually abused children. *Archives of General Psychiatry, 67*, 1114–1119.

Darves-Bornoz, J.M., Lemperiere, T., Degiovanni, A. & Gaillard, P. (1995). Sexual victimisation in women with schizophrenia and bipolar disorder. *Social Psychiatry and Psychiatric Epidemiology, 30*, 78–84.

Denby, C., Winslow, C., Willette, C., Bergen, E., Toole, K., Richardson, K. et al. (2008). *Trauma-Informed: The Trauma Toolkit.* Winnipeg, MB: Klinic Community Health Centre. Retrieved from www.trauma-informed.ca

Dixon, L.B., Dickerson, F., Bellack, A.S., Bennett, M., Dickinson, D., Goldberg, R.W. et al. (2010). The 2009 Schizophrenia PORT psychosocial treatment recommendations and summary statements. *Schizophrenia Bulletin, 36*, 48–70.

Elklit, A. & Shevlin, M. (2011). Female victimization predicts psychosis: A case-control study based on the Danish Registry System. *Schizophrenia Bulletin, 37*, 1305–1310.

Elliott, D.E., Bjelajac, P., Fallot, R.D., Markoff, L.S. & Reed, B.G. (2005). Trauma-informed or trauma-denied: Principles and implementation of trauma-informed services for women. *Journal of Community Psychology, 33*, 461–477.

Fisher, H., Morgan, C., Dazzan, P., Craig, T.K., Morgan, K., Hutchinson, G. et al. (2009). Gender differences in the association between childhood abuse and psychosis. *British Journal of Psychiatry, 194*, 319–325.

Freire, P. (1993). *Pedagogy of the Oppressed* (rev. ed.). New York: Continuum.

French, P. & Morrison, A.P. (2004). *Early Detection and Cognitive Therapy for People at High Risk of Developing Psychosis: A Treatment Approach.* Chichester, UK: John Wiley & Sons.

Goodman, L.A., Rosenberg, S.D., Mueser, K.T. & Drake, R.E. (1997). Physical and sexual assault history in women with serious mental illness: Prevalence, correlates, treatment, and future research directions. *Schizophrenia Bulletin, 23*, 685–696.

Gumley, A. & Schwannauer, M. (2006). *Staying Well after Psychosis: A Cognitive Interpersonal Approach to Recovery and Relapse.* Chichester, UK: John Wiley & Sons.

Hardy, A., Fowler, D., Freeman, D., Smith, B., Steel, C., Evans, J. et al. (2005). Trauma and hallucinatory experience in psychosis. *Journal of Nervous and Mental Disease, 193*, 501–507.

Harris, M. & Fallot, R.D. (2001). Envisioning a trauma-informed service system: A vital paradigm shift. In M. Harris & R.D. Fallot (Eds.), Using Trauma Theory to Design Service Systems [Special issue]. *New Directions for Mental Health Services, 89*, 3–22.

Ivey, A.E. (1995). Psychotherapy as liberation: Toward specific skills and strategies in multicultural counseling and therapy. In J. Ponterotto, J. Casas, L. Suzuki & C. Alexander (Eds.), *Handbook of Multicultural Counseling* (pp. 53–72). Thousand Oaks, CA: Sage.

Jackson, C. & Birchwood, M. (2006). Trauma and first episode psychosis. In W. Larkin
    & A.P. Morrison (Eds.), *Trauma and Psychosis: New Directions for Theory and Therapy* (pp.
    75–100). East Sussex, UK: Routledge.

Jankowski, M.K., Mueser, K. & Rosenberg, S.D. (2006). Psychosis with comorbid PTSD.
    In W. Larkin & A.P. Morrison (Eds.), *Trauma and Psychosis: New Directions for Theory and
    Therapy* (pp. 127–147). East Sussex, UK: Routledge.

Janssen, I., Krabbendam, L., Bak, M., Hanssen, M., Vollebergh, W., de Graaf, R. et al. (2004).
    Childhood abuse as a risk factor for psychotic experiences. *Acta Psychiatrica Scandinavica,
    109,* 38–45.

Kingdon, D.G. & Turkington, D. (2005). *Cognitive Therapy of Schizophrenia*. New York:
    Guilford Press.

Larkin, W. & Morrison, A.P. (2006a). Relationships between trauma and psychosis: From theory
    to therapy. In W. Larkin & A.P. Morrison (Eds.), *Trauma and Psychosis: New Directions for
    Theory and Therapy* (pp. 259–282). East Sussex, UK: Routledge.

Larkin, W. & Morrison, A.P. (Eds.). (2006b). *Trauma and Psychosis: New Directions for Theory and
    Therapy*. East Sussex, UK: Routledge.

Larkin, W. & Read, J. (2008). Childhood trauma and psychosis: Evidence, pathways, and
    implications. *Journal of Postgraduate Medicine, 54,* 287–293.

Lehman, A.F., Kreyenbuhl, J., Buchanan, R.W., Dickerson, F.B., Dixon, L.G., Goldberg, R. et al.
    (2004). The Schizophrenia Patient Outcomes Research Team (PORT): Updated treatment
    recommendations. *Schizophrenia Bulletin, 30,* 193–217.

McGorry, P. (2005). Royal Australian and New Zealand College of Psychiatrists clinical practice
    guidelines in the treatment of schizophrenia and related disorders. *Australian and New
    Zealand Journal of Psychiatry, 39,* 1–30.

Morgan, C. & Fisher, H. (2007). Environmental factors in schizophrenia: Childhood trauma—A
    critical review. *Schizophrenia Bulletin, 33,* 3–10.

Morrison, A.P. (2001). The interpretations of intrusions in psychosis: An integrative cognitive
    approach to hallucinations and delusions. *Behavioural and Cognitive Psychotherapy, 29,* 257–276.

Morrison, A.P., Frame, L. & Larkin, W. (2003). Relationships between trauma and psychosis: A
    review and integration. *British Journal of Clinical Psychology, 42,* 331–353.

Morrison, A.P., Read, J. & Turkington, D. (2005). Trauma and psychosis: Theoretical and clinical
    implications. *Acta Psychiatrica Scandinavica, 112,* 327–329.

Morrison, A.P., Renton, J.C., Dunn, H., Williams, S. & Bentall, R.P. (2004). *Cognitive Therapy for
    Psychosis: A Formulation-Based Approach*. East Sussex, UK: Brunner-Routledge.

Morrissey, J.P., Jackson, E.W., Ellis, A.R., Amaro, H., Brown, V.B. & Najavits, L.M. (2005).
    Twelve-month outcomes of trauma-informed interventions for women with co-occurring
    disorders. *Psychiatric Services, 56,* 1213–1222.

Mueser, K.T., Rosenberg, S.D., Goodman, L.A. & Trumbetta, S.L. (2002). Trauma, PTSD, and the course of severe mental illness: An interactive model. *Schizophrenia Research, 53*, 123–143.

Mueser, K.T., Goodman, L.B., Trumbetta, S.L., Rosenberg, S.D., Osher, F.C., Vidaver, R. et al. (1998). Trauma and posttraumatic stress disorder in severe mental illness. *Journal of Consulting and Clinical Psychology, 6*, 493–499.

Nasser, E.H., Walders, N. & Jenkins, J.H. (2002). The experience of schizophrenia: What's gender got to do with it? A critical review of the current status of research on schizophrenia. *Schizophrenia Bulletin, 28*, 351–362.

National Institute for Clinical Excellence. (2002). *Core Interventions in the Treatment and Management of Schizophrenia in Primary and Secondary Care.* London, UK: Author. Retrieved from www.nice.org.uk/guidance/index.jsp?action=byID&o=10916

National Institute for Health and Clinical Excellence. (2009). *Schizophrenia: Core Interventions in the Treatment and Management of Schizophrenia in Adults in Primary and Secondary Care (Update).* London, UK: Author. Retrieved from http://guidance.nice.org.uk/CG82

Padesky, C.A. (1993, Sept. 24). *Socratic questioning: Changing minds or guiding discovery.* Keynote address delivered at the European Congress of Behavioural and Cognitive Therapies, London, UK.

Read, J. (2005). The bio-bio-bio model of madness. *The Psychologist (UK), 18*, 596–597.

Read, J., Fink, P.J., Rudegeair, T., Felitti, V. & Whitfield, C.L. (2008). Child maltreatment and psychosis: A return to a genuinely integrated bio-psycho-social model. *Clinical Schizophrenia and Related Psychoses, 7*, 235–254.

Read, J., Hammersley, P. & Rudegeair, T. (2007). Why, when, and how to ask about childhood abuse. *Advances in Psychiatric Treatment, 13*, 101–110.

Read, J., McGregor, K., Coggan, C. & Thomas, D.R. (2006). Mental health services and sexual abuse: The need for staff training. *Journal of Trauma and Dissociation, 7*, 33–50.

Read, J., Morrison, A. & Turkington, D. (2005). Trauma and psychosis: Theoretical and clinical implications. *Acta Psychiatrica Scandinavica, 112*, 327–329.

Read, J., Van Os, J., Morrison, A.P. & Ross, C.A. (2005). Childhood trauma, psychosis, and schizophrenia: A literature review with theoretical and clinical implications. *Acta Psychiatrica Scandinavica, 112*, 330–350.

Romme, M.A.J. & Escher, A.D. (1989). Hearing voices. *Schizophrenia Bulletin, 15*, 209–216.

Schachter, C.L., Stalker, C.A., Teram, E., Lasiuk, G.C. & Danilkewich, A. (2009). *Handbook on Sensitive Practice for Health Care Practitioners: Lessons from Adult Survivors of Childhood Sexual Abuse.* Ottawa: Public Health Agency of Canada.

Shevlin, M., Dorahy, M.J. & Adamson, G. (2007). Trauma and psychosis: An analysis of the National Comorbidity Survey. *American Journal of Psychiatry, 164*, 166–169.

Shevlin, M., Houston, J.E., Dorahy, M.J. & Adamson, G. (2008). Cumulative traumas and psychosis: An analysis of the National Comorbidity Survey and the British Psychiatric Morbidity Survey. *Schizophrenia Bulletin, 34,* 193–199.

Shulman, R. (1996). Psychotherapy with "schizophrenia": Analysis of metaphor to reveal trauma and conflict. *The Psychotherapy Patient, 9*(3/4), 75–106.

Tarrier, N. (2007). What's in a name? A commentary on Valmaggia et al.'s "Attention training with auditory hallucinations." *Cognitive and Behavioral Practice, 14,* 144–146.

Taylor, P.J. & Bragado-Jemenz, M.D. (2009). Women, psychosis, and violence. *International Journal of Law and Psychiatry, 32,* 56–64.

Thompson, A., Nelson, B., McNab, C., Simmons, M., Leicester, S, McGorry, P.D. et al. (2010). Psychotic symptoms with sexual content in the "ultra high risk" for psychosis population: Frequency and association with sexual trauma. *Psychiatry Research, 177,* 84–91.

Varese, F., Smeets, F., Drukker, M. Lieverse, R., Lataster, T., Viechtbauer, W. et al. (2012). Childhood adversities increase the risk of psychosis: A meta-analysis of patient-control, prospective- and cross-sectional cohort studies. *Schizophrenia Bulletin, 38,* 661–671.

Young, M., Read, J., Barker-Collo, S. & Harrison, R. (2001). Evaluating and overcoming barriers to taking abuse histories. *Professional Psychology: Research and Practice, 32,* 407–414.

Sheeja, M., Bindroo, B., Devarajan, R., & Solaraman, S. (2006). Quantitative measures and gradients for analyzing the neutral density features assessed the retinal ... Methods, tools. Clinical psychology. 3, 4-9.

Shainkin, K. (2007). Psychology, psych in ... the visitor Wales. ...
Suburban. Studies. 76. Psychologia. 74. 247. (5) 2-6.

...

Thompson, A., Lake, P., Miller, C., Bronson, M., Ayers, J., & Byrne, D. (...). Problems, work, fact with ... method in differences ... the responses problems, diagnosis, and associated with social ... with ...

Chapter 7

Trauma-Informed Body-Centred Interventions

Steven Hughes and Paul Hyman

> *The places where we cringe are our personal edges. They are the doors we have never been quite able to walk through, although we have always known they are waiting for us.*
>
> —*Stephen Levine*

These words describe an experience most of us have felt when we approach the edges of our current growth, awareness and understanding. We often hesitate to embrace change and to take that first step into the unknown. For people who have experienced trauma, taking this kind of risk can be particularly challenging. Laughter yoga and Brain Gym are emerging as promising practices that can support people touched by trauma to move forward on their path to recovery and personal growth and, ultimately, to realize their full potential.

Brain Gym and laughter yoga allow people to experience simple yet powerful ways to make a body/mind connection. Listening to our bodies allows us to access our problems at their physiological roots and get in touch with ourselves. With mind and body working together, we have the potential to access all our interpersonal and intrapersonal capacities. Activating our bodies in a safe, non-threatening environment can help change how we feel.

Doing laughter yoga and Brain Gym is fun and a good way to socialize, release emotions and express ourselves. When these modalities are offered by organizations, they invite participation in a way that can be less intimidating than formal therapeutic interventions for trauma healing. Clients can learn to cope with the effects of trauma without needing to speak directly with a helping professional about the trauma. Laughter yoga and Brain Gym are levellers in other ways as well: they provide benefits to staff as well as clients, with the possibility of integrated sessions where clients and staff participate together.

Trauma and the Body

Trauma profoundly affects the body. Growing scientific evidence indicates that the dynamics of traumatic stress and its symptoms have significant biological components (Ogden et al., 2006). One way to look at trauma is as an out-of-body experience, a separation of the mind and body. People who have experienced physical, sexual or psychological abuse, or other forms of trauma, may withdraw unconsciously and be more disconnected from and less aware of their bodies and how they feel (e.g., pain, tension, pleasure). Some report simply feeling detached, numb or blank. People who have been traumatized need to reconnect with their bodies.

The residual effects of trauma and the complex world we live in can trap people in thoughts about the past and fears about the future. Brain Gym and laughter yoga are body-centred interventions that offer a pathway to dis-identify from the jigsaw puzzle of memories, images, affects and bodily sensations—allowing us to reconnect with joy and playfulness, feel rejuvenated and find hope for a fulfilling future. Helping professionals and their clients can do these techniques together to connect to the present moment.

Body-Centred Techniques for Trauma Recovery

A body-focused approach to trauma recovery is rooted in an understanding that our bodies, emotions and thoughts create a feedback/feed-forward loop. By using the body (rather than cognition or emotion) as an entry point for processing trauma, body-centred techniques directly treat the effects of trauma on the body, which in turn facilitates emotional and cognitive processing. The mind and body need to work together to facilitate trauma recovery.

A body-centred approach addresses the whole person, using cognitive and affective states in combination with sensation to work directly with the nervous system. Clients are taught to be mindful of inner body sensations—to the extent that they are capable of observing their internal experience. They learn to connect what they are thinking (the mind) with what they are feeling (the body).

These techniques have significant benefits for people recovering from trauma:

- Significant change can be achieved without needing to know the client's story of trauma; this is especially useful when symptoms seem to exist for an unknown reason.
- Body-centred techniques have proven to be effective in addressing symptoms and effects of abuse, neglect, trauma and complex syndromes, while minimizing retraumatization and transference (Ogden et al., 2006).
- These techniques use the wisdom of the body and the attunement of the mind/body to move toward release of trauma in the body and to create lasting positive change.
- The practitioner can do less therapy, while the client is empowered as an active participant in recovery.
- These techniques restore self-regulation and return a sense of aliveness, relaxation and wholeness. Based in a trauma-sensitive approach, these techniques work from an empowerment model, maximizing the client's sense of control and creating an atmosphere that is respectful of his or her need for safety, respect and acceptance. Besides creating a safe space, self-regulation techniques allow clients to prepare for therapeutic interventions and stay grounded and present during and after a session, especially when they are alone and possibly feeling vulnerable. Clients talk about wanting to feel grounded: body-centred techniques allow them to experience a visceral whole-body experience in trauma recovery. (For more about grounding techniques, see Najavits, 2001).
- Body-centred, non-verbal techniques assist in the management between hyper- and hypo-arousal trauma states (Ogden et al., 2006). Traumatic stress symptoms are often expressions of incomplete or fixated functions of fight, flight and freeze. Whatever the challenge, it stimulates a fight-or-flight reaction, making the body tense, agitated and eager to do something to relieve the situation. Using body-centred techniques, clinicians can interactively modulate clients' levels of arousal, keeping them from going too far

outside the optimum arousal zone, where it becomes difficult or impossible to process information without dissociating.

Laughter Yoga

> *Momentary experiences of positive emotion can build endur-*
> *ing psychological resources and trigger upward spirals toward*
> *enhanced emotional well-being.*
> —Barbara L. Fredrickson, Positivity

Laughter yoga focuses on the value of laughter as a physical/physiological experience rather than a cognitive/intellectual construct (Mahony et al., 2002). It stimulates the physiological phenomenon of "laughter" without requiring humour as a catalyst. It creates a safe social venue where people can experience laughter, joy and playfulness in the body. The process of laughter yoga seeks to bypass the mind and its relentless propensity to judge (and often criticize) our moment-to-moment experiences. Laughter yoga offers a concrete somatic experience rather than an intellectual or cognitive appreciation of laughter and joy.

Laughter yoga is not a form of "treatment"; however, it does have therapeutic and healing potential as a personal health promotion practice (Davidson et al., 2006; Mora-Ripoll, 2010; Provine, 2000).

Laughter yoga was developed in 1995 by Madan Kataria, a physician in Mumbai, India. Kataria was researching the stress management and health benefits of laughter and decided to form a "laughter club" to test laughter's healing potential first-hand. The key to the popularity and success of laughter yoga is the discovery that laughter can occur without the presence of humour (Kataria, 1999). Many of us have been conditioned to expect laughter to be elicited by something funny. Through laughter yoga, we can directly experience the benefits of laughter without needing to be comedians.

Interest in the idea grew very quickly. There are now estimated to be more than 60,000 laughter clubs in more than 60 countries around the globe. Ironically, numerous studies in the literature examine humour as an intellectual and cognitive process, but relatively few reference the pure study of laughter as a physiological phenomenon (Provine, 2000).

In addition to its physical benefits, laughter yoga can be used to enhance feelings of self-acceptance and to build social skills and confidence in social situations. Within the safety of the laughter yoga group setting, participants can begin to take small interpersonal risks, as the exercises facilitate fun and playful interaction. The exercises begin with an introduction by the leader, followed by a community-building segment in which participants get to know one another. They are reminded that they can opt out of participation at any time if they begin to feel overwhelmed or uncomfortable in the social context of the session.

Although laughter yoga can challenge the boundaries of people's comfort zones, this common experience is articulated, validated and normalized by the leader. With gentle support and encouragement, each participant begins to feel liberated from personal limitations associated with feeling self-conscious or awkward in the group setting. Participants also begin to allow themselves to let go of self-limiting self-talk and their overarching inner critic as they begin to reconnect with a sense of joy and, perhaps for the very first time, to experience the gift of "laughing for no reason."

Participants can also begin to re-experience a sense of joy in their bodies. This can be an important benchmark experience for trauma survivors, whose memories and thoughts about their bodies may be associated with shame, violation and abuse (Herman, 1992).

Brain Gym

Brain Gym is a program (or practice) that involves using 26 basic movements —all learned in the first few years of life—as a way to activate different areas of the brain. They work together to improve cognitive and emotional processing, facilitate learning and enable people to better cope with the effects of trauma. People who have experienced trauma can use Brain Gym to help them self-regulate: it assists them to modulate hyper- and hypo-arousal states and normalize and stabilize arousal patterns. By working through the body, both Brain Gym and laughter yoga allow people to feel more grounded and better able to integrate other aspects of their formal treatment.

Paul Dennison and Gail Dennison (2010), the originators of Brain Gym, became interested in the latest research about the relationship between the left and right hemispheres of the brain. They developed intentional integrative movement activities to help people access cognitive and emotional processes from the hemispheres that may get blocked from trauma and other stressful life situations. Brain Gym draws on techniques from many fields, including developmental optometry, brain research, neurolinguistic programming, motor development, psychology, acupuncture and dance.

In her book, *Smart Moves: Why Learning Is Not All in Your Head* (2005), neurophysiologist Carla Hannaford writes, "Movements awaken and activate many of our mental capacities: [they] integrate and anchor new information and experience into our neural networks" (p. 18).

Brain Gym has been used to help with various mental and physical challenges. It is designed for anyone interested in natural solutions to reducing stress, improving memory, sharpening skills, strengthening technique, making effective changes, improving productivity and enhancing performance. Clients who have done Brain Gym report reduced triggers and symptoms of depression and fewer episodes of anxiety. Brain Gym is also helpful with various multicultural groups because it is non-verbal and therefore may be used with people whose first language is not English.

A pilot of the Problem Gambling Program in Ontario, held at the Donwood Institute in Toronto in 1996, used Brain Gym as part of its stress reduction component. Brain Gym activities worked equally well when introduced at Interval House in Toronto, Canada's first shelter for women and children who experienced domestic violence (Hyman, 2006).

Integrating Brain Gym as a coping strategy and learning readiness model has already demonstrated success (Hyman, 2006). It has worked in the critical acute phase with people in recovery, and has been incorporated as a life-skill tool as people have moved forward, accessing more of their resources and potential for a positive lifestyle change.

Combining Body-Centred Approaches

Doing Brain Gym before and after laughter yoga allows for both modalities to provide maximum benefits. By harnessing them together, people have the flexibility to use these grounding techniques and self-regulate their emotions in different situations and environments. Managing the dynamics of change requires laser-light focus and agility to flow with resilience (Csikszentmihalyi, 1990).

Giving trauma survivors permission to reconnect with their inner childlike playfulness is a gift that allows them to release themselves into the present moment and gain a reprieve from self-negating thoughts and the periodic painful emotional waves that often affect their daily lives (Beckman et al., 2007). Although the mind will continue to run its commentary, with persistence, laughter yoga and Brain Gym can serve as forms of meditation that can help people temporarily release themselves from an overactive inner critic or a repetitive inner dialogue.

Incorporating Body-Centred Techniques within Organizations

> *It's almost impossible to maintain any kind of distance or any sense of social hierarchy when you are just howling with laughter.*
> —*John Cleese,* The Human Face

Mind/body modalities can be successfully embedded at the organizational level, signaling commitment to a non-hierarchical, positive and empowering culture of care.

Traditionally, many health care environments have been influenced by the ubiquitous presence of the medical model and its focus on "symptom management" and pharmacological interventions. Historically, this approach has been intertwined with a patriarchal and custodial approach to treatment, where the clinician is viewed as the expert. The last decade has seen increasing movement toward embracing integrative medicine and recovery-based models of care that are sensitive to the power dynamics between care providers and the recipients of care.

Brain Gym and laughter yoga are modalities or practices connected to the emerging field of positive psychology (Fredrickson, 2009; Seligman & Csikszentmihalyi, 2000; Snyder & Lopes, 2002). The value in examining the positive aspects of human psychology is influencing the new field of positive organizational scholarship—how we can create organizations that are more supportive social environments that nurture personal growth, creativity and collective development (Cameron et al., 2003; Meyer, 2010).

Collective development happens, for example, when Brain Gym or laughter yoga participants who have used the modalities to deal with their own challenges go on to teach the techniques to other individuals in distress. Laughter yoga participants who experience its joy and stress-reducing benefits have often enrolled in training to become laughter yoga leaders. Therapists and staff members have commented that laughter yoga has helped them to manage the insidious impact of vicarious trauma in their lives in a joyful way.

Conclusion

> At the height of laughter, the universe is flung into a kaleidoscope of new possibilities.
> —*Jean Houston,* The Possible Human

A body-centred approach has produced surprising results in dealing with difficult symptoms arising from trauma. The mind/body connection integrates body-centred processes with the higher-brain processes of cognition and feeling, creating a more flexible neurological system and enhancing the capacity to enjoy a wide spectrum of human experiences.

Brain Gym and laughter yoga are congruent with the emerging trauma-informed paradigm because they are practices that therapists and clients can do together and that clients can adopt and practise on their own as part of their self-managed path to recovery. Since Brain Gym and laughter yoga can be practised by anyone, they are not burdened with the baggage of treatment modalities reserved for "psychiatric consumers" or "trauma survivors." In other words, they do not carry the stigma that is often attached to more formal psychiatric and addiction treatment protocols.

Brain Gym and laughter yoga, when offered by health care services and agencies, become part of a trauma-informed organizational culture, promoting safety and easing stress in accessible and enjoyable ways.

References

Beckman, H., Regier, N. & Young, J. (2007). Effect of workplace laughter groups on personal efficacy beliefs. *Journal of Primary Prevention, 28,* 167–181.

Cameron, K.S., Dutton, J.E. & Quinn, R.E. (Eds.). (2003). *Positive Organizational Scholarship: Foundations of a New Discipline.* San Francisco: Berrett-Koehler.

Csikszentmihalyi, M. (1990). *Flow: The Psychology of Optimal Experience.* New York: HarperCollins.

Davidson, L., Shahar, G., Staeheli Lawless, M., Sells, D. & Tondora, J. (2006). Play, pleasure, and other positive life events: "Non-specific" factors in recovery from mental illness? *Psychiatry, 69,* 151–163.

Dennison, G. & Dennison, P. (2010). *Brain Gym: Teachers Edition Revised.* Ventura, CA: Edu-Kinesthetics.

Fredrickson, B.L. (2009). *Positivity: Top-Notch Research Reveals the 3:1 Ratio That Will Change Your Life.* New York: Three Rivers Press.

Hannaford, C. (2005). *Smart Moves: Why Learning Is Not All in Your Head.* Salt Lake City, UT: Great River Publishers.

Herman, J. (1992). *Trauma and Recovery: The Aftermath of Violence—From Domestic Abuse to Political Terror.* New York: Basic Books.

Hyman, P. (2006). A study linking cocaine clients to ADD characteristics as a foundation to study Brain Gym and cocaine recovery. *TRO Research Annual, 1,* 20–24.

Kataria, M. (1999). *Laugh for No Reason.* Mumbai, India: Madhuri International.

Mahony, D.L., Burroughs, W.J. & Lippman, L.G. (2002). Perceived attributes of health-promoting laughter: A cross-generational comparison. *Journal of Psychology, 136,* 171–181.

Meyer, P. (2010). *From Workplace to Playspace: Innovating, Learning, and Changing through Dynamic Engagement.* San Francisco: Jossey-Bass.

Mora-Ripoll, R. (2010). The therapeutic value of laughter in medicine. *Alternative Therapies, 16*(6), 56–64.

Najavits, L.M. (2002). *Seeking Safety: A Treatment Manual for PTSD and Substance Abuse.* New York: Guilford Press.

Ogden, P., Minton, K. & Pain, C. (2006). *Trauma and the Body: A Sensorimotor Approach to Psychotherapy.* New York: W.W. Norton.

Provine, R.R. (2000). *Laughter: A Scientific Investigation.* New York: Penguin Books.

Seligman, M.E. & Csikszentmihalyi, M. (2000). Positive psychology: An introduction. *American Psychologist, 55*, 5–14.

Snyder C.R. & Lopes, S.J. (Eds.). (2002). *Handbook of Positive Psychology*. London, UK: Oxford University Press.

PART 2

TRAUMA-INFORMED PRACTICE FOR DIVERSE CLIENT GROUPS AND IN SPECIFIC SETTINGS

Introduction

Section 1: Diverse Groups

The first section focuses on programs and services for a range of groups or populations that have characteristics requiring either adaptation or a specific approach to working in a trauma-informed manner. Identifying the special needs of such groups is often an emergent process that can arise out of demand from consumer groups, the experiences of practitioners or evolving maturation and specialization processes in practice or system design. In this section, seven groups are discussed as examples of adapted or specialized approaches. Some of these approaches emerged in response to needs that presented themselves, as in the case of the program at the Jean Tweed Centre, while others are designed assuming potential trauma, such as a creative drama program for young people with fetal alcohol spectrum disorder (FASD).

Using an illustrative vignette, Palucka and Lunsky address the challenges in responding to trauma experienced by people with developmental disabilities who are unable to describe or discuss their past trauma. In Chapter 8, they present a trauma-informed way to reframe a set of responses tailored to this population. Given the limitations and differences in the abilities of people with developmental disabilities to communicate and interact with service providers, applying principles of trauma-informed care and service design requires a particular sensitivity: this includes providing strength and resilience training, creating a safe environment that is gender-specific, promoting empowerment and increasing control and choice, minimizing retraumatization and, most important, soliciting direct input from the client and his or her support networks. Palucka and Lunsky highlight the various adaptations that must be made to take developmental disabilities into account.

Agic discusses the impact of trauma, multiple losses, social disruption and economic hardship on the health of refugees. In Chapter 9, she describes how trauma-informed care is an important emerging service provision model that understands and validates the impact of these multiple stressors, rebuilds a sense of control, creates a climate of hope and resilience and facilitates social support. In addition, Agic draws attention to cultural competence in trauma-informed practice by discussing the important differences among cultures in what is considered a traumatic event and in how trauma-related symptoms are expressed and interpreted. She also describes trauma-informed practices that respect different cultural values and beliefs and that meet the social, cultural and linguistic needs of refugees.

In Chapter 10, Bloomenfeld and Rasmussen describe the process of developing trauma-informed practice at the Jean Tweed Centre in Toronto. Observing the abuse and trauma histories of the women coming for substance use treatment, the centre took steps to integrate or "braid" an awareness of trauma into all aspects of its substance use treatment programming and agency structure. For example, trauma-informed principles were integrated into the training of receptionist and clerical staff so that women would be greeted in a context of safety and understanding. The program addresses a wide range of abuse and trauma issues, including terror and political and social oppressions, affecting women. The programming emphasizes containment, collaboration, empowerment and the prevention of retraumatization.

Chapter 11 addresses the challenges of working in a trauma-informed manner with people who have FASD. Harber likens the effects of FASD to the experience of trauma and uses creative drama as an approach to working with young people with FASD dealing with *potential* trauma histories. Creative drama, as distinguished from theatre, addresses real issues and scenarios and functions as a rehearsal for real-life situations. This form of drama uses a range of principles, such as choice, control, containment and prevention of retraumatization, to make the exercises safe and non-threatening.

Clark, in Chapter 12, describes working with girls using an intersectional approach, which deliberately addresses the many factors affecting girls' experiences. She advocates for the importance of girls' groups and, in light of the continuum of trauma in girls' lives, the necessity of making these groups trauma informed. Clark describes a program for Aboriginal girls aged 8 to 12 that recognizes the impact of cultural experiences and specific rites of passage. She illustrates trauma-informed principles, such as containing disclosure, generating externalized views of oppression, developing stronger self-definitions, learning resistance and acknowledging the effects of gender discrimination and racism.

Fallot and Bebout discuss the challenge of working with men with trauma, violence and abuse histories, ranging from child sexual abuse to military combat trauma. In Chapter 13, they describe how gendered characteristics and socialization practices affecting men may prevent them from making certain disclosures and may inhibit their relational skills and emotional expressions, all of which affect treatment approaches and systems design. These issues contribute to difficulties assuming the role of "victim," displaying a full range of emotions and self-regulating. Fallot and Bebout contend that these issues are either magnified in or specific to men and demand particular approaches in care. They stress the importance of developing mutual relationships, building on strengths and "connecting the dots" between current issues and past traumas. They make the critical point that any service provider can address these processes in any part of the helping system.

In Chapter 14, Menzies describes a tailored response to the specific effects of intergenerational trauma among Aboriginal people in Canada. He traces the effects of the residential school system and an assimilationist child welfare system, both of which removed many Aboriginal children from their families over the course of a century. These systems created long-term damage and trauma to Aboriginal people, much of which has become intergenerational in its effects. The costs of identifying cultural transmission and community and individual stability were, and are, high. Menzies describes the accommodations required in trauma counselling to strengthen relationships, cultures and communities. He stresses the importance of considering cultural affinity and adapting counselling approaches to align with how survivors see themselves as Aboriginal. The chapter also highlights the importance of social policy, past, present and future, in affecting trauma and its solutions.

Section 2: Diverse Settings

The second section highlights several issues about the settings in which services are provided. Does it matter where people are being cared for or treated? How does it matter? How can settings such as hospitals become trauma informed? What change processes are required, and how do these processes work? The chapters discuss inpatient, primary care and counselling contexts and consider the processes of creating trauma-informed services and systems.

In Chapter 15, Chaim, Rosenkranz and Henderson describe adaptations in outpatient services for young people with substance use issues that take account of trauma. The program is adapted to the developmental stages of 16- to 24-year-olds and services span the continuum of care from outreach to day treatment services. The program recognizes that many young people, particularly young women, with serious substance use issues have experienced or witnessed trauma, abuse or neglect. To increase youth's commitment and engagement in treatment, efforts are made to empower and involve youth in treatment planning using a harm reduction framework. Staff also considers ways to make the hospital environment more informal and welcoming.

Perivolaris and Pottinger address two contentious procedures in psychiatric units: restraint and seclusion. In Chapter 16, they explain that while inpatients with trauma backgrounds often find these procedures retraumatizing, many service providers see them as methods for reducing aggression and ensuring their own safety and that of other patients. The authors describe the complex process of shifting from restraint use to restraint prevention at a large hospital, the Centre for Addiction and Mental Health in Toronto. Prompted in part by two patient deaths, the change process involved senior leaders identifying the need to evaluate best practices around restraint use and included detailed plans and methods for dealing with resistance to reducing restraint use. Elements of trauma-informed service systems were critical to the initiative, such as fostering empowerment, providing flexibility and developing safety planning.

Baker discusses working with families in the context of a family member's mental health problems in Chapter 17. She discusses how these processes can take place in various settings, designed to increase safety and preserve confidentiality. Baker illustrates how traumatizing illness and/or hospitalization can be for all family members and how introducing a strengths-based collaborative and participatory approach with the family can improve recovery for all. She addresses how the culture of blame can affect mothers in particular, due to historical sexism, and how this needs to be directly addressed.

In Chapter 18, Akman and Rolin-Gilman discuss another hospital-based setting, a dedicated women's inpatient psychiatric unit. This unit was developed to provide safety for women with substance use or mental health issues and was designed to attend to the intersections of these issues with violence and trauma. The unit aims to promote wellness, not just provide treatment. Client empowerment is encouraged by emphasizing each woman's role in determining her own treatment goals. In addition, all procedures are continuously revisited, and specific procedures responding to dangerous situations are deliberately designed to prevent or reduce retraumatization.

Umaña addresses the challenges of providing trauma-informed service in primary health care in a community clinic for a specific client group—immigrant and refugee women with HIV/AIDS. As described in Chapter 19, this context features numerous factors that contribute to trauma and that require consideration in providing service. These factors include culture, circumstances of infection, stigma and isolation. Umaña describes a comprehensive enhancement of a primary care service to include community-based research, community partnerships, multidisciplinary responses, erasure of wait times and the overarching integration of trauma-informed service and system improvements.

These examples drawn from various settings show the importance of questioning practices, designing change management processes and developing client-centred approaches that empower clients and are sensitive to wide-ranging trauma. They illustrate the difficulties involved in changing procedures, practices and service design to include more trauma-informed approaches and to maintain consciousness and reflexivity while doing so.

The examples presented in Part 2 of this book are in no way meant to represent all groups for whom trauma-informed practice is important or all settings where trauma-informed practice is being developed. The differential experiences of trauma experienced by lesbian, gay, bisexual, transgendered, transsexual, two-spirit, intersex and queer people; women leaving violent relationships; veterans with posttraumatic stress disorder; people who are incarcerated and forensic clients have all come to our attention in developing this book. This awareness underlines the importance of responding in trauma-informed ways to the specific needs of different groups at the systemic, program and individual levels. Indeed it is important—as contributors to this book have often achieved—to see the linkages with health equity and harm reduction processes, as we develop and apply a trauma-informed framework in our support of people with mental health and substance use issues.

empowerment is encouraged by emphasizing each woman's role in determining her own treatment goals. In addition, all procedures are thoroughly explained, and specific procedures respond to and dangerous situations are deliberately designed to prevent or reduce retraumatization.

Our shelters serve those challenges of providing trauma-informed care in primary health care in community clinics, a service often clients are immigrant and refugee women with HIV/AIDS. As one clinic's example of this group of women mentioned often that trauma-informed care means that it requires consideration in providing service. It also means including relationships of the practice alongside and isolation. Through described the examples that they express a sense of community work to help them meet their own basic needs. Community groups, offering additional support for women in their own living and the overriding importance of trauma-informed care and support to help women.

These examples drawn from various settings show the importance of providing trauma-informed care to women at various project levels and developing a genuine considered approach that empowers clients and are sensitive to wide-ranging situations. They illustrate the difficulties involved in changing practices, policies, and service design to include more trauma-informed responses and to maintain conditions and trauma-life affirming.

The editors have worked with individual clients, managed programs, overseen organizations, and trained practitioners within systems to help to train-informed practice systems developed. The differential experiences of women employed by becoming more familiar with the work has been has spent in developing an awareness more consistent relationships with the research settings, these are programs in are interrelated and for many clients have all experienced attention to developing this basic understanding to the important role of supporting trauma-informed work in the specific trends at different points at the systemic, program, and individual levels. Indeed, it is important—as contributors to this book have often acknowledged—to mental and health care, entities, and trauma organizations, clients, we develop and apply a trauma-informed framework in our support of people with mental health and addictive-ness issues.

PART 2

SECTION 1: DIVERSE GROUPS

Chapter 8

Working in a Trauma-Informed Way with Clients Who Have a Developmental Disability

Anna M. Palucka and Yona Lunsky

People with developmental disabilities are far more likely to be victimized than the general population, yet have fewer resources to deal with these experiences. Their response to the trauma may also be different. Therefore, trauma-informed practice with this population requires certain modifications. The goal of this chapter is to demystify the tailored approach to trauma-informed care for people with developmental disabilities. It addresses the types of trauma they may experience, the impact of cognitive impairments on how they may report trauma and how to apply a trauma-informed approach in work with people who have developmental disabilities.

In general, developmental disability refers to impairments in cognitive functioning accompanied by impairments in adaptive skills that emerge in the developmental period (prior to age 18). The term developmental disability[1] allows for inclusion of individuals whose IQ might be a little higher but who nevertheless have significant cognitive and functional difficulties. People with fetal alcohol spectrum disorders and autism spectrum disorders (ASD) are also considered to have developmental disabilities. Individuals with ASD may have ways of understanding and interpreting their social and non-social world that are different than those of neurotypical individuals.[2] They may experience

---

1. Diagnostic criteria for mental retardation in DSM-IV: Intellectual functioning markedly below average (IQ below 70–75, or two standard deviations below the mean); impairments in at least two areas of adaptive functioning; onset before age 18. (The term "mental retardation" will be replaced by "intellectual disability" in DSM-5.)
2. For more about "social stories" among people with ASD, see www.thegraycenter.org.

relatively minor events, such a falling off a bicycle or losing an object of attachment, as traumatic. Their difficulties in communicating and interacting socially and their behaviours associated with ASD will affect how they communicate and process their experiences.

Working with individuals with developmental disabilities who have experienced trauma often requires working with caregivers (family members or paid staff), and depending on the source of trauma, recognizing that abuse is not the only type of trauma the person may have experienced. The involvement of caregivers can be crucial, as many people with developmental disabilities do not live independently and may need others' assistance for transportation, decision-making and implementing treatment strategies. If it is safe to do so, it is these caregivers who can provide information about personal and clinical history, significant relationships, dreams and goals or preferences.

The following vignette illustrates key elements of trauma-informed practice involving a person with a developmental disability and those who work with her.

> Tracy is 34 years old but looks and acts like a teenager. She has moderate intellectual disability and attention-deficit/hyperactivity disorder. She was admitted to hospital because her group home placement broke down due to her aggression. On one occasion, she entered a bedroom of another resident at night and started to punch him. Her records indicate that she experienced physical and emotional abuse and severe neglect in her family home. She was sexually assaulted by a stranger when she was 19, but her family refused the offer of counselling at that point. More recently, after Tracy left home, her sisters disclosed that they were sexually abused by their father and suspected that Tracy, too, might have been abused. Group home staff wanted Tracy to engage in psychotherapy, but following the initial evaluation, the therapist felt that she would not be able to tolerate it. Behavioural approaches were unsuccessful and staff continued to request individual therapy to help with challenging behaviours: Tracy was highly reactive, impulsive, intrusive and pushy, and at times of distress, she would become combative and verbally and physically aggressive, display sexualized behaviour and speak in a deep masculine voice.
>
> In hospital, Tracy presented with high anxiety and agitation, excitability, need for attention and exaggerated display of somatic complaints, including leg or

stomach pain and difficulty swallowing. Given her dramatic presentation, somatic complaints might have been easily dismissed as attempts to engage staff, particularly since she would settle in response to staff reassurance; however, medical examination revealed underlying medical conditions. Further observations identified triggers to her agitation that seemed to be directly related to her experience of neglect and trauma: triggers included doing something incorrectly, such as spilling her drink; being criticized, ignored or dismissed; being sent for time out; perceiving unfairness or rejection; noticing attention being given to someone else; hearing other people breathing loudly or making "noises"; and having her family visit her. Attempts to talk with Tracy about those issues led inevitably and rapidly to behavioural escalation. The intervention approach was shifted from therapy and behavioural contingencies (i.e., providing consistent consequences for specific behaviours, such as cancelling an outing if she was verbally aggressive to staff) to a focus on staff understanding and being sensitive to Tracy's experiences, both past and present. To support Tracy, staff had to keep the present impact of her history of trauma at the forefront of all interactions and acknowledge and validate her experiences. That was particularly important given the neglect and secrecy she had experienced with her family.

A trauma-informed plan of care was developed that emphasized the role of staff in addressing Tracy's trauma-related behavioural difficulties. It included:

- educating staff about the effects of trauma on Tracy, her triggers and the importance of validating her experiences and how to tailor the teaching of self-soothing skills using visual aids
- creating a safe environment through recognizing and minimizing situations and responses that might be retraumatizing, such as sending Tracy for time out when she was upset about attention given to another client
- providing choices and increasing opportunities for positive experiences
- assisting Tracy to use calming strategies, employing specially tailored comic strips that illustrate deep breathing
- establishing a working relationship with Tracy's family
- developing a support network beyond paid staff; for example, encouraging Tracy to attend her local church.

Tracy's story illustrates how helpful trauma-informed practice can be, regardless of whether clients are able to describe their experiences as related to trauma. The therapeutic team's awareness of how trauma may be expressed is critical to trauma-informed services. With this awareness, the team can support the client by using creative approaches to applying the practices of creating safety, providing opportunities for relational connections and teaching skills.

The Nature of Trauma for People with Developmental Disabilities

In addition to issues such as sexual abuse, as illustrated by Tracy's story, there are other sources of trauma for people with developmental disabilities. Clinicians may not always consider the types of trauma that affect them and how their response to trauma may be different.

Abuse

People with developmental disabilities are more likely to experience emotional, physical and sexual abuse and life-threatening neglect than the general population. As in Tracy's case, this abuse is more likely to be perpetrated by someone they know rather than a stranger. They experience high rates of bullying and teasing by peers in youth and even in adulthood. One in three is sexually abused before age 18 and women are at higher risk than men of being victimized and revictimized. People with developmental disabilities who have been sexually abused may display sexualized behaviour (including sexual threats or accusations) under stress. Some individuals with developmental disabilities remain at lifelong risk for repeated trauma: acquiescence, social naiveté, poor judgment and social skills and a reluctance, fear or inability to disclose abuse make them more likely to experience traumatic events. Higher-functioning individuals may repeatedly place themselves in abusive or exploitive situations because of a desire to present as normal or to have relationships with "normal people."

Loss through Separation, Abandonment or Death

Loss can be experienced by being separated from or abandoned by family—being placed in a foster or group home or institution—or from the death of a parent. In these situations, the person with a developmental disability is often removed from the family home and placed in the care of strangers. This means the person loses not only his or her parent, but a way of life and his or her possessions. Women with mild developmental disabilities, as with other women, may experience trauma when they give birth to children they are unable to care for, or when children are removed from their care. They may continually re-experience the loss of the mother role through exclusion from the child's life, for example, being denied participation in significant events such as birthdays due to concerns about their behaviour.

Natural Disasters, War, Displacement and Accidents

Caregivers, and sometimes clinicians, can wrongly assume that people with developmental disabilities are not aware of, or that they can be sheltered from, the psychological impact of a natural disaster, war, displacement or accident. Even when individuals are clearly aware of their circumstances, it might be difficult to determine their actual understanding and experience of the trauma. For example, a young woman with a mild developmental disability whose parents and several siblings were killed during Rwanda's genocide when she was 14 repeatedly expressed the desire to "go back home." When looking at the impact of these events, the clinician may find it helpful to consider how a similar situation might affect a young child who is reliant on a caregiver who has been harmed or killed.

Hospitalization

There are several factors to consider in relation to hospitalization and trauma. People with developmental disabilities experiencing mental health issues are generally hospitalized for difficulty managing aggression or for displaying self-injurious or severely disruptive behaviour. These behaviours are often precipitated by or exacerbated by significant life events in the preceding months and indicate the person's difficulties in dealing with them. Being admitted to hospital can be very traumatic, particularly if it involves the use of force and police. The hospital environment itself can be traumatizing for people with developmental disabilities.

FACTORS THAT CONTRIBUTE TO HIGH RISK OF (RE)TRAUMATIZATION IN HOSPITAL

- use of intrusive interventions such as time out, seclusion, mechanical and chemical restraints
- being assigned to or being restrained by a staff member of the same sex as an abuser
- witnessing others being restrained
- being assaulted or witnessing assaults by co-patients (not feeling safe)
- separation from family (caregivers)
- separation from familiar environment and routines
- prolonged admissions
- not understanding reason for hospitalization and not knowing for how long (forever)

WAYS TO MINIMIZE THE RISK OF (RE)TRAUMATIZATION IN HOSPITAL

- Assign same-sex staff to assist with personal hygiene (two staff if needed).
- Use least restraint policy: understand escalation continuum and use prevention; allow person to select preferred mode of restraint when required.
- Address vulnerability: Separate female bedrooms from male bedrooms.
- Debrief incidents that involve or are witnessed by the individual.
- Avoid hospitalization or keep it to a minimum.
- Facilitate caregiver contact and visits.

Impact of Cognitive Impairments on Reporting Trauma

People with developmental disabilities have a range of cognitive impairments that affect their ability to understand what has happened to them and to communicate the trauma to someone else. Impairments may occur in these areas:

Concrete thinking: People with developmental disabilities may have difficulty identifying their emotional or internal experience. They may actually not realize that what happened to them was traumatic or wrong, and that they could talk to someone about it.

Communication issues: They may not have words to explain their experience and may express it through their behaviour instead, or express it in ways that are misunderstood by others.

> Individuals with developmental disabilities may experience their own thoughts or memories as voices. Their reporting of voices telling them upsetting things or telling them to do things may be misdiagnosed as psychotic.

Attention and memory issues: They may not be able to recall significant details of a traumatic experience, such as the names of people or places involved. Or they may confuse details and provide inconsistent information at different times, so that people do not believe them.

Concept of time: They may not be able to report when things happen and their report might be confusing, with remote events being reported as recent.

> ### HOW SERVICE PROVIDERS CAN COMPENSATE FOR CLIENTS' COGNITIVE DIFFICULTIES
>
> - Be explicit about interventions.
> - Provide clear explanations, using:
>   - concrete language
>   - short sentences
>   - visual aids (drawings, photos)
>   - frequent repetition.
> - Check for understanding (ask clients to explain in their own words).
> - Allow time for processing.
> - Provide engaging and fun activities.
> - Repeat information over several sessions.
> - Record sessions so the client can listen or even view them again.

A Trauma-Informed Approach with People Who Have Developmental Disabilities

This section applies and adapts the principles of trauma-informed practice articulated by Elliot et al. (2005) to the realities of people with developmental disabilities.

Recognize the impact of victimization and trauma on the person's behaviour and coping strategies. The person's childhood history may be unknown. Bizarre or disturbed behaviour might signal that the person is re-experiencing trauma or extreme distress, or that she or he is trying to self-soothe in the best way possible. It can be important, as in Tracy's situation (see p. 110), for the service provider to consider unrecognized trauma as an explanation for disturbed behaviour and to seek to understand it.

QUESTIONS ABOUT TRAUMA FOR SERVICE PROVIDERS TO CONSIDER

- When did the trauma occur?
- What is the nature of the trauma?
- What symptoms has the individual experienced?
- What support and treatment have been received?
- Is there a previous history of trauma? (McCarthy, 2001)

  Note: These questions are not intended to be posed directly to the client; rather they are questions for service providers to keep in mind.

Identify recovery from trauma as a primary goal. Recovery from trauma should be a primary goal of treatment, as it would be with any other population. Specialized services—for developmental/dual diagnosis and trauma—need to be integrated into treatment. Furthermore, trauma work with this group extends beyond the individual with a developmental disability; when it is safe to do so, caregivers need to be involved, as their support can be critical to the recovery process. Caregivers may need education about trauma in general and about issues specific to the person in their care to better understand the person's behaviour and their own comfort level and ability to assist the person.[3]

Empower the individual. Be aware of a tendency that people with developmental disabilities have to acquiesce to caregivers or treatment providers. Recognize that they might feel that they did something wrong and may get in trouble if they reveal abuse. It is important to teach about privacy in interaction (e.g., not talking about sensitive or private topics in public places, checking with the person whether information he or she revealed may be shared with caregivers) and that saying no or refusing things does not mean the person is being unco-operative.

Maximize choices and control over recovery. People with developmental disabilities may have little sense of self-agency. They may not have skills to identify and express preferences and might need to be taught in small steps.

---

3. For more information about supporting a person with a disability who is experiencing posttraumatic stress disorder, see www.dimagine.com.

Provide them with situations where they can choose and assert preferences (e.g., what to wear or eat, where to go). Emphasize opportunities for positive experiences such as engaging in fun activities or fostering relationships with supportive others.

Create an environment that is safe, respectful and accepting. Take time to understand how the person communicates. Include people the person feels safe with, even in the therapy itself. Carefully consider the choice of therapist. This includes considering gender-specific services (i.e., a female therapist for a female client), or specialized dual diagnosis services, particularly if a diagnosis of psychotic spectrum disorder is being considered.

Create a predictable and consistent environment. Be aware of clients' current living circumstances: if they live somewhere they do not want to be and which is interpersonally stressful, they may need help to recognize and deal with that.

Emphasize strengths and resilience over pathology. See the person as someone to be admired rather than as a problem to be solved, recognizing his or her resilience in the face of impairments and traumas (Wilson & DuFrene, 2008). Identify and focus on relative strengths or the things the person enjoys doing.

Minimize possibilities for retraumatization. It is important to work with caregivers whose role is to protect the person from revictimization. Recognize that the person may be at risk in any placement—in the community as well as in an institutional setting (jail or hospital).

Be culturally competent and competent around the "culture" of developmental disability. In addition to being sensitive to the person's racial and cultural background, it is important to appreciate the different ways trauma might be expressed by people with developmental disabilities. Use your creativity to modify your interactions and treatment interventions to compensate for the cognitive impairment. You may have to adjust your expectations about what is helpful; take cues from the person about what type of interactions he or she finds supportive.

Solicit input from clients with developmental disabilities directly. Soliciting client input is an important aspect of providing trauma-informed services for any population. Even if it is more difficult to obtain input from people with developmental disabilities, try to find ways to elicit feedback and consider it, even if it is limited (e.g., using simplified visual analogues of rating scales—smiling/upset faces). We recognize the possible importance of including caregivers, but not at the cost of excluding the person with the disability from being central and sharing his or her own perspective and experience of the services.

> Monica is 40 years old and lives semi-independently with limited hours of support. She was admitted to hospital because of concerns about her aggressive behaviour, for which she was criminally charged. In contrast to her relatively high cognitive and adaptive abilities, Monica presented in a very childlike way in her speech and emotional reactions. In hospital, she described hearing the voices of her dead parents. She heard her mother, who had abused, neglected and later abandoned her, telling her to hurt herself or damage things. Monica was very distressed by hearing this. The voice of her father, on the other hand, was very protective, telling her mother to "shut up" or telling Monica to ignore her.
>
> The main intervention was to explore Monica's experience of the voices and "give" her power over them. In a concrete way, she decided to use a visual aid to help her contain the voices—she would "lock her mother (the voice) in a closet." This helped her to stop paying attention to her mother's voice and stop getting distressed by it.

Conclusion

The concept of trauma should be viewed very broadly in developmental disabilities; it is important to understand what is traumatizing for the person. Given the high probability of trauma in the lives of people with developmental disabilities, all interventions should be trauma sensitive, emphasizing coping, safety, choice and having a voice. It is also crucial to involve caregivers and help them understand the person's behaviours in relation to trauma. The presence of trauma should become part of the clinical formulation, provide a framework for understanding the person's experiences and be taken into account when planning supports and interventions. Hospitalization should be carefully considered because it will likely (and potentially unavoidably) be traumatizing.

References

Elliott, D.E., Bjelajac, P., Fallot, R.D., Markoff, L.S. & Reed, B.G. (2005). Trauma-informed or trauma-denied: Principles and implementation of trauma-informed services for women. *Journal of Community Psychology, 33*, 461–477.

McCarthy, J. (2001). Post-traumatic stress disorder in people with learning disability. *Advances in Psychiatric Treatment, 7,* 163–169.

Wilson, K.G. & DuFrene, T. (2008). *Mindfulness for Two: An Acceptance and Commitment Therapy Approach to Mindfulness in Therapy.* Oakland, CA: New Harbinger.

Chapter 9

Trauma-Informed Care for Refugees

Branka Agic

Armed conflicts, political repression and massive human rights violations have forced millions of people to flee their homes and seek refuge in other countries. As a party to the 1951 Convention relating to the Status of Refugees, Canada has an obligation to protect refugees facing prosecution.[1] Through its refugee protection system,[2] Canada accepts more than 25,000 refugees annually. Since World War II, Canada has accepted more than one million refugees (Citizenship and Immigration Canada, 2010).

Research examining the mental health of refugees has consistently found a high prevalence of trauma-related problems in this population (Cardozo et al., 2004; Fazel et al., 2005; Kirmayer et al., 2011). Failing to adequately address the complex mental health needs of refugees who are trauma survivors may worsen their health and negatively affect the integration process (Blanch, 2008; Gardiner & Walker, 2010).

This chapter outlines the key determinants of refugee mental health, describes the impact of trauma and explores the evidence base for trauma-informed care for refugees.

---

1. The 1951 Refugee Convention, which established the United Nations High Commissioner for Refugees (UNHCR), defines a refugee as a person who "owing to a well-founded fear of being persecuted for reasons of race, religion, nationality, membership of a particular social group or political opinion, is outside the country of his nationality, and is unable to, or owing to such fear, is unwilling to avail himself of the protection of that country" (UNHCR, 1951/2003, p. 14).
2. The Canadian refugee system includes the Refugee and Humanitarian Resettlement Program for people seeking protection from outside Canada and the In-Canada Asylum Program for people making refugee protection claims from within Canada (Citizenship and Immigration, 2010).

Trauma as a Risk Factor for Mental Health Problems in Refugees

Most refugees experience traumatic events and difficult situations, such as violence, persecution, multiple losses, social disruption and economic hardship, that are associated with adverse mental health outcomes (Rubinstein & Kohli, 2010). Research reveals high prevalence rates of psychiatric disorders, particularly posttraumatic stress disorder (PTSD) and depression, among refugee populations (Fazel et al., 2005; Hollifield et al., 2002; Karunakara et al., 2004; Mollica et al., 2001). More severe reactions are associated with a higher degree, duration and frequency of exposure to traumatic events. Risk factors that may predispose refugees to mental health problems and disorders include being subject to or witnessing torture, physical and sexual violence, imprisonment, internment in refugee camps, prior history of mental illness and loss of family members (Porter & Haslam, 2005; Watters, 2001). Vulnerable groups include children, unaccompanied minors, adolescents and older adults (Mikus Kos at al., 2011).

Since the second half of the 20th century, civilian populations have increasingly become subject to widespread human rights violations, with women and girls constituting the majority of victims. In the past few decades, the frequency and brutality of sexual violence against women and girls—including rape, sexual slavery, enforced pregnancy and forced prostitution—have reached alarming rates in contemporary armed conflicts (Mazurana & Carlson, 2006; Ward & Marsh, 2006).

Mass rape during armed conflicts has become a strategic weapon of war, ethnic cleansing and genocide in many settings. Between 20,000 and 50,000 women and girls were raped during the war in Bosnia in the early 1990s; during the Rwandan genocide, an estimated 250,000 to 500,000 women and girls were raped; it is believed that in the Democratic Republic of the Congo, 200,000 women and girls have been raped since 1998 (United Nations, 2009, n.d.).

Despite the high incidence of sexual assault and rape among refugee women, this crime is largely under-reported because of societal and cultural stigma attached to it. Victims are often viewed as defiled. They rarely receive medical treatment or emotional support. Women who became pregnant are often ostracized by their families and communities.

Exposure to multiple traumatic events is correlated with a greater negative impact on health. Evidence shows that stresses experienced after migration play a significant role in determining the severity of mental health problems. Trauma can be compounded by daily struggles experienced due to low socio-economic status, unemployment, social isolation, the uncertain status and experiences of discrimination and isolation and other life stressors (Porche et al., 2009; Wilson et al., 2010). The occurrence of mental health problems in refugees has been repeatedly reported years after traumatic exposure (Smid et al., 2012).

The impact of trauma can be debilitating, affecting every aspect of refugee life, including work, interpersonal relationships, parenting and social life. Trauma can also lead to poor physical health and substance use problems. To ensure refugees' successful resettlement and integration into Canadian society, it is critical to identify and properly address the unique mental health needs of this population.

Trauma-Informed Care for Refugees

Trauma-informed care is an emerging model for providing refugee-sensitive mental health services that understand and validate the impact of multiple stressors; recognize the meaning of trauma and healing within the cultural context; create a climate of hope and resilience; rebuild the person's sense of control; facilitate social support and promote recovery and successful integration into the host society (Blanch, 2008).

Being Aware of Pre-migration Trauma and Post-migration Stressors

Trauma-informed care for refugees recognizes the profound effects of pre-migration trauma on refugees' health and validates their experiences of injustice and the loss of household, social status and social structure that compound the experience of trauma.

Almost all refugees have at least one traumatic experience that is an important part of their life history. Yet many refugees are reluctant or emotionally unable to share their personal story (Harvard Program in Refugee Trauma, 2011), particularly when it involves being tortured or raped. Concealing these kinds of experiences creates considerable barriers for service providers to adequately addressing clients' mental health needs. Familiarity with the common characteristics of survivors of war or torture trauma is important for providing appropriate support and preventing more serious problems. Warning signs of a possible trauma history include but are not limited to a history of civil war in the country of origin; reluctance to disclose pre-migration experiences; fear of groups and authority figures; missing, tortured or killed family members; a history of imprisonment; somatic symptoms with no known physical cause; and mental health symptoms such as sleep problems, depression, being easily startled and avoidance (Johnson, 2005).

It is also important to keep in mind that mass violence can directly and indirectly cause serious medical problems, including injuries, chronic pain, HIV/AIDS, hypertension, cardiovascular disease and diabetes. Using alcohol and other drugs to cope with sleep and anxiety problems can lead to substance use issues (Johnson, 2005). A longitudinal study of Bosnian refugees revealed serious disability associated with the mental health effects of violence, as well as premature death related to the negative health effects of chronic depression in older adults (Mollica et al., 2001). Post-migration stress interferes with healing and recovery. Simich et al. (2006) found that refugees are 2.6 to 3.9 times more likely to suffer common PTSD symptoms if they suffer from financial difficulties in their host countries. In Canada, refugees are consistently overrepresented among the poor. Their increased susceptibility to poverty creates difficulties in accessing basic needs, such as food and adequate housing (Kazemipur & Halli, 2001).

Growing evidence shows that the provision of basic needs, such as housing and income, has a positive effect on refugees' ability to cope with trauma and on their general well-being, as well as improving treatment outcomes (Blanch, 2008; Mollica et al., 2002; Vasilevska & Simich, 2010). When asked what will help them get better, most refugees identify socio-economic factors rather than psychiatric or medical assistance (Watters, 2001). Therefore, when working with a refugee client, it is important to ask not only about the person's pre-migration experiences, but also about his or her housing situation, ability to find work and availability of social support.

Trauma-informed service providers recognize the contribution of resettlement difficulties to refugees' psychological and social problems and facilitate links to other services, such as housing assistance, employment support and family reunification.

The service provider should address the client's priorities in sequence, from most immediate or pressing to least pressing. Treatment plans should be adapted to the client's most immediate needs. This may include referral to services that assist in documenting torture or persecution for the refugee determination decision, language classes, help finding housing and work or addressing other health issues before moving toward more sensitive mental health issues (Benedek & Wynn, 2011; Gorman, 2001; Vasilevska & Simich, 2010).

Focus on Safety, Respect and Trust

Because of their experiences of persecution due to ethnic, religious or political background, many refugees find it difficult to trust anyone again. Even though the new country is relatively safe and secure, refugees may continue to feel unsafe after their arrival. Mistrust, particularly of authority figures, is a significant barrier to care. Refugees may be reluctant to disclose a trauma history for fear that the disclosure can be used against them (Tribe, 2002).

Trauma-informed care for refugees works toward developing feelings of safety and trust. This requires cultural sensitivity and respect, understanding of linguistic needs and the importance of using qualified interpreters and case management efforts.

Refugees are more likely to heal if health care providers show empathy and interest and allow adequate time to develop rapport and a trusting relationship (Gardiner & Walker, 2010). Becoming aware of the political situation in the client's country of origin and core cultural values may be helpful in developing a trust-based relationship. Addressing refugees' immediate needs conveys respect for their rights, well-being and autonomy (Gorman, 2001).

Refugees who are trauma survivors are particularly vulnerable to retrauma-tization (Bemak et al., 2003; Schwarz-Langer et al., 2006) Trauma-informed services are designed specifically to avoid retraumatizing those who seek assistance, whether or not they are seeking specific treatment for trauma. This includes awareness and prevention of potential triggers. For example, history taking and the assessments and hearings associated with the refugee determination process often trigger traumatic memories and worsen symptoms (Benedek & Wynn, 2011). For refugees who have been tortured by health care providers, routine physical exams may be very stressful and bring back memories of the torture. Unexpected loud noises can trigger an exaggerated startle response in survivors of bombing or shooting. Respecting the client's wish not to discuss trauma is important (Gardiner & Walker, 2010).

Service providers also need to be sensitive to gender and ethnic issues. Women who are survivors of sexual violence may feel more comfortable with female service providers. Refugees who were persecuted by members of their own cultural group may prefer service providers from a different cultural group (Allimant & Ostapiej-Piatkowski, 2011).

All clients who are not fluent in English should be offered a professional interpreter. The client's preference for someone with a particular ethnicity and of a certain gender should be respected where possible. Refugees from ethnic or religious minority groups may not feel comfortable with interpreters from majority groups responsible for their persecution. If the interpreter is perceived by the refugee client as biased, the client may not feel comfortable discussing personal issues (Canadian Council for Refugees & Sojourn House, 2010).

Focus on Strengths and Resilience

Refugees have the capacity to deal with hardship and deprivation and have a strong motivation to succeed. They should not be viewed as helpless victims of circumstance, but rather as people with extraordinary coping skills and resilience (Guyot, 2007; Rubinstein & Kohli, 2010; UNHCR, n.d.). Refugees should be acknowledged as "active survivors in a new environment" (Vasilevska & Simich, 2010). Blanch (2008) notes that even people who display severe trauma-related symptoms in some areas of functioning may show remarkable resilience in others.

Trauma-informed services build on the refugees' inner resources, prioritize skill building, encourage active participation in mental health programs and aim to expand support networks. Active participation "prevents the harmful helplessness and enforced dependence which drain their energy" (World Health Organization, 1996, p. 133).

The loss of family and social support can compound the experience of trauma. Trauma-informed care encourages refugees to become engaged with social support networks. For example, programs offered through settlement or social service agencies, such as a befriending program, that match clients with volunteers or mutual supports groups, have the potential to break down isolation and promote mental health (Canadian Centre for Victims of Torture, 2009).

Strong community support decreases resettlement stress, alleviates emotional distress and promotes refugee mental health (Beiser, 2010; Beiser et al., 2003; Simich et al., 2004). Beiser (2009) suggests that, at least in the short and medium term, the availability of a like-ethnic community is one of the strongest promoters of resilience in refugees.

Rebuilding a Sense of Control

Refugees are victims of circumstances beyond their control and usually have very few options about where they go or what they do. Being a refugee means being deprived of power and control, living in exile and depending on others for such basic needs as food and shelter. Trauma-informed care creates opportunities for survivors to rebuild a sense of control. Regaining a sense of control and responsibility for their lives is a part of healing and recovery (Miller & Rasco, 2004).

The key components of this approach involve empowering refugees to take a central role in their health and linking them to community resources. This means that refugees are active participants with choice and control over their treatment options and care, while service providers are responsive to their needs and choices.

Refugees are frequently unaware of the impact of trauma on their health and well-being. Gaining an understanding of the effects of trauma is important to the healing process. Health education should focus on normalizing trauma experiences, reducing stigma attached to mental health problems and exploring available treatment options (Johnson, 2005).

Prolonged disability status and dependence on others are generally not helpful. The Harvard Program in Refugee Trauma (2011) stresses the critical importance of actively involving trauma survivors in their own recovery. The areas of highest therapeutic potential include work, volunteering and spirituality. Survivors of war or organized violence often find comfort and healing from trauma through religion and spirituality. Work and volunteering provide survivors with a sense of worth, structured daily life and opportunities for socialization. Activities in these areas should be strongly encouraged (Harvard Program in Refugee Trauma, 2011; Johnson, 2005).

The ability to speak English or French is essential to refugee empowerment. Language skills help refugees to find employment and increase their access to services. These skills also provide opportunities for socialization (Beiser, 2010). However, due to trauma-related problems such as lack of concentration, memory problems or distrust of strangers, some refugees may have difficulties staying in regular ESL classes. Referral to a language program specially designed for survivors of war or torture is often helpful (Canadian Centre for Victims of Torture, 2009).

Refugees' social world has been destroyed or seriously damaged. Families are frequently separated for prolonged periods. Family members may have been killed or are missing. Trust in others has often been diminished by traumatic pre-migration experiences. Ethnic communities are considered a significant source of support for refugees. Linking survivors with the community-based organizations is often effective in reconstructing healthy relationships with others and increasing social connections (Blanch, 2008; Johnson, 2005).

Cultural Competence

Culturally competent trauma-informed care is increasingly recognized as a necessity for quality mental health care. Culture plays a key role in mental health, mental illness and help-seeking behaviour. It influences how people respond to trauma, how they express and communicate their symptoms, how they cope and what type of help they prefer (Blanch, 2008; Brown, 2008; Hinton & Lewis-Fernandez, 2010).

Research has found many commonalities in the way that people from different cultures react to traumatic events. However, there are also important differences across cultures in what is considered a traumatic event and how trauma-related symptoms are interpreted and expressed (Gorman, 2001). For example, research found that Tibetans consider witnessing the destruction of religious symbols as more traumatic than imprisonment or torture. For Rwandan genocide survivors, not being able to perform morning ceremonies and traditional funerals for the dead is very upsetting, due to cultural beliefs about the spiritual status of those who have not received those ceremonies (Hinton & Lewis-Fernandez, 2010).

Trauma-related symptoms in refugees may be missed if service providers are looking for symptoms that are normative in western populations (Blanch, 2008; Hinton & Lewis-Fernandez, 2010). Mental health problems may be attributed to many different causes, including witchcraft, voodoo, offending ancestor spirits, karma transmitting past life sins or soul loss (Johnson, 2005; Kohrt & Hruschka, 2010). In many refugee groups, local culture-specific syndromes represent a key response to trauma (Hinton & Lewis-Fernandez, 2010). For example, Hinton et al. (2009) report that Cambodian refugees tend to interpret nightmares as a sign of physical and spiritual vulnerability and/or a potential attack by ghosts. This frequently leads to the performance of specific practices and rituals aiming to force out attacking forces and protect the victim.

The biomedical approach to mental health problems that western medicine uses may not fit well into the framework of beliefs held by refugees from culturally different backgrounds. For example, for some refugees, restoring dignity may be more important than healing trauma symptoms (Blanch, 2008). Cultural competence is considered a core requirement for mental health professionals working with culturally diverse clients (Bhui et al., 2007). Culturally competent trauma-informed care respects different cultural values, beliefs and practices; reflects a willingness to learn about other cultures; and tailors services to meet clients' social, cultural and linguistic needs (Betancourt et al., 2002).

Conclusion

The assumption that all refugees are severely traumatized and need trauma treatment is incorrect (Blanch, 2008; Brundtland, 2000). Blanch (2008) states that trauma-specific services should be available to those who need them, in particular refugees who display severe and persistent trauma symptoms, but that the key principles of trauma-informed care—awareness, safety, respect, choice and empowerment—meet the basic mental health needs of all refugees, regardless of their experiences.

References

Allimant, A. & Ostapiej-Piatkowski, B. (2011). Supporting women from CALD backgrounds who are victims/survivors of sexual violence: Challenges and opportunities for practitioners. *ACSSA Wrap, 9.* Retrieved from www.aifs.gov.au/acssa/pubs/wrap/wrap9/w9.pdf

Beiser, M. (2009). Resettling refugees and safeguarding their mental health: Lessons learned from the Refugee Resettlement Project. *Transcultural Psychiatry, 46,* 539–583.

Beiser, M. (2010, Summer). Compassionate admission and self-defeating neglect: The mental health of refugees in Canada. *Canadian Issues,* 39–44.

Beiser, M., Simich, L. & Pandalangat, N. (2003). Community in distress: Mental health needs and help-seeking in the Tamil community in Toronto. *International Migration, 41,* 233–245.

Bemak, F., Chi-Ying Chung, R. & Pedersen, P.B. (2003). *Counseling Refugees: A Psychosocial Approach to Innovative Multicultural Interventions.* Westport, CT: Greenwood Press.

Benedek, D.M. & Wynn, G.H. (Eds.). (2011). *Clinical Manual for Management of PTSD.* Washington, DC: American Psychiatric Publishing.

Betancourt, J., Green, A. & Carrillo, E. (2002). *Cultural Competence in Health Care: Emerging Frameworks and Practical Approaches.* New York: The Commonwealth Fund.

Bhui, B., Warfa, N., Edonya, P., McKenzie, K. & Bhugra, D. (2007). Cultural competence in mental health care: A review of model evaluations. *BMC Health Services Research, 7*(15). Retrieved from www.biomedcentral.com/bmchealthservres/

Blanch, A. (2008). *Transcending Violence: Emerging Models for Trauma Healing in Refugee Communities.* Alexandria, VA: National Center for Trauma-Informed Care.

Brown, L.S. (2008). *Cultural Competence in Trauma Therapy: Beyond the Flashback.* Washington, DC: American Psychological Association.

Brundtland, G.H. (2000). Mental health of refugees, internally displaced persons and other populations affected by conflict. *Acta Psychiatrica Scandinavica, 102,* 159–161.

Canadian Centre for Victims of Torture. (2009). *Befriending: Creating a therapeutic bond with the community.* Retrieved from http://ccvt.org/publications/online-publications/befriending-creating-a-therapeutic-bond-with-the-community

Canadian Council for Refugees & Sojourn House. (2010). *Welcome to Canada: The Experience of Refugee Claimants at Port-of-Entry Interviews.* Retrieved from http://ccrweb.ca/files/poereport.pdf

Cardozo, B.L., Oleg, O., Bilukha, C., Gotway, C., Irshad, S., Wolfe, M. et al. (2004). Mental health, social functioning and disability in postwar Afghanistan. *JAMA, 292,* 575–584.

Citizenship and Immigration Canada. (2010). *Backgrounder: More support for resettled refugees.* Retrieved from www.cic.gc.ca/english/department/media/backgrounders/2010/2010-03-29.asp

Fazel, M., Wheeler, J. & Danesh, J. (2005). Prevalence of serious mental disorder in 7000 refugees resettled in western countries: A systematic review. *The Lancet, 365,* 1309–1314.

Gardiner, J. & Walker, K. (2010). Compassionate listening: Managing psychological trauma in refugees. *Australian Family Physician, 39,* 198–203. Retrieved from www.racgp.org.au/afp

Gorman, W. (2001). Refugee survivors of torture: Trauma and treatment. *Professional Psychology: Research and Practice, 32,* 443–451.

Guyot, J. (2007). Child and youth participation in protracted refugee situations. *Children, Youth and Environment, 17,* 159–178.

Harvard Program in Refugee Trauma. (2011). *Treatment plan.* Retrieved from http://hprt-cambridge.org/?page_id=69

Hinton, D.E., Hinton, A.L., Pich, V., Loeum, J.R. & Pollack, M.H. (2009). Nightmares among Cambodian refugees: The breaching of concentric ontological security. *Culture, Medicine and Psychiatry, 33,* 219–265.

Hinton, D.E. & Lewis-Fernandez, R. (2010). The cross-cultural validity of post-traumatic stress disorder: Implications for DSM-5. *Depression and Anxiety, 0,* 1–19. Retrieved from www.dsm5.org/Research/Documents/CulturePTSD_Published.pdf

Hollifield, M., Warner, T.D., Lian, N., Krakow, B., Jenkins, J.H., Kesler, J. et al. (2002). Measuring trauma and health status in refugees: A critical review. *JAMA, 288,* 611–621.

Johnson, D.R. (2005). *Helping Refugee Trauma Survivors in the Primary Care Setting.* St. Paul, MN: Center for Victims of Torture. Retrieved from www.cvt.org/resources/publications

Karunakara, U.K., Neuner, F., Schauer, M., Singh, K., Hill, K., Elbert, T. et al. (2004). Traumatic events and symptoms of post-traumatic stress disorder amongst Sudanese nationals, refugees and Ugandans in the West Nile. *African Health Sciences, 4*(2), 83–93.

Kazemipur, A. & Halli, SS. (2001). The changing colour of poverty in Canada. *Canadian Review of Sociology, 38,* 217–238.

Kirmayer, L.J., Narasiah, L., Munoz, M., Rashid, M., Ryder, A.G., Guzder, J. et al. (2011). Common mental health problems in immigrants and refugees: General approach in primary care. *Canadian Medical Association Journal, 183,* E959–E967. Retrieved from www.cmaj.ca

Kohrt, B.A. & Hruschka, D.J. (2010). Nepali concepts of psychological trauma: The role of idioms of distress, ethnopsychology and ethnophysiology in alleviating suffering and preventing stigma. *Culture, Medicine and Psychiatry, 34*, 322–352.

Mazurana, D. & Carlson, K. (2006). *The Girl Child and Armed Conflict: Recognizing and Addressing Grave Violations of Girls' Human Rights*. New York: United Nations Division for the Advancement of Women. Retrieved from www.un.org

Mikus Kos, A., Peren-Klinger, G. Gorenenberg, M., Mollica, R., DeMartino, R. & Petevi, M. (2011). *Draft Guidelines for the Evaluation and Care of Victims of Trauma and Violence.* Retrieved from http://hprt-cambridge.org/?page_id=88

Miller, K.E. & Rasco, L.M. (2004). An ecological framework for addressing the mental health needs of refugee communities. In K.E. Miller & L.M. Rasco (Eds.), *The Mental Health of Refugees: Ecological Approaches to Healing and Adaptation* (pp. 1–64). Mah Wah, NJ: Lawrence Erlbaum.

Mollica, R.F., Cui, X., McInnes, K. & Massagli, M.P. (2002). Science-based policy for psychosocial interventions in refugee camps: A Cambodian example. *Journal of Nervous and Mental Disease, 190*(3), 158–166.

Mollica, R., Sarajlic, N., Chernoff, M., Lavelle, J., Vukovic, I.S. & Massagli, M. (2001). Longitudinal study of psychiatric symptoms, disability, mortality, and emigration among Bosnian refugees. *JAMA, 286*, 546–554.

Porche, M.V., Fortuna, L.R. & Rosenberg, S. (2009). *Community Dialogue and Needs Assessment for Trauma Informed Systems of Care for Resettled African Refugee Youth in New Hampshire.* Retrieved from www.endowmentforhealth.org

Porter, M. & Haslam, N. (2005). Predisplacement and postdisplacement factors associated with mental health of refugees and internally displaced persons: A meta-analysis. *JAMA, 294*, 602–612.

Rubinstein, L. & Kohli, A. (2010). *Mental Health Services during and after Armed Conflict: The State of Knowledge and Practice.* Washington, DC: United States Institute of Peace. Retrieved from www.usip.org

Schwarz-Langer, G., Deighton, R.R, Jerg-Bretzke, L., Weisker, I. & Traue, H.C. (2006). Psychiatric treatment for extremely traumatized civil war refugees from former Yugoslavia: Possibilities and limitations of integrating psychotherapy and medication. *Torture, 6*, 69–80.

Simich, L., Hamilton, H. & Khamisa Baya, B. (2006). Mental distress, economic hardship and expectations of life in Canada among Sudanese newcomers. *Transcultural Psychiatry, 43*, 418–444.

Simich, L., Mawani, F., Wu, F. & Noor, A. (2004). *Meanings of Social Support, Coping and Help-Seeking Strategies among Immigrants and Refugees in Toronto.* (Toronto CERIS working paper No. 31). Toronto: Joint Centre of Excellence for Research on Immigration and Settlement.

Smid, G.E., van der Velden, P.G., Gersons, B.P.R. & Kleber, R.J. (2012). Late-onset posttraumatic stress disorder following a disaster: A longitudinal study. *Psychological Trauma: Theory, Research, Practice, and Policy, 4*, 312–322.

Tribe, R. (2002). Mental health of refugees and asylum-seekers. *Advances in Psychiatric Treatment, 8*, 240–248.

United Nations. (2009). *Violence against women.* Retrieved from www.un.org/en/events/endviolenceday/pdf/UNiTE_TheSituation_EN.pdf

United Nations. (n.d.). *Ending violence against women and girls.* Retrieved from www.un.org/en/globalissues/briefingpapers/endviol/index.shtml

United Nations High Commissioner for Refugees. (1951/2003). *Convention and Protocol relating to the Status of Refugees.* Geneva, Switzerland: Author. Retrieved from www.unhcr.org/3b66c2aa10.html

United Nations High Commissioner for Refugees. (n.d.). *Who are the refugees?* Retrieved from www.the-ecentre.net/resources/e_library/doc/RD%20Who%20Are%20the%20Refugees.pdf

Vasilevska, B. & Simich, B. (2010). A review of international literature on refugee mental health practices. *Canadian Issues, 33*–38. Retrieved from http://canada.metropolis.net/publications/index_e.html

Ward, J. & Marsh, M. (2006, June). *Sexual violence against women and girls in war and its aftermath: Realities, responses, and required resources.* Briefing paper prepared for the Symposium on Sexual Violence in Conflict and Beyond, Brussels, Belgium. Retrieved from www.unfpa.org/emergencies/symposium06/docs/finalbrusselsbriefingpaper.pdf

Watters, C. (2001). Emerging paradigms in the mental health care of refugees. *Social Science and Medicine, 52*, 1709–1718.

Wilson, R.M., Murtaza, M. & Shakia, Y. (2010). Pre-migration and post-migration determinants of mental health for newly arrived refugees in Toronto. *Canadian Issues, 45*–49. Retrieved from http://canada.metropolis.net/publications/index_e.html

World Health Organization. (1996). Mental health of refugees. Retrieved from http://helid.digicollection.org/en/d/Jh0223e2html

Chapter 10

The Evolution of Trauma-Informed Practice at the Jean Tweed Centre

Julia Bloomenfeld and Tammy Rasmussen

The Jean Tweed Centre was established in Toronto in 1983 as a substance use treatment centre for women, at a time when understanding of the relationship between trauma and substance use was just starting to emerge. While Jean Tweed has always applied a gender-specific lens in working with women, it was in the early 1990s that we began incorporating a trauma-informed approach in our substance use services. This chapter describes the genesis and framework for Jean Tweed's trauma-informed service model for working with substance use and gambling concerns, key aspects of providing trauma-informed care in the residential program and our more recent evolutions in trauma-informed practice.

The Genesis

Beginning in the late 1980s, clinical reviews confirmed that more than 80 per cent of women using Jean Tweed's services had experienced abuse. As we listened to women's stories, we learned about their use of substances to cope with trauma. We also saw the impact of trauma on women's experiences of treatment. As the centre became more conscious of the multifaceted impact of trauma, it was apparent that changes were necessary. Jean Tweed needed to become more knowledgeable about trauma and how it affects survivors seeking treatment for substance use and to change some of its traditional practices.

The critical first step was committing to build the infrastructure needed to provide trauma-informed services. Next, the centre hired an external consultant to provide intensive clinical training over a six-month period. The training provided a baseline of knowledge about trauma and its connection to substance use problems, and a common language for discussions. Over the years, it has been important to maintain agency-wide training to keep pace with emerging evidence-based approaches. Because all staff contribute to the overall atmosphere of safety and comfort that a woman experiences, non-clinical staff were included in aspects of the training. These sessions provided them with background and context for the kinds of situations they might encounter, such as women calling or arriving in distress. This kind of orientation is vital, as the reception a woman receives at the front door conveys a strong message about how she will be treated. For clinical staff, ongoing individual supervision, group consultation and regular team meetings provided a forum to enhance skills. These meetings also offered opportunities to discuss themes such as transference, countertransference and vicarious trauma.

The organizational strategies to promote a trauma-informed approach included changing our hiring practices. We began screening resumés and formulating interview questions to explore candidates' attitudes toward, and experience working with, trauma survivors. Similarly, individual professional development plans incorporated continued growth in trauma-informed care as a requirement.

The Paradigm Shift

Two pivotal shifts accompanied these strategies. The first was a shift in thinking: we left behind the notion that substance use and trauma are unconnected and should be dealt with separately. The leading principle going forward was that an understanding of the impact of trauma must be braided into all programs. The second shift involved capacity. Through training and education, Jean Tweed increased its capacity to provide trauma-informed programs. Service-level changes flowed out of this transformation. While all of the programs are now trauma informed, for purposes of illustration here, we will focus on practice examples drawn from our residential program.

Judith Herman's model (1992) for working with trauma strongly influenced the development of Jean Tweed's approach. The process of change around substance use problems has commonalities with the three stages outlined in Herman's model—safety, remembrance and mourning, and reconnection. In early-stage work for both trauma and substance use problems, the emphasis is on creating safety; the time orientation is the present; and the focus is on self-care. Women in this stage are supported to develop new coping skills. In terms of women's safety, the goals related to substance use problems and trauma recovery centre on establishing external and internal safety. External safety concerns arise from elements in women's physical or living environments that put them at risk. Many of the women who use the services at Jean Tweed, for example, may be living with an abusive partner, or without stable housing. Internal safety issues may include intense and difficult feelings, intrusive memories and physiological difficulties.

In the residential program, the focus remained on substance use problems, but treatment was delivered within a trauma-informed model. Jean Tweed created an affirming environment where a woman could name trauma as a concern, make the links between her substance use and her experience of trauma and learn positive coping strategies.

This trauma-informed approach was combined with trauma-specific programming. Hiring a trauma counsellor meant that women in continuing care who were ready for later-stage trauma work could get individual counselling. A Seeking Safety (Najavits, 2002) group, open to women across programs, provided a dual focus on first-stage substance use and trauma work. Initially, Jean Tweed's trauma lens focused on issues of abuse that occurred within the family. Over time, as our understanding of diversity and anti-oppression grew, we became aware of a much wider spectrum of oppression, terror and other forms of violence and trauma, politically and socially driven, that affect women on varied levels—within marginalized groups, such as immigrants, and across generations. With this awareness, our trauma lens expanded.

What evolved from this new framework was a trauma-informed continuum of services that encompassed a theoretical model for an integrated approach, an organizational infrastructure and changes to and expansion of programs. A parallel transfer of knowledge occurred with the integration of services to address problem gambling.[1]

1. Readers interested in a full description of the development of the Jean Tweed Centre's model will find it in "A braided recovery: Integrating trauma programming at a women's substance use treatment centre." In N. Poole & L. Greaves (Eds.), *Highs and Lows: Canadian Perspectives on Women and Substance Abuse* (pp. 365–371). Toronto: Centre for Addiction and Mental Health.

Trauma-Informed Practice

In a residential environment, specific concerns for trauma survivors may include physiological reactions, such as sleep disturbances, relational challenges and affect dysregulation. The literature about trauma-informed care highlights a number of principles that assist in responding to these concerns. These principles also influence our clinical decisions related to individual counselling, group facilitation and workshop content (Moses et al., 2003). Four of the key principles shaping our work include:

- avoiding retraumatization
- empowering women
- working collaboratively and with flexibility
- recognizing trauma symptoms as adaptations.

Avoiding Retraumatization

A residential treatment setting for substance use and gambling problems needs to pay special attention to how trauma-related material is woven into the program to avoid overwhelming women. Early in Jean Tweed's work with trauma, workshops were introduced to provide general information about trauma and managing trauma responses such as flashbacks. However, the sessions were overwhelming and women were frequently scared to attend. Some coped through avoidance, for example, by not paying attention or dissociating; others were triggered into painful memories and flashbacks. We learned from these experiences that psychoeducation and discussions about trauma should be "braided" into discussions related to substance use and gambling issues. For example, a workshop that teaches grounding skills is relevant to both substance use and trauma recovery. We also learned about the need to follow a woman's lead. For example, in relapse prevention, women often identify situations and emotions related to past trauma that put them at risk of using substances or gambling. Once women raise these issues, counsellors are prepared to provide support by identifying and teaching safe coping skills.

It is equally important to prevent retraumatization by supporting women to pace themselves. In the past, it was quite common in group therapy for women to move quickly into giving details of their traumatic history. This often led women to shut down in subsequent groups, as this level of disclosure was retraumatizing for the woman sharing the information and/or for other group members. Now, when trauma stories emerge in group, the therapeutic emphasis is on identifying the impact of trauma in the present. Linking trauma to substance use and gambling, and the importance of learning alternative coping skills, is the focus. This emphasis on the containment of sharing traumatic details and the focus on developing coping skills are affirmed by the literature related to first-stage trauma work (Haskell, 2001; Najavits, 2002). Women may want to share some details of their trauma in individual counselling sessions, where together with the therapist they can assess the safety and impact of this disclosure.

Empowering Women

Many clients are ashamed and overwhelmed by their trauma responses and believe they are "crazy." In the program, psychoeducation is used to help women better understand and normalize their trauma responses and the connections to substance use and gambling. The information the counsellor offers is based on what each woman is able to integrate at a particular time (Van der Hart et al., 2006). Skill development also promotes a sense of power and competency. For example, learning to regulate intense and overwhelming emotions and body sensations through strategies such as grounding and self-soothing can be empowering, particularly as these sensations are often triggers for substance use or gambling. Self-awareness, including awareness of personal strengths, and building upon assertiveness skills further increase women's empowerment, making them better able to know and take care of their needs. The knowledge women have gained, together with the coping skills they have learned, supports a shift from reacting to trauma triggers toward more safely and effectively responding to them.

Working Collaboratively and with Flexibility

The residential environment offers a community experience with a clear structure and set of norms. For many women, this type of experience promotes a sense of safety. However, for some, this environment can exacerbate trauma responses such as nightmares, insomnia, self-harm and recurring flashbacks. There are often women in the program who are making their first attempt to cope without the use of substances or gambling, and these trauma reactions can overtake their participation in the program. At times, a woman may feel like she is experiencing more harm than benefit. She becomes torn between her desire to stay in the program and the desire to stop the pain.

Trauma-informed practice has led us to be more flexible about the structure and expectations of the program. An emphasis on "guidelines" rather than "rules" expands the space around women for whom "treatment as usual" has created barriers. Counselling is collaborative. As much as possible, the counsellor will work with each woman to explore strategies for self-care, with openness to adjusting a guideline or offering a modified program to reduce the intensity.

Recognizing Trauma "Symptoms" as Adaptations

An important principle of trauma-informed care is the understanding that "symptoms" related to trauma are actually coping strategies developed to manage the traumatic experience (Haskell, 2001; Moses et al., 2003). In the residential program, we often observe relational patterns rooted in past traumatic experiences, often from childhood. Najavits (2006) identifies boundaries in relationships as a specific area of concern for survivors of trauma. Relationships may be "too close" (p. 155), such as when there is "excessive care-taking of others at the cost of self-care," or "too distant" (p. 155). Behaviours such as hostility or aggression can be scary for other participants and negatively affect the group's safety. The patterns and their impact are intensified in the residence, where women share space and tasks of community living. These patterns are also seen in how women interact with staff.

Prior to adopting a trauma-informed approach, some of these responses might have been perceived in negative ways—as "difficult" or "resistant"— or connected exclusively to a woman's substance use or gambling, whereas the caretaking behaviour might have been overlooked or even rewarded. A trauma-informed lens helps us to view these behaviours as coping strategies and to respond in non-judgmental ways that avoid shaming. Counsellors integrate education about boundaries in relationships and look for opportunities to assist women in developing new ways of relating to others. Sometimes, such as in the case of aggression, a woman is unable to shift her behaviour enough to maintain group safety, and a transfer to another program is required. In this situation, the counsellor's ability to present hope and maintain a trauma-informed view will support a woman who is struggling with self-esteem and feelings of shame; it may also help her to maintain a therapeutic connection to the centre.

Trauma-Informed Evolutions

Harm Reduction

Over the past several years, many service providers have embraced the idea of incorporating strategies that can reduce the harm of substance use and gambling problems on people's lives. Where in the past treatment focused strictly on stopping substance use, harm reduction expanded the lens of what is worthy of attention and support. Harm reduction sparked many changes for the centre. At various stages of healing, many trauma survivors in treatment may not feel ready or able to manage their trauma responses without using substances or gambling. Hence, the idea of reducing the harm of substance use or gambling—without necessarily stopping altogether—is consistent with a trauma-informed approach: supporting a woman at her own pace, working with the goals she establishes for herself, promoting choice and acknowledging her autonomy and control over her own life.

The integration of harm reduction resulted in a greater inclusion of programming geared to a variety of substance use or gambling-related goals. We also shifted our language; for example, we moved away from references to positive urine screens as "dirty" and negative urine screens as "clean," because such terms conveyed judgment and elicited shame. The routine practice of urine screening at Jean Tweed was also reconsidered. While initially the intention behind screening was to protect group safety, we now recognize that the practice can reduce trust and evoke trauma responses related to betrayal of physical and emotional boundaries. As a result, we have moved away from routine screening in the residential program, although there are times when urine screening still happens. For example, a woman may request screening as an external measure to increase her safety, or staff may use screening when concerns about group safety cannot otherwise be resolved.

The shift to a harm reduction model sometimes created dissonance. To protect the residence as a safe place, women are asked to not use substances or gamble. The tendency in the past has been to view any instance of substance use or gambling as an indication of a lack of readiness for an intensive program or of too great a risk to other participants. However, when a trauma survivor who is attending treatment uses a substance or gambles, critical reflection of its meaning and impact is helpful. The gains in coping skills the woman has learned are not erased. Instead, the event often consolidates her knowledge of the connection between her use of substances or gambling and her trauma history. A deeper focus on building safety skills emerges. Coming to a decision about how to respond to an instance of substance use requires a skilled counselling team in order to balance the needs of both the individual and the group.

Mindfulness

As part of adapting our practices and programs to be congruent with a trauma-informed approach, staff was offered training in mindfulness. Roshchild (2010) notes that "since the 1990's mindfulness has increasingly gained respect as a tried and true asset for trauma recovery. It is even now advocated by many in the mainstream of trauma treatment and research" (p. 7). Jon Kabat-Zinn (1994) defines mindfulness as "paying attention in a particular way; on purpose to the present moment and non-judgmentally" (p. 4).

In our experience, mindfulness can help to minimize retraumatization when a woman in the program is experiencing the somatic, cognitive and/or emotional experiences of trauma. By guiding her to observe and report on her experience in the present moment, which engages the prefrontal cortex of the brain, the woman "has" an experience rather than "being" it (Ogden et al., 2008). She is then more able to remain grounded and differentiate the past from the present, thereby maintaining a sense of safety. Aspects of mindfulness are now integrated into individual and group work.

Clinical meetings are also guided by a mindfulness approach. This safe and supportive context provides an opportunity for staff to engage in reflexive practice. Clinical cases are discussed, as well as the enactments or counter-transferences that can occur with clients. Grounding the discussions is the concept that "it is skillful to know when we are not being skillful" in our work with clients (B. Laskin, community practice discussion, April 21, 2010).

Conclusion

Women who have experienced trauma may turn to substances or gambling—not as ways to harm themselves, but as ways to keep themselves alive in the face of overwhelming psychic pain. As an agency dedicated to the empowerment of women, it is important for us at Jean Tweed to be aware of the incredible resilience and courage of the women we serve. The transformations that women make as they shake loose the control that substance use, gambling and trauma have had over their lives are a reminder of the power of trauma-informed care. The evolution of trauma-informed practice at Jean Tweed, while positive and exciting, has challenged our thinking and revealed many complexities of practice. As the women with whom we work seek to master skills to heal from trauma and substance use and gambling issues, we seek to shape a treatment environment in which this may happen.

References

Haskell, L. (2001). *Bridging Responses: A Front-Line Worker's Guide to Supporting Women Who Have Post-traumatic Stress.* Toronto: Centre for Addiction and Mental Health.

Herman, J. (1992). *Trauma and Recovery: The Aftermath of Violence—From Domestic Abuse to Political Terror.* New York: Basic Books.

Kabat-Zinn, J. (2005). *Wherever You Go, There You Are: Mindfulness Meditation in Everyday Life.* New York: Hyperion.

Moses, D., Reed, B., Macelia, R. & D'Ambrosio, B. (2003). *Creating Trauma Services for Women with Co-occurring Disorders: Experiences from the SAMHSA Women with Alcohol, Drug Abuse and Mental Health Disorders Who Have Histories of Violence Study.* Retrieved from www.nationaltraumaconsortium.org

Najavits, L.M. (2002). Seeking Safety: *A Treatment Manual for PTSD and Substance Abuse.* New York: Guilford Press.

Najavits, L.M. (2006). Managing trauma reactions in intensive addiction treatment environments. *Journal of Chemical Dependency Treatment, 8,* 153–161.

Ogden, P., Minton, K. & Pain, C. (2006). *Trauma and the Body: A Sensorimotor Approach to Psychotherapy*. New York: W.W. Norton.

Roshchild, B. (2010). *8 Keys to Safe Trauma Recovery: Take-Charge Strategies to Empower Your Healing*. New York: W.W. Norton.

Van der Hart, O, Nijenhuis, E. & Steele, K. (2006). *The Haunted Self: Structural Dissociation and the Treatment of Chronic Traumatization*. New York: W.W. Norton.

Chapter 11

Show Not Tell...

Trauma-Informed Creative Engagement with Youth Who Have FASD

Mary Harber

Trauma-informed practice has been successfully enacted in expressive therapies often used with children and youth as a way to address the effects of trauma. This chapter describes how a creative drama intervention called Theatre We ARE is being used with young people with fetal alcohol spectrum disorder (FASD) in British Columbia as a way to attend to both their disability and potential experience of trauma.

Adolescence, FASD and the Experience of Trauma

The combined effects of having FASD, experiencing trauma and going through adolescence pose certain challenges for youth with FASD. People with FASD have difficulty with various issues, including cognition, learning, communication and executive functions such as memory, sequencing and cause and effect (Streissguth, 1997). They also experience problems in social, behavioural and adaptive functioning (Riley et al., 2011).

Like people with FASD, many children who have been traumatized also have trouble with learning, concentration and attention (Baker & Jaffe, 2007, as cited in Bellamy & Hardy, 2010). They can have difficulty in social functioning, coping with stress and relationships. According to Putnam (2006), children and youth who have trauma histories experience lower social competence, difficulty recognizing their own and others' emotional states, cognitive and attention problems, affective mood regulation issues and difficulty with identity and self-esteem. Henry et al. (2007, as cited in Bellamy & Hardy, 2010) explain:

> The combination of fetal alcohol exposure and a history of trauma is more damaging to children than trauma alone. Combined, the neurodevelopmental consequences result in an increased risk for learning disabilities, poor coping strategies, and inability to control emotional responses. These developmental deficits result in higher levels of negative behaviors because traumatized children are more likely to over-react or shut down in the face of stress. (p. 5)

In addition to FASD and trauma, transitional and developmental issues must be considered. Developmentally, youth are exploring the meaning of the world and how they "fit." Baizerman and Erickson (2000) see this as a time for exploration and excitement around learning about one's self. However, creating emotional safety and supporting identity development for youth with disabilities can be potentially intimidating for care providers.

Creative Drama

Creative drama focuses on the experience of participants (Way, 1967). It is "an improvisational, non-exhibitional, process-oriented form of drama, where participants are guided by a leader to imagine, enact, and reflect on experiences real and imagined" (Youth Stages, n.d.). The difference between theatre and creative drama is doing and being (creative drama) and pretending and performing (theatre). Creative drama explores real-life situations, problem solving, modelling and rehearsing using potential and actual lived experiences. This approach to learning appeals to the kinesthetic learning style of many people with FASD and other brain-based disabilities.

Creative drama offers an externalized form of expression that is important to feeling safe, while allowing participants to be free to discuss difficult issues; it is a way to place a unique mark on experiences and feelings. Active engagement also allows youth to experience their feelings without fear of social repercussion —they cannot draw or take a photo of the "wrong" thing. This provides a sense of safety, which is critical when engaging youth who have FASD and a history of trauma. These youth are often in helping systems that are "deficit" oriented and may have learned to shut down in times of stress in response to anxiety about making "mistakes." Youth with FASD need to see their strengths and be given permission to express who they are in healthy, non-judgmental ways.

Creative drama provides a forum in which to explore healthy relationships and boundaries that can address the relational needs of adolescents in general and those with FASD. Young people must have opportunities to form healthy relationships with others, to feel like they are recognized, that they are important and that they belong to a larger community.

Drama techniques may mistakenly be seen to lack containment, boundaries and safety. The concern is that the person may be acting out a scenario or engaging in an activity that could represent a traumatic event or that could trigger feelings around an event. This possibility is not a reason to avoid this type of engagement; rather, it provides an opportunity to incorporate containment strategies, as described below. Nash and Rowe (2000) recognize the potential for playback—a form of creative drama using real-life stories of participants— to bring up difficult and distressing thoughts and feelings, while acknowledging that many things can potentially act as triggers, whether they be video games, television or movies, and that risk can only ever been managed and reduced but never eliminated.

Trauma-Informed Principles Embedded in Creative Drama Interventions

Creative drama is currently being used with a group of young adults with FASD and autism spectrum disorders to support the transition to adulthood, promote community inclusion and develop social skills. The following three principles of trauma-informed practice are embedded in this work:

1. **Choice and control:** Practitioners ensure physical and emotional safety by setting clear tasks and boundaries for participants. Creative drama supports

choice and control for each person, as well as power sharing, collaboration and skill building. Every measure is taken to reduce potential harm as opposed to shutting down participants' examination of their experiences. Representational expression (acting, art, story metaphor, etc.) provides an opportunity to take a familiar situation and see it in new ways (Cohen et al., 1995).

2. **Preventing retraumatization:** Drama is used in a way that facilitates an understanding of participants' issues, without reliving any trauma they may have experienced. Participants who need to deal with individual trauma issues are referred to trauma-specific services.

3. **Creating safety:** Various measures are taken to create safety and ensure that participants have the freedom to express who they are and how they feel without judgment. Concrete measures are taken to ensure the youths' safety while still allowing them freedom, using drama techniques. For example, all drama activities have a built-in "freeze" component, whereby the leaders or others can stop a scene during an improvisational skit and move it in another direction. We also talk about what we saw and what we might do differently if we were to re-story a scene.

Example 1

Two participants act out a scene in which they are two friends going to a movie. One person begins by telling the other that he or she doesn't really like the other's choice of movie and would like to see something different. The scene continues on with the two friends getting into an argument over the choice of movie.

As the scene unfolds, you may notice a participant getting upset or agitated. At this point, you would say "freeze," approach the two participants, tap one of them out of the scene and start a different track. For example, you may respond with "Well, I understand that you don't want to see a movie—let's go for ice cream." Any other participant can also call "freeze" and take over a spot in the scene. Interrupting the scene in this way helps to regulate what is happening and ensures that a sense of safety remains. The activity can be very playful and fun, often allowing participants to use their imagination.

Example 2

Two participants decide to do a scene about making a difficult life decision. They ask others to play different people in the scene to help them act out the issue—for example, taking a job, experiencing a friendship conflict or school problems, dealing with money.

Once the scene (short time-frame) is finished, the rest of the group debriefs and talks about how it felt, and offers strategies and advice for dealing with the presented issue.

Beyond doing this expressive work, Theatre We ARE, which was named by the group, created an educational presentation for the community. This group consisted of five youth and two adolescent mentors from the community, and was facilitated with a co-leader model. This configuration provided support as well as peer mentoring. The group wrote three scenes that present issues related to FASD. The scenes reflect participants' own experiences. The first scene examines struggles in classroom learning, teaching expectations and peer relationships. The second scene is about a young person who works in a retail store and is trying to manage job responsibilities while struggling with memory and sequencing issues and not wanting to look inept. The final scene is about understanding the commercial exchange of money, such as buying a coffee. The scene highlights the difficulty individuals may experience when they may not understand the cost of an item or the math involved in the transaction. This is an important scene, as some individuals find this type of pressure publicly embarrassing.

Conclusion

Through their educational presentations to the community and their own expressive work as a group, Theatre We ARE participants support one another, make risk possible and share fears and concerns about their own lives. They use drama as an avenue for self-expression that respects their voice and need for control over their own stories. Creative drama has enormous potential for people with FASD to safely express their experiences in a way that takes into account and increases understanding of their challenges with adaptive functioning.

References

Baizerman, M.L. & Erickson J.B. (2000, January). Adolescence is not a medical condition. *CYC-Online*. Retrieved from www.cyc-net.org/cyc-online/cycol-0100-adolescence.html

Bellamy, S. & Hardy, C. (2010). *Northern Attachment Network Review #4: Trauma, Learning and Fetal Alcohol Spectrum Disorder*. Retrieved from www.fasdoutreach.ca

Cohen, B.M., Barnes, M.M. & Rankin, A.B. (1995). *Managing Traumatic Stress through Art: Drawing from the Center*. Baltimore: Sidran Press.

Nash, S. & Rowe, N. (2000). *Safety, Danger and Playback Theatre*. Retrieved from http://playbacktheatre.org

Putnam, F.W. (2006). The impact of trauma on child development. *Juvenile and Family Court Journal, 57*, 1.

Riley, E.P., Clarren, S., Winberg, J. & Jonsson, E. (2011). *Fetal Alcohol Spectrum Disorder: Management and Policy Perspectives*. Weinheim, Germany: Wiley-Blackwell.

Streissguth, A. (1997). *Fetal Alcohol Syndrome: A Guide for Families and Communities*. Baltimore: Paul H. Brookes.

Way, B. (1967). *Development through Drama*. Atlantic Highlands, NJ: Humanities Press.

Youth Stages. (n.d.). *What Is Creative Drama?* Retrieved from www.youthstages.com/CreativeDrama/index.asp

Chapter 12

Girls' Groups and Trauma-Informed Intersectional Practice

Natalie Clark

Girls' groups provide a space for girls to find their own voices, make connections and honour relationships in their lives at a time when they often feel disconnected—from family, peers, their culture, school, community and themselves (Bell-Gadsby et al., 2006).

The Canadian Women's Foundation report *Girls in Canada* (Calhoun Research and Development/Recherche et développement et al., 2005) defines a gender-specific girls' program as a "single-sex program intentionally designed to respond to the specific needs and strengths of the girls it serves" (p. 55). The report explains the rationale for these programs: "There is no one experience of being a girl. Gender combines with race, socio-economic status, sexual orientation and dis/ability status to shape girls individually and collectively, and programs for girls reflect such diversity" (p. 55).

Girls' groups have the potential to provide a unique model to support and identify young women's health needs when offered within a trauma-informed intersectional framework. Research suggests that there is a significant need for gender-specific girls' programming, especially within ethno-specific communities, impoverished neighbourhoods and rural and northern regions. Girl-specific programs have had overwhelmingly positive results, giving girls the opportunity to address, critique and develop their ideas, experiences and imaginings.

Unfortunately, despite the growing popularity of girls' groups in the community and in schools, and the constant presence of a continuum of trauma in many girls' lives, many groups do not apply a trauma-informed or intersectional and culturally safe model. However, the need for such a model is evident in research indicating that gender intersects with issues of racism, violence and abuse in girls' lives and that these issues must be addressed together (Jiwani, 1999; McCreary Centre Society, 2004, 2005; Taefi et al., 2008). From my 20 years of practice and research with girls, I know that girls often do not disclose abuse and trauma, and many do not seek treatment; as a result, they engage in high-risk behaviours or "strategies of disconnection." They may misuse substances; engage in self-harming behaviours, such as cutting and disordered eating; have suicidal thoughts or attempt suicide; and experience emotional outbursts, display high energy and appear disconnected from others and from systems in their lives. Girls who do seek treatment and who use these forms of coping are often further labelled and pathologized within the health care system, rather than being honoured for the creativity they use to survive or understood for the meaning they attach to these coping strategies (Clark & Hunt, 2011).

Applying an Intersectional Approach

Many girls who are disadvantaged and marginalized by society do not see themselves or their unique needs reflected in mainstream girls' group programming (Clark & Hunt, 2011). Girls who are marginalized due to intersecting factors such as race, class and geography often experience even higher rates of violence, daily acts of sexual harassment and racism (Jiwani, 1998). The Alliance of Five Research Centres on Violence, in one of the few studies examining violence and girls through an intersectional lens, described effective programs as recognizing "how gender, race, class, sexuality, disability, and age intersect in particular ways to shape women's and girls' experiences of violence and their access to programs and services" (Blaney, 2004, p. vi).

Intersectionality, a concept and framework developed by indigenous and African-American feminist activists and coined by critical race scholar Kimberlé Crenshaw (1989), is an important component of any trauma-informed practice. The term describes the oppression produced structurally and experienced and resisted individually and collectively through and across diverse social categories of identity simultaneously. Intersectionality, as Jessica Yee (2011) describes it, is not new to indigenous peoples—it is the way they have always thought. Indigenous communities, prior to colonization, had multiple categories of gender and holistic understandings and approaches to health. Many had strong matrilinear traditions and complex systems of governance and systems of treaty and peacemaking processes. There is growing recognition that the concept of intersectionality "complements growing discussions about the complexity and multiplicities involved in being indigenous, in the category of indigeneity, and in indigenous people's health and well-being" (De Leeuw & Greenwood, 2011, p. 54).

Through a trauma-informed and intersectional approach, the groups that my colleagues and I have developed provide girls with the opportunity to explore their experiences of abuse, sexual exploitation, body image and violence, as well as their strengths, diversity and daily lived realities in a safe and non-threatening environment (Bell-Gadsby et al., 2006; Clark & Hunt, 2011).

My current work in partnership with the Aboriginal community and school district has involved developing a culturally safe model for Aboriginal girls' groups within a framework that reintroduces indigenous cultural teachings of girlhood, or "rites of passage." The model for the group was developed in a unique format—with youth, elders, community leaders and practitioners in a traditional circle and facilitated by an elder in the community. This talking circle identified the key issues for Aboriginal youth in our community and how to address them. Through partnerships with community, the school district and elders, the goal of these groups is to provide Aboriginal/First Nations girls, aged eight to 18, with a safe space in which to explore issues affecting their daily lives.

Aboriginal adolescent girls begin to identify themselves by their race at a time when there are strong societal messages about who is and who is not desirable. The groups support the girls to resist societal stereotypes and develop healthy definitions of themselves as Aboriginal/First Nations girls. Research has found that strong cultural beliefs and values provide a protective resilience for youth and are linked to positive health outcomes and decreased risk factors, including achievement, self-esteem and less risky drug and sex activities (Chandler & Lalonde, 2008; McCreary Centre Society, 2005). Specifically, research has linked cultural rites of passage groups for African-American girls with fewer risk factors and greater protective factors in these areas (Belgrave et. al., 2004; Constantine et al., 2006).

A trauma-informed and intersectional girls' group locates the source of girls' challenges within structural and systemic problems such as racism, poverty, sexism and the intersections of these in their lives. We support the young women in healthy resistance to these problems and in their efforts to move back into connection with themselves and others. We do this through a range of trauma-informed strategies of naming, educating and supporting healthy resistance strategies[1] (Robinson & Ward, 1991).

Key Trauma-Informed Practices

Trauma-informed practice allows us to provide girls with safety, support and the tools to deal with trauma and its effects in their daily lives within an intersectional framework. Key trauma-informed practices that inform my work include truth-telling and conscious use of self; safety and containment; naming and noting; and fostering healthy resistance strategies, as adapted from the *It's A Girl Thang: A Manual on Creating Girls Groups* (Bell-Gadsby et al., 2006). These practices are elaborated on below.

Truth-Telling and Conscious Use of Self

A specific strategy for facilitators is "truth-telling," or directly naming and challenging negative cultural messages, such as those about gender or race. Service providers can introduce girls to role models, such as youth activists like Jessica Yee, who have spoken up or resisted racism or sexism.[2] I have brought books or speakers to girls' groups that provide examples of girls and women resisting violence and speaking up about oppression and trauma. Girls were hungry for their stories. I realized that they needed to hear from other girls like themselves and from Aboriginal women and role models who had resisted violence and abuse and ultimately colonization. The girls wanted

1. For more information on resistance, see Robinson & Ward's (1991) article, "A belief in self far greater than anyone's disbelief: Cultivating resistance among African American Female Adolescents," in *Women and Therapy, 11,* 87–104. The authors present two different forms of resistance to oppression—healthy resistance (liberating) and survival resistance (survival oriented).
2. For more information about Jessica Yee's work with the Native Youth Sexual Health Network, visit http://nativeyouthsexualhealth.com/aboutourfounder.html.

to hear the specific strategies that these women used, whether they were political, legal, artistic or therapeutic.

Service providers may also choose to share their own strategies for resisting violence and oppression and tell stories that provide the girls with under-standing, tools and strategies for coping with daily challenges. In my groups, I share my experiences of growing up with a solo parent living on income assistance and some of the ways I resisted the limitations of our financial situation by, for example, buying clothes at thrift stores. This strategy is then used in the group: we take the girls to a thrift store, where they shop for themselves and another on a limited budget. We discuss how we can resist societal marketing and messages about what one should wear, while practising self-expression through what we wear. I tell the story of going to a school counsellor after feeling judged by a teacher who said he felt sorry for me. The counsellor encouraged me to share the impact of this comment with this teacher, even pulling him out of class. I still recall the power I felt walking down the hall and interrupting his class to share my anger about his comments. When I did, the teacher cried. I contrast how I coped in this situation with other times when I would get into fights.

Having self-awareness is key, as group facilitators will be challenged to share aspects of their own lives and struggles. Articulating these experiences can be difficult, as we have often been socialized to be silent about these issues. Thoughtful use of self-disclosure means ensuring that you tell stories where you have found resolution and that you focus on how what you are disclosing will be relevant or beneficial to the girls, rather than what it will mean for you personally. Central to this practice is the importance of grounding in your own experience and considering the intersections of power and privilege within your own life. The girls I have worked with often ask who I am and why I care. We must be ready to answer these questions.

From the work of bell hooks (1999) and others, we know that assisting girls to develop an "oppositional gaze" is crucial: in other words, supporting them to resist stereotypes and to replace these with strong and affirming messages and images of themselves. This includes naming and challenging negative cultural messages and abuse of power and its sources in society. Sharing strategies for coping with sexual harassment, racism or other abuses of power is an important skill. For example, in the Aboriginal girls' groups, we often invite Aboriginal young women as role models to share their own stories and strategies of how they negotiated adolescence.

Safety and Containment

Addressing issues of safety and containment in the group and within individual relationships is key to allowing girls the opportunity to learn and grow. Dealing with issues of trauma and abuse and challenges related to identity and development is also important. In the group setting, the onus is on the facilitator to create a feeling of safety.

Strategies for creating safety include:

- beginning and/or ending each group with a circle where each girl's voice is heard
- providing weekly reminders of confidentiality and limits
- gently and consistently interrupting if a girl is about to disclose or share too much
- providing girls with the opportunity to disclose individually, if you think they want to disclose, rather than in a group format. (If they do disclose, remind them of the limits of confidentiality and that the therapist is required to report the abuse and provide support and follow-up.)
- encouraging and supporting a girl's choice to speak and share her truth, and introducing breathing, journaling and other tools to help contain the impact of strong emotions
- sharing power with the girls through group decision-making models; creating agendas and topics for the groups; and inviting the girls to assist with the group in as many ways as possible, such as creating the calendar of events, choosing the name of the group or the time the group happens.

Addressing physical, emotional, mental, spiritual and cultural safety is crucial to trauma-informed practice. Cultural safety means allowing the user of the health service to define if the service feels safe for her:

> The main themes of cultural safety are that we are all bearers of culture and that we need to be aware of and challenge unequal power relations at the level of individual, family, community, and society.

> Cultural safety draws our attention to the social, economic, and political position of certain groups within society, such as the Maori people in A/NZ or Aboriginal peoples in Canada. Cultural safety reminds us to reflect on the ways in which our health policies, research, education, and practices may recreate the traumas inflicted upon Aboriginal peoples. (University of Victoria Continuing Studies, n.d.)

With girls' groups, this means that not only is the group informed by and understanding of the history of colonization and residential schools, but also that it recognizes the ongoing impact of colonization in the girls' lives. In contrast to cultural competence, where the service provider determines the competence of the participants, usually based on their attending training, cultural safety puts the receiver of the service, in this case the girls, in the role of identifying whether the group is culturally safe for them.

Naming and Noting

Naming and noting involves embracing the intersections of who the girls are and who we are as facilitators by naming and noting experiences of racism, sexism and trauma. This helps girls to connect across differences, rather than pretend that we are all the same or that differences do not exist. Within the group, girls are given the analytical tools to situate themselves within larger power systems and institutions, and to then problematize ideals around girlhood, health and other norms. Through this process, the girls can identify how their lives are shaped by intersecting societal processes and can explore creative ways to question or undermine the hold these processes have on their lives. Rather than asking "What is wrong with me and how can I better fit into society's ideals?," the girls are encouraged to ask "What is wrong with societal norms, and what ideals do I hold true for my own vision of health?"

This questioning involves directly naming and identifying the girls' strengths and special skills. Girls exist within a society that often makes them feel hypervisible, or under the gaze of others, but not truly "seen." By naming and noting, we help girls to develop their gifts and provide tools, such as writing and art workshops and beadwork, to make these gifts visible.

Fostering Healthy Resistance

A trauma-informed practice with girls reframes their coping and resistance as strategies to meet their needs in the here and now and survive in an environment or society that is oppressing them. This is adapted from the groundbreaking work of Robinson and Ward (1991), who examined African-American girls' strategies of resistance. However, girls' resistance strategies often do not challenge the source of the problem, and are instead a form of dissociation that involves "loss to the conscious self of knowledge or feelings that have become dangerous to know and feel" (Gilligan et al., 1995, p. 26). Service providers can encourage girls to name the true source of their problems, and assist them with strategies that demand change in the structural environment, including policies and programs that are oppressing them (Gilligan et al., 1995).

A recent study by Peled and Cohavi (2009) examined the experiences of girls in Israel running away from home, and concluded that understanding Israeli girlhood "requires a consideration of layers of social marginality other than those of gender and age, such as race, class and immigration status" (p. 740). The researchers explored the shifting meaning that society has attached to running away, from labelling it as youth rebellion, to the current practice of viewing girls who run away as victims of abuse and violence. The authors acknowledge that most runaway girls identify histories of sexual abuse as the reason for leaving home and have higher rates of posttraumatic stress disorder and substance abuse. Peled and Cohavi (2009) also identify and name the strength of these girls

> in [their] ability to give up their homes and oppose familial and cultural norms in order to care for themselves, to save their bodies and souls from abuse, rejection, and humiliation. . . [in so doing, they work to] facilitate a change in their life situations, and to make their voices heard above the silence imposed on them. (p. 747)

A strengths-based approach focuses on making girls' strengths and resistance visible. Girls are encouraged to express themselves creatively by publishing their writing and displaying their art. While girls often do not report or speak about incidents of date rape and violence in their interpersonal relationships, through art-based methods they are able to tell these stories and express their feelings about them, even if they aren't comfortable disclosing them more directly. In this way, the girls are introduced to new ways of coping that increase their sense of power and agency, rather than leaving them feeling further pathologized.

Shifting away from self-blame and demanding change

We work with the girls to shift the blame from themselves and support them in moving from "survival" resistance strategies, such as dropping out of school to avoid seeing the boys, to naming the issues and demanding change. The girls created a poster that said, "Hey, do you want to get laid?" and then went on to identify the conditions under which rape occurs, including their own date rape experiences. The poster was then displayed in a central place in the youth centre these boys attended, and remained there, unmarked, for a number of years. This clearly told the boys at the centre about the girls' resistance. The girls also discussed safety strategies, such as using a buddy system; always having a friend with them who doesn't drink alcohol; and, if they choose to drink or use substances, taking a harm reduction approach, rather than binge drinking, which often resulted in blackouts.

Identifying strategies to cope with anger

Another example of helping girls shift to healthy resistance is asking them to identify how they cope daily with their anger (e.g., attacks on one another, cutting and other self-harming strategies) and then move toward identifying the true source of their anger (racism, violence against women, sexual harassment). The girls then make a collage of the real things they are angry about, such as abuse and racism, and throw the plate with their collage against the wall (wearing safety goggles). From this activity, they learn to move from daily coping strategies for anger to naming the structural issues about which they are actually angry. Throwing the plate teaches them that there can be safe ways to release anger in the body. The girls then pick one piece of the broken plate that they will keep to make something creative from their anger. Through such activities, girls' groups can reinforce and provide tools for healthy resistance and self-expression.

Framing Trauma Discourse within a Social Justice Framework

Two questions, adapted from Jennifer White (2009), encapsulate a social justice approach that views girls' strategies as resistance and recognizes how trauma discourse is often part of Aboriginal girls' ongoing colonization.

- What are the consequences of locating risk and trauma within girls or specific types of girls (i.e., racialized or Aboriginal girls)? What about placing it within society and structural barriers?
- What fresh possibilities might be opened up by thinking about girls and trauma in other ways? For example, what difference does it make, if any, to understand and locate their coping within oppressive social practices, such as colonization, and structural racism?

Education about Trauma and Resistance

Trauma is a constant presence in the lives of the girls we work with. In educating the girls about trauma, girls' groups frame the girls' experiences as resistance strategies to oppose a system or relationships that are oppressing or abusive to them. The girls are encouraged to see the links between their individual behaviour and coping mechanisms, and their resistance to abuse, violence and daily experiences of oppression within society. Girls are encouraged to name and centralize the location of the problem outside of themselves. With more than 53 per cent of girls experiencing sexual harassment and body-based harassment daily in schools (McCreary Centre Society, 2004), health care practitioners need to recognize that trauma includes more than direct experiences of violence. Trauma can also be experienced by racism, sexism and the intersections of these in girls' lives. In a study of violence and young women of colour in British Columbia, most girls identified racism as the number one form of violence they experienced. Many of these young women, particularly those in rural communities, have few safe places or services to access (Jiwani, 2006). It is important that girls understand that trauma exists on a continuum and that their choices and resistance exist within a framework that allows them to name their experiences of sexism and racism.

Conclusion

In my practice and writing about girls' groups, my colleagues and I have developed a model that widens the lens for situating and responding to the experience of trauma. We caution that trauma-informed practice must not further label and pathologize girls. Even the definitions of "trauma" and "PTSD" are medicalized terms and are culturally bound and limited. A focus on trauma as an individual health problem prevents and obscures a more critical, historically situated focus on social problems under a (neo)colonial state that contribute to violence. We need programs that provide safer spaces for girls to address their intersecting and emergent health needs, without furthering the discourse and construction of indigenous girls and women as being at risk. Programs such as rites of passage groups that resist medical and individual definitions of trauma, and use an intersectional framework that shifts from the individual as the problem, help girls to understand and locate their coping as responses to larger structural and systemic forces, including racism, poverty, sexism, colonialism and a culture of trauma. Even when educating girls about the biological impact of trauma (e.g., understanding triggering and fight-or-flight responses), it is important to frame their reactions and coping within a social justice approach that views these strategies as resistance, and names and understands how current trauma discourse and services are often part of the ongoing colonization of Aboriginal girls.

References

Bell-Gadsby, C., Clark, N. & Hunt, S. (2006) *It's A Girl Thang: A Manual on Creating Girls Groups*. Vancouver: McCreary Youth Foundation.

Belgrave, F.Z., Reed, M.C., Plybon, L.E., Butler, D.S., Allison, K.W. & Davis, T. (2004). An evaluation of Sisters of Nia: A cultural program for African American girls. *Journal of Black Psychology, 30*, 329–343.

Blaney, E. (2004). *PRISM: Probing Rural Issues—Selecting Methods to Address Abuse of Women and Girls: (E)valu(at)ing "Better" Practices and Reflexive Approaches*. Fredericton, NB: Muriel McQueen Fergusson Centre for Family Violence Research.

Calhoun Research and Development/Recherche et développement, C. Lang Consulting & Savoie, I. (2005). *Girls in Canada 2005*. Toronto: Canadian Women's Foundation.

Chandler, M.J. & Lalonde, C.E. (2008). Cultural continuity as a moderator of suicide risk among Canada's First Nations. In L. Kirmayer & G. Valaskakis (Eds.). *Healing Traditions: The Mental Health of Aboriginal Peoples in Canada* (pp. 221–248). Vancouver: UBC Press.

Clark, N. & Hunt, S. (2011). Navigating the crossroads: Exploring rural young women's experiences of health using an intersectional framework. In O. Hankivsky (Ed.), *Health Inequities in Canada: Intersectional Frameworks and Practices* (pp. 131–146). Vancouver: UBC Press.

Constantine, M.G., Alleyne, V.L, Wallace, B.C. & Franklin-Jackson, D.C. (2006). Africentric cultural values: Their relation to positive mental health in African American adolescent girls. *Journal of Black Psychology, 32,* 141–154.

Crenshaw, K. (1989). Demarginalizing the intersection of race and sex: A black feminist critique of antidiscrimination doctrine, feminist theory and antiracist politics. *University of Chicago Legal Forum, 1989,* 139–167.

De Leeuw, S. & Greenwood, M. (2011). Beyond borders and boundaries: Addressing indigenous health inequities in Canada through theories of social determinants of health and intersectionality. In O. Hankivsky (Ed.), *Health Inequities in Canada: Intersectional Frameworks and Practices* (pp. 53–70). Vancouver: UBC Press.

Gilligan, C. Taylor, J.M. & Sullivan, A. (1995). *Between Voice and Silence: Women, Girls, Race and Relationship.* Cambridge: Harvard University Press.

hooks, b. (1999). The oppositional gaze: Black female spectators. In S. Thornham (Ed.), *Feminist Film Theory: A Reader.* Edinburgh, UK: Edinburgh University Press.

Jiwani, Y. (1998). *Violence against Marginalized Girls: A Review of the Current Literature.* Vancouver: FREDA Centre for Research on Violence against Women and Children.

Jiwani, Y. (1999). *Violence Prevention and the Girl Child: Phase One Report.* Vancouver: FREDA Centre for Research on Violence against Women and Children.

Jiwani, Y. (2006). *Discourse of Denial: Mediations of Race, Gender, and Violence.* Vancouver: UBC Press.

McCreary Centre Society. (2004). *Healthy Youth Development: Highlights from the 2003 Adolescent Health Survey III.* Retrieved from http://mcs.bc.ca/pdf/AHS-3_provincial.pdf

McCreary Centre Society. (2005) *Raven's Children II: Aboriginal Youth Health in B.C.* Retrieved from www.mcs.bc.ca/pdf/Ravens_children_2-web.pdf

Peled, E. & Cohavi, A. (2009). The meaning of running away for girls. *Journal of Child Abuse and Neglect, 33,* 739–749.

Robinson, T. & Ward, J.V. (1991). A belief in self far greater than anyone's disbelief: Cultivating resistance among African American female adolescents. In C. Gilligan, A. Rogers & D. Tolman (Eds.). *Women, Girls and Psychotherapy: Reframing Resistance* (pp. 87–104). New York: Haworth Press.

Taefi, N., Czapska, A., Webb, A. & Aleem, R. (2008). *Submission to UN Committee on the Elimination of All Forms of Discrimination against Women at Its 7th Periodic Review of Canada.* Retrieved from www2.ohchr.org/english/bodies/cedaw/docs/ngos/CEDAW_Submission-FINAL.pdf

University of Victoria Continuing Studies (n.d.). *Cultural Safety: Module 2: Peoples' Experiences of Oppression* (online course). Victoria, BC: Author. Retrieved from http://web2.uvcs.uvic.ca/courses/csafety/mod2/glossary.htm

White, J. (2009, February). *Doing Youth Suicide Critically: Interrogating the Knowledge Practice Relationship.* Victoria, BC: School of Child and Youth Care, University of Victoria.

Yee, J. (Ed.). (2011, November). Presentation to Intersectionality Reading Group, Simon Fraser University, Vancouver.

Chapter 13

Acknowledging and Embracing "the Boy inside the Man"

Trauma-Informed Work with Men

Roger Fallot and Richard Bebout

The core values of a trauma-informed culture of care are safety, trustworthiness, choice, collaboration and empowerment (Fallot & Harris, 2008). For both men and women, for both consumers and staff members, these values pervade trauma-informed programs. They stand as necessary antidotes to the toxic effects of violence in the lives of trauma survivors. To the extent that a program embodies these five values in every contact, every physical setting, every activity and every relationship, it can claim to be "trauma informed." However, because of the powerful effect of gender role socialization, these values may be enacted differently for men and women. Therefore, it is equally important for programs to be "gender responsive," considering the unique needs of men and women in their services and service settings (Covington et al., 2008). In this chapter, as we discuss the assumptions guiding our work with male trauma survivors, we also highlight the simultaneous and overlapping development of trauma-informed, gender-responsive organizational cultures.

Prevalence, Impact and Disclosure

Experiences of violence are pervasive in the lives of men and boys. Community surveys in the United States indicate that more than 50 per cent of men have been exposed to at least one traumatic event (Kessler et al., 1995). In metropolitan urban areas, these numbers may be even higher; in one survey, men reported, on average, 5.3 distinct traumatic events in their lives, with people who are poor, non-white and less educated experiencing more violence than others (Breslau et al., 1998). Men diagnosed with severe mental health problems have reported even higher rates of exposure to violence than the general population. Mueser et al. (1998) found that more than 35 per cent of these men reported childhood sexual abuse, and 25 per cent reported sexual assault in adulthood; nearly half indicated that they had been physically assaulted with a weapon in adulthood.

The oft-cited "culture of violence" among men is thus extremely broad, including emotional, physical and sexual violence, as well as community or street violence, institutional violence (e.g., jail, prison, shelter, psychiatric hospitals) and military and combat trauma. The consequences of traumatic violence for men are similarly broad: posttraumatic stress disorder (though at lower rates than women), anger, aggression and other interpersonal difficulties; substance use problems; depression; and physical health problems. Though boys and men are more likely to "externalize" their responses to trauma than are girls and women, they also have a full range of emotional and physical sequelae.

Partly because of the power of male gender role socialization (see below), men often under-report the occurrence of traumatic violence and frequently minimize its impact on their lives. Men who learn not to show vulnerability are unlikely to acknowledge "victimization." Because they participate in the same culture of masculinity, service providers frequently under-recognize the prevalence and impact of violence among men.

One of the first lessons in a trauma-informed, gender-responsive culture of care for men is straightforward: service providers need to ask men about their history of exposure to violence as early as possible in the intake process. Framing this as exposure to "violence" is more likely to elicit disclosure than using language addressing "abuse" or "trauma," both of which may tap into men's fears of appearing weak. Prefacing questions with some data about the pervasiveness of violence and its broad impact may also make it easier for men to discuss their histories. For those men whose initial response is positive, service providers can then follow up with a more comprehensive trauma assessment, include that assessment in a collaborative recovery plan and refer interested men to trauma-specific services (those that focus directly on the sequelae of trauma and on facilitating trauma recovery). For men whose initial response is negative, providers may revisit the questions later, after a working, collaborative relationship has been established.

Core Assumptions of Trauma-Informed, Gender-Responsive Care

Assumption 1

Although men and women experience overlapping types of traumatic events and often exhibit similar short- and long-term sequelae, gender role expectations dramatically colour not only the initial experience of trauma, but also the survivor's narrative explanation and responses to trauma. Consequently, it is essential for male survivors, and trauma-informed service providers seeking to engage them, to examine the impact of male gender role socialization on men's experiences of traumatic violence. Without this kind of analysis, men will be less willing or able to seek and accept help. Culturally held messages about what it means to be a "real man" emphasize toughness and independence and substantially limit the range of emotions that men are allowed to express publicly and even to acknowledge privately. And yet, the ability to tolerate vulnerability, to risk connection and to accurately label a range of negative and positive emotions is essential for recovery to proceed.

Before engaging effectively in explicit trauma-specific work, men may need to address and strengthen different basic skills than women. In particular, men need time and support to gain comfort with and expand their emotional vocabulary. Whereas women may enter trauma services already able to acknowledge vulnerability and common emotions associated with trauma, many men find it difficult to label, describe and perhaps experience a wide range of emotions, especially the "softer" ones. Similarly, the most common narratives of male development emphasize growth toward independence and self-sufficiency; relationships are often decidedly secondary in men's socialization. Gender-responsive and trauma-informed service settings help men to accurately label experiences, to develop a shared vocabulary of emotional and relational life and to heighten men's awareness of connections between current struggles and past experiences of violence.

To facilitate a safe and trustworthy environment of care, service providers need both to understand these gender-related patterns and to be cautious in pacing their expectations about men's deeper engagement in services. A man who is reluctant to talk about his emotional or relational life is not necessarily "resistant" or "in denial." He may simply have a limited ability to express himself in ways more common in a "therapeutic" culture. Slowing the expected rate of disclosure and open discussion, for example, enhances these men's sense of safety.

Assumption 2

Male trauma survivors face a "disconnection dilemma," an almost irresolvable conflict between their identity as men and their experiences of powerlessness and vulnerability associated with violent victimization. Acknowledging fear and loss of control is tantamount to weakness and threatens their core identity as men. Many men resolve this dissonance by cutting off thoughts and feelings tied to victim experiences. Being "a man" is incompatible with being "a victim," yet both sets of experiences carry a strong emotional "charge." Just as the like-poles of magnets repel, men are unable to stably hold together their images of themselves as "man enough" with their experiences of victimization and the unacceptable feelings of fear and vulnerability they engender. If men are defined by strength, courage, toughness and control, there is no room for experiences of victimization and fear.

Because of this potential for disconnection, it is crucial to explore the relationship between experiences of trauma and male gender role expectations. Exploring the pervasive messages boys and men get about the way "real men" think, feel and act can reduce their magnetic charge and begin to make it possible for men to bring both parts of self with them into services.

Service providers who acknowledge the importance of these gendered messages convey that they are not "blaming the victim;" this acknowledgment enhances the provider's image as safe and trustworthy and strengthens the possibility of meaningful collaboration. By empathizing with the disconnection dilemma and by drawing explicit attention to it, service providers communicate that they are willing to follow the consumer's lead in any discussion of trauma-related concerns.

Assumption 3

Many male trauma survivors display all-or-nothing responses in their approach to emotional and relational issues throughout their lives. For example, men may express only extremes of rage or timidity, and either easy trust or pervasive mistrust. The subtle beauty of grey is lost.

Developing a broader range of options for expressing emotions and for being in relationships is a key trauma recovery skill for men. A trauma-informed, gender-responsive system for men must recognize a range of typical male adaptations, including hard-shelled withdrawal (think armadillos) and aggressive posturing (think bears or porcupines) as preferred stances. These masks are moulded both by the real and perceived danger men have faced and by the "male code." Service providers must recognize the adaptive inevitability of these positions and develop helpful responses that gradually allow men to cope in more flexible and less automatic ways.

Staff members who realize that men frequently cope with stressors by enacting common male gender role messages therefore have an alternative way to think of the angry, aggressive male consumer. Knowing that scared people scare others, just as hurt people hurt others, helps reduce the likelihood that staff will react in counterproductive ways and will instead seek ways to increase everyone's sense of safety. De-escalation techniques (e.g., speaking in a low, even tone and asking questions rather than making demands) are more likely to make sense to, and be used successfully by, staff members who understand the connections between traumatic violence and anger.

Assumption 4

For both men and women, trauma frequently severs core connections to family, community and ultimately to the self. For men, these experiences reinforce the need to maintain at least the appearance of interpersonal self-sufficiency and emotional control.

Broad-based recovery work in a trauma-informed system aims not only at the reconnecting skills of emotional, cognitive and behavioural self-recognition but also of *relational mutuality*. In a society where men are often expected to exercise power and assert authority, men who have experienced the abuse of power are left with unique knowledge of its interpersonal dangers.

Men become more open to collaborative relationships with service providers who offer to share meaningful power in a way that gives consumers maximum choice and voice in their recovery and life goals. Trauma-informed providers shift from the more traditional stance of "Here is what I can do to fix you" to one that asks, "How can you and I work together to meet your goals for recovery and healing?" Men who have been sensitized to the abuse of power in previous relationships may need to hear this message repeatedly and in a variety of contexts.

Assumption 5

People who experienced repeated trauma in childhood have often been deprived of the opportunity to develop a range of skills for coping and self-regulation necessary for effectively managing in an adult world. Growing up in an unsafe, often chaotic environment means living in "survival mode," where a limited number of skills are acquired and get used repeatedly.

Trauma-informed systems of care adopt a skills-oriented approach to recovery work and provide formal and informal opportunities for psychoeducation. All service providers, not just trauma clinicians, learn to recognize and underscore the connections between abuse histories and current skill deficits.

Motivational interviewing techniques are among the primary ways in which choice and control become consumer priorities. Repeated invitations for men to examine the advantages and disadvantages of alternative responses are important tools for engaging men in experimenting with new, potentially less costly behaviours. Developing needed skills is a way clients can feel empowered, without actually engaging in "treatment." For example, staff may support men in learning and practising relaxation skills as an alternative way to cope with anger and excessive anxiety.

Assumption 6

While certain abilities may have been adversely affected by violence and abuse, trauma survivors nonetheless bring an array of skills and strengths to the recovery process.

Acknowledging the genuinely miraculous strength and courage men have shown, simply that they are "still standing," helps to resurrect hope and motivate men to engage in further recovery. Helping men to remember and to own even small successes and to recognize budding new skills encourages them to continue in their recovery efforts. Men who have had good friendships, for example, may be able to use these experiences to explore the ingredients necessary to trust and to risk appropriate self-disclosure. Or men who have exhibited emotional self-control skills at work may be able to transfer those skills to more intimate relationships. There is no better avenue to empowerment than by acknowledging existing strengths. Recognition of this sort may be "water in the desert" for male survivors who have heard only how their behaviour and attitudes are destructive to themselves or others.

Assumption 7

We assume that some dysfunctional behaviours and/or "symptoms" may have originated as legitimate coping responses to trauma.

Reframing specific problematic behaviours—distrust, hypervigilance, hair-trigger aggression—as reflections of understandable attempts to cope with abuse is a key element in trauma recovery. Recognizing the necessity and adaptive health embedded in actions or feelings that appear so unhealthy is often a pivotal step that gradually frees men to try another way. Reframing is in itself empowering, in that the person can attribute a different meaning to something without shaming or blaming himself, and learn about himself in the process, as a prelude to choosing other ways of coping.

Assumption 8

All attempts to cope with trauma have advantages and disadvantages, benefits and costs. The advantages or disadvantages may be physical (e.g., survival), emotional (e.g., minimizing distressful feelings), cognitive (e.g., developing certain beliefs about oneself and the world), behavioural (e.g., avoiding potentially dangerous situations) or spiritual (e.g., considering life to be meaningless or without purpose).

Focused on simply managing the effects of trauma, many survivors are unclear about the full range of costs and benefits involved in their coping strategies. Opportunities to clarify the advantages and disadvantages of various coping styles can occur in different contexts. Male survivors benefit from seeing this kind of "cost-benefit" analysis. It helps them to accept and reframe some of the problems associated with their coping attempts—and to see more explicitly the often hidden or minimized negative consequences. Trauma-informed values emphasize both choice and empowerment, expanding men's freedom to choose the most helpful and least costly coping methods and highlighting their capacity to develop the requisite recovery skills for meeting life goals.

Trauma-Specific Treatment

This book's focus is on trauma-informed care rather than trauma-specific treatment, so we devote the majority of this chapter to practice examples not tied directly to the relief of posttraumatic stress or related symptoms. However, much of our most intimate knowledge about men's trauma recovery comes from developing, implementing and training clinicians in the Men's Trauma Recovery and Empowerment model (M-TREM), a group approach that features a 24-week psychoeducational curriculum geared specifically to men. The model builds on extensive experience with, and empirical support for, the Trauma Recovery and Empowerment model developed by Harris (Fallot & Harris, 2002; Harris, 1998).

The model has been implemented in many mental health and addiction treatment settings, homeless programs and in jail diversion and other criminal justice settings. Perhaps of special interest are several initiatives to modify M-TREM for work with military veterans. One of the central insights of that work is the extent to which military culture and "warrior ideals" amplify the male messages and masculine gender-role ideals we have discussed. As with men in general, a key component of work with veterans is finding safe ways for soldiers to access and express otherwise unacceptable thoughts, feelings and behaviour patterns and reframe them as normal responses to trauma, in a way that is fundamentally countercultural.

Conclusion

Promoting recovery within a trauma-informed, gender-responsive culture of care becomes everybody's job. All staff within trauma-informed systems of care —not just trauma clinicians but case managers, addiction counsellors and housing and employment specialists—have opportunities to assist men to accurately label and modulate emotional states, to increase the range of options available to them to manage their lives and to cope with their trauma experiences. Any service provider in any encounter can help connect the dots in new ways so that current problems become understandable in light of bad things that have happened in the past. Exploring the connections between violence on one hand and psychological, substance use and interpersonal problems on the other occurs throughout the care system. Greater self-awareness and access to a wider range of emotional experiences create the possibility of a correspondingly expanded repertoire of coping and healing responses. Recognizing feelings or relationship patterns early on, and accurately, for example, is a starting point for increased control and self-expression in the relatively unexplored middle ground, or grey area, of the continuum.

Men in mental health and addiction treatment—like men nearly everywhere —commonly go to extraordinary lengths to hide and protect "the boy inside the man," as Antwone Fisher (2001) describes it in a poem featured in his autobiography, *Finding Fish*. At the very least, it is incumbent on us all to recognize that boy and nurture him, and to make our systems of care places where he might feel safe enough to show himself and risk opening himself to a different kind of human connection that will allow him to heal.

References

Breslau, N., Kessler, R., Chilcoat, H., Schultz, L. Davis, G. & Andreski, P. (1998). Trauma and posttraumatic stress disorder in the community: The 1996 Detroit Area Survey of Trauma. *Archives of General Psychiatry, 55,* 626–632.

Covington, S.S., Burke, C., Keaton, S. & Norcott, C. (2008, November). Evaluation of a trauma-informed and gender-responsive intervention for women in drug treatment. *Journal of Psychoactive Drugs, 40*(Suppl. 5), 387–398.

Fallot, R.D. & Harris, M. (2002). The Trauma Recovery and Empowerment model (TREM): Conceptual and practical issues in a group intervention for women. *Community Mental Health Journal, 38,* 475–485.

Fallot, R.D. & Harris, M. (2008). Trauma-informed services. In G. Reyes, J.D. Elhai & J.D. Ford (Eds.), *Encyclopedia of Psychological Trauma* (pp. 660–662). Hoboken, NJ: John Wiley & Sons.

Fisher, A.Q. (2001). *Finding Fish: A Memoir.* With M.E. Rivas. New York: HarperCollins.

Harris, M. (1998). *Trauma Recovery and Empowerment: A Clinician's Guide for Working with Women in Groups.* New York: Free Press.

Kessler, R.C., Sonnega, A., Bromet, E., Hughes, M. & Nelson, C.B. (1995). Posttraumatic stress disorder in the National Comorbidity Survey. *Archives of General Psychiatry, 52,* 1048–1060.

Mueser, K.T., Goodman, L.B., Trumbetta, S.L., Rosenberg, S.D., Osher, F.C., Vidaver, R. et al. (1998). Trauma and posttraumatic stress disorder in severe mental illness. *Journal of Consulting and Clinical Psychology, 66,* 493–499.

Chapter 14

An Intergenerational Trauma-Informed Approach to Care for Canada's Aboriginal Peoples

Peter Menzies

Helping professionals have only recently learned how historical public policies that disadvantaged and isolated Aboriginal families and communities continue to have ripple effects throughout many Aboriginal communities today. Understanding these historical policies, including the Indian Act, the residential school system and child welfare legislation, is important when providing therapeutic intervention with Canada's Aboriginal Peoples. Recent research on intergenerational trauma is helping to inform new healing strategies for Aboriginal individuals, families and communities. As a therapist with more than three decades of experience in individual and family counselling, I offer my own evolved methodology for working with Aboriginal people that includes exploring intergenerational trauma with the client. This chapter explores the impact of Canada's public policies on Aboriginal Peoples and offer intervention strategies using a trauma-informed approach.

Canadian Public Policy

Canadian historical social policy around Aboriginal Peoples has been criticized for deliberately trying to "remov[e] the Indianness out of the Indian" (Titley, 1986, p. 75) by systematically eradicating the values, beliefs and way of life of Canada's First Peoples and assimilating them into mainstream Canadian culture (Churchill, 1995).

The Indian Act

The Indian Act, 1876, gave the federal government the power to set out the terms and conditions by which Aboriginal Peoples would be treated within Confederation. First, it established the federal government as "guardian" of Aboriginal Peoples. The act gave Ottawa the right to define who was and who was not Aboriginal, to create reserves and to impose hierarchy and decision-making authorities that did not reflect traditional values and practices. The act restricted the mobility of Aboriginal Peoples within the country, outlawed ceremonies and trading with settlers, denied legal counsel and the right to vote and forced communities to relocate. In effect, the Indian Act gave authority to Ottawa to control the everyday life of Aboriginal Peoples (Royal Commission on Aboriginal Peoples, 1996).

More recent attempts have been made to redress some of the act's most blatant shortcomings by addressing the bias against Aboriginal women in relationships with non-Aboriginal men with the passing of Bill C-31 in 1985. However, the Indian Act continues to fuel significant discourse within Aboriginal communities and among Canada's legislators as the debate for self-government continues.

Residential Schools

Through partnership with Christian institutions, including the Anglican, Catholic, United and Presbyterian churches, an estimated 100,000 Aboriginal children were placed in the residential school system between 1840 and 1983 (United Church of Canada, 1994). Residential schools were designed to civilize or "westernize" the children, remove their Indian identity and integrate them into mainstream Canadian society (Royal Commission on Aboriginal Peoples, 1996). A statement in 1920 by the head of the Department of Indian Affairs, Duncan Campbell Scott, best demonstrates the harsh attitude of government officials toward Canada's Aboriginal population:

> I want to get rid of the Indian problem. I do not think as a matter of fact, that the country ought to continuously protect a class of people who are able to stand alone. . . . Our objective is to continue until there is not a single Indian in Canada that has not been absorbed into the

> body politic and there is no Indian question, and no Indian
> Department, that is the whole object of this Bill. (Titley, 1986, p. 50)

This policy resulted in the forced removal of children from their families for
months, even years at a time. Parents refusing to hand over their children were
threatened with imprisonment and other consequences, including reduced
food rations. Many children attending these schools lost their language,
culture, identity and spiritual beliefs, as well as a sense of belonging to family,
community and nation. Many children experienced physical, sexual, emotional,
spiritual and psychological abuse (Assembly of First Nations, 1994; Royal
Commission on Aboriginal Peoples, 1996). This public policy was embraced
by governments for more than a century, with the last residential school in
Canada not closing until 1996 (Thatcher, 2005).

Child welfare policies

With the closing of residential schools, child welfare systems became the new
vehicles of assimilation. In 1983, researcher Patrick Johnston introduced the
term "the Sixties Scoop" to identify the overwhelming number of Aboriginal
children removed from their communities by child welfare authorities. Many
parents who had attended residential schools as children were so overwhelmed
by their experiences that they were unable to care for their children. Issues
such as abandonment, neglect, alcohol abuse, poor parenting skills and lack
of supervision became the predominant grounds for apprehension.

Many child welfare workers had no understanding of Aboriginal traditions,
culture and history. Taking a crisis intervention approach to child welfare
meant that services to support children in their home were non-existent
(Andres, 1981; Johnston, 1983; Richard, 1989; Timpson, 1990). In 2006,
an estimated 27,000 Aboriginal children were in the care of child welfare
agencies across Canada (Assembly of First Nations, 2006). Child welfare
institutions have now replaced residential schools as instruments of assimilation.

Establishing a Therapeutic Framework for Intervention with Aboriginal People

The impact of these policies has resulted in the loss of self, family and community ties. In order to work effectively with Aboriginal people, we need a therapeutic framework that recognizes the role of public policies on individuals, families and communities.

Understanding the Individual

Across North America, various theories—such as residential school syndrome and split feather syndrome—have been developed over the past three decades to help therapists broaden their understanding of how public policies related to Aboriginal Peoples have affected individual behaviours. These theories attempt to explain a range of behaviours presented by Aboriginal people who have been separated from their families as a result of residential school programs or child welfare systems. Intergenerational trauma extends the focus of the trauma beyond the individual's experience to include the social context of family, community and all First Nations.

Residential school syndrome

Many writers (Corrado & Cohen, 2003; Stout & Kipling, 2003) have documented the abuses and harm experienced by Aboriginal children who attended residential schools. Brasfield (2001) and Chrisjohn and Young (1997) developed assessment models of Aboriginal people who attended residential schools by modelling the criteria after the Diagnostic Statistical Manual of Mental Disorders (DSM), which classifies disorders identified in modern psychiatry and provides descriptions to assist in diagnosis and treatment. Chrisjohn and Young describe residential school syndrome as:

> . . . a personality disorder manifested in an individual's specific behavioral action of (1) obliterating another people's way of life by taking the children of the group away from their parents and having them raised in ignorance of, and/or with contempt for, their heritage;

while (2) helping himself/herself to the property of the target group. (p. 84)

The diagnosis is based on a collection of individual behaviours, including recurrent intrusive memories, nightmares, flashbacks, lack of personal insight, detachment from others, relationship difficulties, diminished interest and participation in Aboriginal cultural activities, anger management difficulties, impaired concentration, inadequate parenting and abuse of alcohol or other drugs.

Split feather syndrome
The impact of social policies on Aboriginal children is not only isolated within the Canadian policy realm. American researcher Carol Locust (1998) found that Indian children who entered the child welfare system in the United States tended to lose their identity and culture. Locust's research noted that Indian children in care experienced the loss of family, culture, heritage, language, spiritual beliefs and tribal affiliation, as well as having the sense of growing up being different. These children reported that the cultural isolation and loss of familial connections left them feeling isolated from both mainstream and Indian culture. Without belonging to either culture, many described their socialization as being split between two worlds. This split resulted in long-term emotional and psychological problems. Locust (1998) maintains that these problems are the result of a deeply felt connection with the birth culture while living outside of that reality. While the research on split feather syndrome is primarily American based, the effects of removing children from their unique cultural and social norms through child welfare systems cannot be disregarded when assessing their behaviour (Archibald, 2006).

Intergenerational Trauma

Only within the last two decades has intergenerational trauma been offered as a broader framework from which we can better understand the legacy of government public policies (Braveheart-Jordan & De Bruyn, 1995; Gagne, 1998; Lederman, 1999; Waldram, 1997). Removing children from the home for long periods has diminished opportunities for family values, parenting knowledge and community behaviour to be transmitted between generations

(Payukotayno, 1988; Van de Sande, 1995). The cumulative impact of trauma experienced by both children and their parents as a result of Canada's residential school policy continues to have consequences for subsequent generations of children. The Aboriginal Healing Foundation (2001) has noted:

> Many passed the abuse they suffered on to their children, thereby perpetuating the cycle of abuse and dysfunction arising from the residential school system. Subsequent generations of children were left with the consequences of what happened to their parents and grandparents. They grew up without the opportunity to learn their language, to have traditions and cultural knowledge passed down to them, or to be a part of a strong and healthy family and community. (p. 7)

Like the residential institutions where their parents, grandparents and great grandparents were sent, the foster care and adoption system created another generation of children who have been subjected to psychological, emotional, sexual and physical abuse. Isolation from families and Aboriginal identity was intensified when some children were sent for adoption to other countries, including the United States (Bagley et al., 1993). Lederman (1999) observed:

> Children's Aid Societies perpetuated the same beliefs as residential schools: that a well-meaning White, cultural institution was better than a Native child's family and community. Many, perhaps even most, of the child welfare workers were compassionate and well-intentioned. But, however well-meaning Children's Aid Society intrusions may have been, they further continued the traumatization of Native people and likely compounded it. (p. 64)

Nadjiwan and Blackstock (2003) noted that these societies failed to recognize Aboriginal traditions:

> Ethnocentric child welfare practices based on Euro-western models did not take into account First Nations values, beliefs, responsibilities, and child care practices and continued to marginalize First Nations' efforts to care for their own children despite the pervasive failure of mainstream approaches in the residential school system. (p. 17)

Trauma is attributed to external factors, which significantly influence individual, family and community behaviours. By externalizing trauma, the therapist enters into a relationship with the client that explores the impact of history on the client's presenting issues.

Posttraumatic Stress Disorder

Although professionals have often used a diagnosis of posttraumatic stress disorder (PTSD) to understand Aboriginal addiction and mental health issues, recent literature suggests that this diagnosis ignores the role of intergenerational issues. A PTSD diagnosis does not connect the individual's experience to broader, systemic conditions that perpetuate and exacerbate the individual's experience (Waldram, 2004).

Gagne (1998) also noted that the effect of the residential school experience was felt beyond the generation that attended the school: "At least two subsequent generations were also 'lost.' The children of these students became victims of abuse as their parents became abusers because of the residential school experience" (p. 363).

The impact of trauma, as a result of social history, has to be carefully considered within the context of the individual's lived experience, rather than simply focusing on individual pathology. However, therapeutic intervention must consider the external influence of trauma as experienced by the individual.

Indicators of Intergenerational Trauma

Although the literature describes intergeneration trauma and notes its causes in historical events, I conducted a study that took a step further and presented clinical indicators of intergenerational trauma (Menzies, 2006). The study, which focused on Aboriginal homeless men, used a qualitative methodology involving interviews with men from different age categories, a focus group, and interviews with key Aboriginal stakeholders who work with homeless Aboriginal men. The findings revealed certain behaviours and psychological responses among Aboriginal men who were directly and indirectly affected by public policies related to Aboriginal Peoples. The responses were grouped into four indicator areas: individual, family, community and nation.

Individual indicators: Lack of a sense of "belonging," identification, or affiliation with a specific family, community, culture, or nation; feeling of "abandonment" by caregivers; limited or no information about one's culture of birth, including language, customs, belief systems, spirituality; one or more "flight" episodes from a caregiver environment as a youth; inability to sustain personal or intimate relationships; being present-oriented, not future-oriented; low self-esteem; limited education and employment history; history of substance misuse; history of involvement with the criminal justice system, precipitated by substance misuse; and involvement with the mental health system.

Family indicators: Chronic or episodic family violence, including physical, sexual, emotional, and/or verbal abuse of children by adults in the household; lack of emotional bonding between parents, siblings, and extended family members; denial of cultural heritage by older family members; perpetuation of negative stereotypes within the family of birth or caregiver environment; irregular contact or the absence of contact with caregiver family members; and concealed misuse of alcohol and other drugs that crosses generations.

Community indicators: Unconcealed misuse of alcohol and other drugs among community members; lack of cultural opportunities, including transmission of language skills, history, traditional values, and spirituality; unwillingness to "reclaim" community members; and low levels of social capital (Putnam, 2000), including trust, reciprocal helping relations, and social engagement.

Nation indicators: Popularization of negative stereotypes through mainstream media; social policies that perpetuate colonialization of Aboriginal peoples on an individual family and community basis; lack of support for holistic programs and services targeting Aboriginal needs; and lack of support for community self-determination.

While the research focused on the experiences of Aboriginal men, my extensive experience in working with Aboriginal communities over two decades would support extrapolating these indicators as also relevant to the experiences of women and youth. Further research is needed to confirm and expand the indicators for other Aboriginal subpopulations.

Identity

To work effectively with Aboriginal people, it is important to find out how the individual perceives himself or herself as an Aboriginal person. McKenzie and Morrissette (2003) developed a framework for working with Aboriginal people, which involves asking clients to identify how they express their cultural awareness across a continuum ranging from "traditional" to mainstream" to "non-traditional." Along this continuum, there is transition to and from each of the three main cultural strata. The three main forms of cultural expression are outlined below:

Traditional

Within this category, individuals express their cultural identity as distinct from mainstream society, in some cases removing themselves from dominant society to live according to traditional lifestyle and spirituality. In other cases, the traditionalist may leverage some practices from mainstream society, such as working and living within the mainstream culture, while still asserting his or her unique Aboriginal identity.

Mainstream

This category includes individuals who struggle to integrate traditional values into their primarily Euro-Canadian world view. They may recognize the historical impact that cultural conflicts have had on the evolution of Aboriginal Peoples in Canada, but are more likely to share the values and belief systems of mainstream society. They often have shifting views or may be ambivalent about the values within traditional Aboriginal culture, but may be open to exploring their situation or leveraging traditional practices in their healing.

Non-traditional

This group includes individuals who have been assimilated into dominant society and are merely spectators of Aboriginal culture and those who have been marginalized or alienated from their traditions and belief systems. Individuals in the latter group struggle with both their Aboriginal identity and their sense of belonging to the dominant society. They are not comfortable in either world. Without a sense of identity that is linked to a collective, individuals may drift into other groups or organizations as they seek a sense of belonging in other types of "community."

By understanding how individuals express their relationship to their culture, the therapist can help clients build their own understanding of how their issues relate to broader issues within their family, community and nation.

Working with Aboriginal People

Aboriginal healing seeks to restore a balance between the mental, spiritual, emotional and physical well-being of the person (Hart, 2002). As individuals are strengthened, their family, community and nation will benefit from a process of healing that seeks to reconnect and strengthen social supports. Working with Aboriginal people requires the therapist to develop trust, respect, openness and honesty so that the client will feel safe and secure within the therapeutic environment. Given the extensive impact that public policies have had on Aboriginal people, many seeking service will come from traumatized backgrounds, so developing a trusting therapeutic relationship may take longer to nurture.

Determining the level of trauma and degree of assimilation is the next point in the assessment process. Asking clients a series of questions about their family and personal history, their thoughts about being Aboriginal and where they see themselves as Aboriginals can provide insight into where the imbalances exist in their lives. Through this assessment process, the therapist can help the client gain insight into how public policies have affected them and how these policies have contributed to the development of their identity.

In the therapeutic process, clinicians must be prepared to understand and leverage the cultural context of the client and be prepared to adapt conventional counselling techniques to effectively meet the needs of their Aboriginal clients (Morrissette, 2008). By helping clients to establish their cultural affinity and explore their personal and family histories in relation to public policy, the therapeutic relationship shifts the client's understanding of his or her externalized behaviours as being self-driven to seeing them within a broader social context. This allows the therapist and client to explore individual externalized behaviours in a new way.

Given that this is a process of discovery, the therapist should partner with other helpers, such as elders, cultural teachers and Aboriginal counsellors. Aboriginal ceremonies and celebrations can be used as part of the treatment intervention strategy.

Conclusion

Aboriginal Peoples have been affected by centuries of colonization. Too many interventions focus on the individual's behaviour without acknowledging the impact of public policies. Awareness of colonization and the impact it has had on Aboriginal people can guide the therapist in the counselling relationship. Intergenerational trauma can be an explanation for the array of mental health and substance use issues that Aboriginal people are experiencing today. Therapists need to acknowledge the role of public policy in severing the physical, mental, emotional and spiritual ties among Aboriginal people, and consider the implications of intergenerational trauma on individuals, families, communities and nations.

References

Aboriginal Healing Foundation. (2001). *Program Hand Guide* (3rd ed.). Ottawa: Author.

Andres, R. (1981). The apprehension of Native children. *Ontario Indian, 46,* 32–37.

Archibald, L. (2006). *Decolonization and Healing: Indigenous Experiences in the United States, New Zealand, Australia and Greenland.* Ottawa: Aboriginal Healing Foundation.

Assembly of First Nations. (1994). *Breaking the Silence.* Ottawa: Author.

Assembly of First Nations. (2006). *Leadership Action Plan on First Nations Child Welfare.* Ottawa: Author.

Bagley, C., Young, Y. & Scully, A. (1993). *International and Transracial Adoptions: A Mental Health Perspective.* Brookfield, VT: Avebury.

Brasfield, C.R. (2001). Residential school syndrome. *BC Medical Journal, 43,* 78–81.

Braveheart-Jordan, M. & De Bruyn, L. (1995). So she may walk in balance: Integrating the impact of historical trauma in the treatment of Native American Indian women. In J. Adelman & G. Enguidanos (Eds.), *Racism in the Lives of Women: Testimony, Theory and Guides to Ethnoracist Practice* (pp. 345–369). New York: Haworth Press.

Chrisjohn, R. & Young, S. (1997). *The Circle Game: Shadow and Substance in the Residential School Experience in Canada.* Penticton, BC: Theytus Books.

Churchill, W. (1995). *Since Predator Came: Notes from the Struggle for American Indian Liberation.* Littleton, CO: Aigis.

Corrado, R.R. & Cohen, I.M. (2003). *Mental Health Profiles for a Sample of British Columbia's Aboriginal Survivors of the Canadian Residential School System.* Ottawa: Aboriginal Healing Foundation.

Gagne, M. (1998). The role of dependency and colonialism in generating trauma in First Nations citizens. In Y. Danieli (Ed.), *International Handbook of Multigenerational Legacies of Trauma* (pp. 355–372). New York: Plenum Press.

Hart, M. (2002). *Seeking Mino-Pimatisiwin: An Aboriginal Approach to Healing.* Halifax, NS: Fernwood.

Johnston, P. (1983). *Native Children and the Child Welfare System.* Ottawa: Canadian Council on Social Development.

Lederman, J. (1999). Trauma and healing in Aboriginal families and communities. *Native Social Work Journal, 2,* 59–90.

Locust, C. (1998). Split feathers: Adult American Indians who were placed in non-Indian families as children. *Pathways, 13,* 1–5.

McKenzie, B. & Morrissette, V. (2003). Social work practice with Canadians of Aboriginal background: Guidelines for respectful social work. *Envision: The Manitoba Journal of Child Welfare, 2*(1), 13–39.

Menzies, P. (2006). Intergenerational trauma and homeless Aboriginal men. *Canadian Review of Social Policy, 58,* 1–24.

Morrissette, P. (2008). Clinical engagement of Canadian First Nations couples. *Journal of Family Therapy, 30,* 60–77.

Nadjiwan, S. & Blackstock, C. (2003). *Caring Across the Boundaries: Promoting Access to Voluntary Sector Resources for First Nations Children and Families.* Ottawa: First Nations Child and Family Caring Society of Canada.

Payukotayno: James and Hudson Bay Family Services & Tikinagan Child and Family Services. (1988). *As Long As the Sun Shines: From Generation to Generation.* Moosonee, ON: Author.

Putnam, R. (2000). *Bowling Alone: The Collapse and Revival of American Community.* New York: Simon & Schuster.

Richard, K. (1989). Kenn Richard fights racism within child welfare. *Metropolis, 2*(11), 3–4.

Royal Commission on Aboriginal Peoples. (1996). *Report of the Royal Commission on Aboriginal Peoples. Volume 1: Looking Forward, Looking Back.* Ottawa: Supply and Services Canada.

Stout, M.D. & Kipling, G. (2003). *Aboriginal People, Resilience and the Residential School Legacy.* Ottawa: Aboriginal Healing Foundation.

Thatcher, R. (2005). Residential school abuse and its legacy: A backgrounder and updates. *Circle Talk, 1*(3), 10–14.

Timpson, J.B. (1990). Indian and native special status in Ontario's child welfare legislation. *Canadian Social Work Review, 7,* 49–68.

Titley, E.B. (1986). *A Narrow Vision: Duncan Campbell Scott and the Administration of Indian Affairs in Canada.* Vancouver: University of British Columbia Press.

United Church of Canada. (1994). *Residential Schools.* Toronto: Author.

Van de Sande, A. (1995). Native and mainstream parenting programs. *Native Studies Review, 10*(1), 1–20.

Waldram, J. (1997). The Aboriginal Peoples of Canada. In I. Al-Issa & M. Tousignant (Eds.), *Ethnicity, Immigration and Psychopathology* (pp. 169–187). New York: Plenum Press.

Waldram, J. (2004). *Revenge of the Windigo: The Construction of the Mind and Mental Health of North American Aboriginal Peoples.* Toronto: University of Toronto Press.

PART 2

SECTION 2: DIVERSE SETTINGS

Chapter 15

Considering Trauma in Outpatient Substance Use Treatment Planning for Youth

Gloria Chaim, Susan Rosenkranz and Joanna Henderson

The Youth Addiction and Concurrent Disorders Service (YACDS) at the Centre for Addiction and Mental Health in Toronto works with youth, aged 16 to 24, who have substance use concerns, frequently with concurrent mental health and related concerns, and their families. We offer a broad range of services that span the continuum of care from outreach and early intervention to day treatment.

The overall program philosophy incorporates a youth-centred, developmentally sensitive perspective with an appreciation of how social determinants of health, including sex, gender and diversity, affect development (Dell & Poole, 2009). The program's developmental approach recognizes that protective and risk factors, both internal and external to the youth, interact throughout development to give rise to the strengths youth possess and the challenges they face when they enter treatment. This perspective also understands that youth in this age range, who are transitioning out of adolescence into adulthood, are moving toward increasing autonomy, independence and responsibility. Our program appreciates the many risks and challenges associated with this stage of life, and the numerous life changes youth of this age are often negotiating.

Our program also recognizes that many youth who face substance use problems and related concerns have experienced traumatic events during their development (e.g., Clark et al., 1997). YACDS recently conducted research revealing that youth entering the service had had high rates of exposure to physical, sexual and emotional abuse, as well as other potentially traumatic events. Approximately two-thirds of youth report exposure to emotional abuse or neglect, one third report exposure to physical abuse or witnessing domestic violence and approximately 20 per cent report experiences of sexual abuse (Rosenkranz et al., 2012).

These findings are consistent with a large body of research indicating the prevalence of substance use problems among youth with trauma histories (e.g., Clark et al., 1997). Also consistent with much research in this area (e.g., Ballon et al., 2001; Titus et al., 2003) are our findings that rates of maltreatment and trauma tended to be higher among females, though a number of males entering our service had also experienced potentially traumatic events. For example, approximately 40 per cent of females reported a sexual abuse history, compared to 7 per cent of males; and 40 per cent of females reported a physical abuse history, compared to 24 per cent of males (Rosenkranz et al., 2012). Females were more likely to report exposure to multiple forms of maltreatment or trauma. Thus gender is an important factor in considering trauma when supporting youth with substance use problems.

We found that trauma-related symptoms were elevated among youth with histories of potentially traumatic events, and that many of these youth believed their use of substances was connected to their histories of traumatic experiences (Rosenkranz & Henderson, 2009). Youth who reported trauma or maltreatment histories tended to report more severe substance use problems than youth without such histories (Chaim & Henderson, 2009). They also experienced more severe negative consequences of their use (Rosenkranz et al., 2012).

Findings also suggest that trauma history may affect the degree and source of motivation for accessing treatment, with potential implications for treatment engagement (Rosenkranz et al., 2011). We found that people with trauma or abuse histories may be motivated to enter treatment because of the shame associated with their substance use. However, research has demonstrated that motivation characterized by high levels of shame is not associated with greater treatment engagement (Wild et al., 2006). Knowing that shame may motivate people to enter, but not stay in, treatment, it will be important to enhance other, more positive forms of motivation to encourage people to continue to attend.

These findings point to the importance of using a trauma-informed perspective in our service. In order to be responsive to our clients' needs, assessment and treatment planning are conducted in a trauma-informed way. The overarching principles that guide our assessment and treatment planning—creating safety and empowering youth—reflect this trauma-informed approach, but also respond to the needs of youth who do not report trauma histories. This chapter describes the trauma-informed treatment planning conducted in our program. We include specific examples of practices where possible, and the voices of our youth and staff throughout.

Empowerment in Treatment Planning

Treatment planning is a collaborative process between client and clinician, guided by the assessment results, and considering the client's interests and preferences. Within a harm reduction framework, treatment plans aim to create safety in the lives of youth and to empower them to make positive changes.

Individual treatment plans are developed to address the specific needs of each client. Treatment options include a motivational interviewing–based group to enhance motivation for change, cognitive-behavioural therapy groups for co-occurring depression or anxiety and substance use, a skills-building group emphasizing the development of coping skills, and Seeking Safety, a manualized intervention designed to address co-occurring trauma symptoms and substance use (Najavits, 2002). Individual treatment and case management are available, as are psychological assessment and psychiatric consultations. Recreation, cooking, art, music and health groups are also offered.

Involvement and Control in Goal Setting

Youth are often told "what is good for them," what changes they "need" to make, what their goals should be, what their treatment plan should look like and who should be involved in their treatment. Recognizing that a significant aspect of healthy development for youth who are transitioning from adolescence into adulthood is increased autonomy, our staff empowers youth to contribute to the development of their own treatment plans. This focus on empowering youth also allows for those who have had little control over previous experiences (e.g., trauma) to have new experiences in which the control for the direction their lives will take is placed back in their hands. Staff members partner with youth to help them formulate their own goals, and to work with them in achieving the goals through engaging in the services they choose. In the words of one client:

> When I came here I was given the ability to choose what substances I wanted to work on, and what I didn't. I was able to set my own goals, no one was telling me "You're doing this," which I think has happened to me in a lot of other programs. That was cool—that you're able to set your own goals and work at your own pace. When I talk to my case manager, he asks "Is this cool, does this work?" (Nick, age 20)

Harm Reduction

Harm reduction and minimizing risk are crucial in addressing the needs of youth. The choices and pacing in the approach are a good fit for youth who are seeking autonomy, and this approach fits with the recognition that some amount of substance use is developmentally normative for youth.

> I went to a different program before this that was abstinence based and 12-step. It was kind of a culture shock coming here, but not in a bad way. I was really surprised to find how easygoing it was. I think that's why a lot of people are resistant to treatment, they expect it to be very moralistic and uncomfortable. I think [a harm reduction approach] took the fear of change and the fear of help away. (Nick, age 20)

Choice about Family Involvement

As a part of treatment planning, youth are encouraged to consider the extent to which they want family to be involved in their treatment. Family involvement in youth treatment has been shown to increase retention and improve treatment outcomes (see Hogue & Liddle, 2009). The benefits of including family in treatment are balanced with recognition of the importance of youth empowerment, as well as a trauma-informed approach. Recognizing that family may be a source of support for some, a source of trauma for others and at times a combination of both, youth are empowered to make decisions regarding family involvement in their treatment. Guided by staff, youth identify who is important in their lives, whom they consider to be family and whom they would like to engage in the treatment process with them.

Choice in Treatment Options

Non-traditional treatment options are included in the choices available to youth. Through satisfaction surveys and annual focus groups, youth have identified that the opportunities to participate in music, art, recreation and cooking groups as adjuncts to traditional treatment are engaging and increase motivation to attend the program. These program components also provide alternative ways for youth to express themselves and connect with others. The program integrates some of these opportunities into the program schedule on an ongoing basis, and also arranges special events through community collaborations, such as inviting a DJ to lead a workshop for the youth and engaging a yoga instructor to lead yoga classes.

Making Connections between Trauma and Current Coping Strategies

Youth with trauma histories often engage in risky behaviours that put them at risk for further traumatic experiences. Self-endangering behaviours, such as excessive substance use, self-harming, unhealthy eating and involvement in emotionally or physically dangerous interpersonal interactions and relationships (e.g., abusive relationships, risky sexual behaviours), may be ineffective coping strategies that youth have developed to deal with distressing situations or memories. For these youth, assistance in connecting their current behaviours and feelings to their past experiences can help them develop an alternative self-understanding that is not laden with negative judgments. This can help youth to begin making choices that will reduce their current risks and harms.

> I think it is important to take the opportunity to normalize and validate behaviour and choices that a person might otherwise judge harshly

and blame themselves for, to encourage them to consider their choices in light of past experience over which they may have had no control, and to help them develop skill in self-compassion. (Chris, social worker)

[Acknowledging the impact of trauma] can be a lot more validating than carrying a diagnosis or a label, like "borderline personality disorder." (Susan, psychiatrist)

A focus on learning and practising alternative coping skills can be very effective in reducing the potential for harm and increasing a sense of self-efficacy and self-worth. Assisting youth in developing coping skills is a key component of our program and is a central part of many of our group and individual interventions.

I smoke a lot less pot now because I used to do it as a reaction to being upset. When you have other coping skills you have other things you can do. When you learn other coping skills, you might still use on the weekends or whatever, but it's not the only method you have for calming down. (Alex, age 20)

Creating Safety

Creating a sense of emotional and physical safety is central to a trauma-informed program. To mitigate the potential for treatment to be traumatizing or retraumatizing (i.e., to trigger painful memories or replicate elements of past experiences), creating a safe environment is essential, as is considering factors that may be uncomfortable or distressing for youth. Considerations include using respectful language, clarifying youth rights and responsibilities, paying attention to self-endangering behaviours, assessing each client's readiness to engage in group treatment, considering aspects of the physical environment and attending to staff safety.

We strive to give youth an opportunity to have a different experience . . . to have a safe experience; their experience of the world is that it's dangerous, unsafe. . . . We want to make that different.
(Joanne, manager)

Levelling Power Imbalances

Youth rights and responsibilities are discussed when youth enter the program, and again at the outset of the various treatment components to ensure that youth are well informed about what they are entitled to and what they may expect. A focus on youth rights and responsibilities acknowledges and attempts to address the potential impact of the power imbalance and dynamics inherent in a therapeutic environment. Attention paid to confidentiality, language, respect and other strategies for maintaining safety aim to reduce the power imbalance and increase a sense of comfort and safety for youth. In groups, youth have the opportunity to contribute to the establishment of group rules and norms, to help them feel as safe and comfortable as possible within the group.

> . . . with regard to maintaining an environment that is emotionally safe for staff and clients—I was thinking about how we as a whole are aware of the importance of language—making certain that we use terms and discuss topics that are appropriate and anti-oppressive, for example, gay-positive language, inclusive language, addressing issues related to all marginalized communities and racialized groups. I think this is extremely critical in the work we do and the way in which we communicate with one another. (Saadia, social worker)

Expressing Distress Safely

Throughout the program, staff members make a particular priority of attending to youth distress and self-endangering behaviours. All staff have participated in training in cognitive-behavioural therapy, dialectical behaviour therapy, the trauma-informed approaches emphasized in the Seeking Safety program, mindfulness and grounding techniques and crisis management. In group and individual treatment settings, staff members work with youth in teaching, practising and evaluating strategies for distress tolerance and affect regulation.

On a regular basis, staff members check in with clients regarding safety. Safety plans are developed proactively with all youth identified to be at high risk for suicidality or self-harming behaviour. If safety concerns are anticipated, staff members collaborate with one another, as well as with youth and families, to develop a plan that minimizes risk. Resources for crisis intervention services are regularly provided to youth and posted in staff offices and waiting areas. In addition, groups are co-facilitated, so that if a crisis should arise, there is the capacity to respond to the person requiring attention, as well as attend to the needs of the group.

> A lot of our groups are co-facilitated, and we try to run our evening groups at the same times, meaning that there are many team members around . . . if there is a crisis, then there are others to help. We're all in the same hallway, so if you are expecting a client who might be a higher-risk client, you can knock on your neighbour's door and let them know. (Stacy, child and youth worker)

Tailoring for Readiness and Gender-Specific Needs

Treatment planning considers the varying backgrounds and presentations of youth and offers modifications to content as appropriate (e.g., stress management activities may be part of a treatment plan, but grounding may be emphasized rather than relaxation). Prior to referring youth to groups, staff determines whether they are group-ready in order to ensure safety and a positive therapeutic experience for the youth and other group members. Youth must be able to contain talk of self-harm, stay sufficiently present and focused to access the content of the group, manage aggressive and impulsive behaviour and, if they have a psychotic illness, be stable. Group content can be offered individually for youth who are not yet able or willing to participate in groups. Considerations are also made regarding group composition (e.g., gender-specific groups) and therapist gender matching.

> [For the Seeking Safety group, we think] about whether we want to have males and females in the same group. . . . Also sensitivity to issues such as if a female was assaulted by a male, you would think about that before recommending a male therapist for that client. (Allison, psychologist)

> If they're triggered by questionnaires, before they leave, we make sure they feel safe and have had an opportunity to talk to someone and there's been an opportunity to address any triggers. (Janis, psychologist)

Building a Safe and Welcoming Environment

The physical environment of the program should create a sense of warmth, welcoming and belonging. Informal furnishings, artwork and magazines in the waiting area contribute to an atmosphere that is not institutional, despite the program being housed in a large hospital. Posters and brochures offer information about issues and programs that respond to the diversity of youth presenting to the program. Attention is paid to minimizing the presence of objects and artwork that may trigger distressing memories and harmful behaviours. Hospital regulations also require regular review of the physical environment, including the space, for any items that may be used to cause harm to self or others.

Ensuring Staff Safety

In order to provide trauma-informed and sensitive service, staff members require a safe space to address their own issues related to working with a challenging population with complex needs. Staff members attend regular team meetings to discuss youth needs and treatment plans, as well as staff issues and concerns related to the work. Discussions and education ensure that staff members have the required competence, confidence and support.

> The program takes staff safety into account . . . when there have been issues in a group, making sure that staff have people they can turn to, to talk about events that have occurred. Supervision, staff meetings, having somebody available if you're feeling upset about this event, somebody is present for clinician support.
> (Janis, psychologist)

Conclusion

This trauma-informed approach to treatment planning is an essential aspect of the YACDS. It is integral to our understanding of, and ability to address, the needs of youth with substance use, mental health and related concerns. Integrating a trauma-informed and sensitive perspective has been an evolving process. Youth and staff feedback, along with emerging new evidence, is regularly sought to further inform a model and approach that aims to be truly responsive to youth needs.

References

Ballon, B.C., Courbasson, C.M.A. & Smith, P.D. (2001). Physical and sexual abuse issues among youths with substance use problems. *Canadian Journal of Psychiatry, 46*, 617–623.

Chaim, G. & Henderson, J. (2009, March). *From data to the right services.* Paper presented at the Looking Back, Thinking Ahead Conference: Using Research to Improve Policy and Practice in Women's Health, Halifax, NS.

Clark, D.B., Lesnick, L. & Hegedus, A.M. (1997). Traumas and other adverse life events in adolescents with alcohol abuse and dependence. *Journal of Child and Adolescent Psychiatry, 36*, 1744–1751.

Dell, C. & Poole, N. (2009). *Applying a Sex/Gender/Diversity-Based Analysis within the National Framework for Action to Reduce Harms Associated with Alcohol and Other Drugs and Substances in Canada.* Ottawa: Canadian Centre on Substance Abuse. Retrieved from www.nationalframework-cadrenational.ca/images/uploads/file/sex-diversity-paper-bil.pdf

Hogue, A., & Liddle, H.A. (2009). Family-based treatment for adolescent substance abuse: Controlled trials and new horizons in services research. *Journal of Family Therapy, 31*, 126–154.

Najavits, L.M. (2002). *Seeking Safety: A Treatment Manual for PTSD and Substance Abuse.* New York: Guilford Press.

Rosenkranz, S. & Henderson, J. (2009, June). *Perceived use of substances to cope with traumatic stress: Association with treatment motivation among youth.* Symposium conducted at the 70th annual convention of the Canadian Psychological Association, Montreal.

Rosenkranz, S.E., Henderson, J.L., Muller, R.T. & Goodman, I.R. (2011). Motivation and maltreatment history among youth entering substance abuse treatment. *Psychology of Addictive Behaviors, 26*(1), 171–177. doi: 10.1037/a0023800

Rosenkranz, S.E., Muller, R.T. & Henderson, J.L. (2012). Psychological maltreatment in relation to substance use severity among youth. *Child Abuse & Neglect, 36*, 438–448.

Titus, J.C., Dennis, M.L., White, W.L., Scott, C.K. & Funk, R.R. (2003). Gender differences in victimization severity and outcomes among adolescents treated for substance abuse. *Child Maltreatment, 8*, 19–35.

Wild, T.C., Cunningham, J.A. & Ryan, R.M. (2006). Social pressure, coercion, and client engagement at treatment entry: A self-determination theory perspective. *Addictive Behaviors, 31*, 1858–1872.

Chapter 16

Using a Trauma-Informed Approach to Guide the Journey of Restraint Prevention

Athina Perivolaris and Ann Pottinger

This chapter describes one journey of restraint and seclusion prevention using a trauma-informed approach so that others working on similar initiatives may learn from the experience. It discusses the relationship between trauma and restraint use, organizational readiness for restraint prevention and trauma-informed strategies for use in inpatient mental health settings. This chapter also addresses the tensions between professional and client perspectives on safety—between professionals who often view the restraint as a means to provide safety and clients who can experience emotional distress, which can negatively affect the therapeutic relationship.

Challenging the Use of Restraints to Ensure "Safety"

Many people who come to a psychiatric unit as inpatients have been abused or have experienced other trauma. Some have self-harmed. They generally enter the hospital hoping to feel safe, heal and recover while they are there. Unfortunately, professional actions based on good intentions to provide safety can end up harming clients. What professionals interpret as safety for both themselves and for clients is diametrically opposed to what clients often experience as feeling safe. Professionals need to reflect on certain "safety" practices, such as the use of restraints, and their potential to harm. They must also explore the relationship between trauma and the use of restraint and seclusion.

For decades, restraints have been used for safety purposes. Despite broad evidence of their risks and a lack of evidence to support any therapeutic value (Silas & Fenton, 2000), restraints continue to be used based on the assumption that they keep people safe. Staff tends to look at the end point of aggression or escalating behaviour and therefore sees limited options for preventing the aggressive event or for envisioning alternative strategies. Yet the use of seclusion and restraint is unsafe, harmful and traumatizing, especially for clients who have already experienced trauma. Restraint use can also traumatize staff and others who observe a person being restrained.

Potential for Retraumatization

Clients with mental health and substance use issues have often experienced violence, abuse and abandonment that predispose them to being retraumatized. Ninety per cent of people with mental health problems have been exposed to trauma (Cusack et al., 2004). One in 10 people in Canada experience posttraumatic stress disorder ("Trauma-informed," n.d.). Sixty-seven per cent of people in substance use treatment report histories of childhood abuse and neglect, and 34 to 53 per cent of them have experienced childhood sexual or physical abuse (National Association of State Mental Health Program Directors, 2005). Being in seclusion or physical restraint can make traumatic experiences resurface. The very act of being restrained can evoke negative memories of physical and sexual abuse. Being locked in a room alone may stir up previous feelings of fear and abandonment.

Many clients with childhood trauma histories have a heightened or pronounced response to certain triggers that cause them to relive past trauma experiences. Part of being trauma informed is understanding that "our brains are sculptured by our early experiences. Maltreatment is a chisel that shapes a brain to contend with strife, but at the cost of deep, enduring wounds" (Teicher, 2000, pp. 66–67). There is a synergistic relationship between trauma-informed care and restraint reduction: a trauma-informed approach reduces restraint use, and reduction in restraint use minimizes trauma and retraumatization. Fostering this synergy is foundational in an organization's restraint prevention journey.

Within hospital environments, there is a tendency to rely on rules and methods of external control that disempower and traumatize clients rather than using approaches that foster empowerment, resiliency, healing and recovery. Power, control and coercive practices in such settings are represented, for example, by the use of locks and keys, the condescending demeanor and harsh tone of staff members, labelling clients through stigmatizing language and applying rigid disciplinary practices and focusing on tasks in a way that overshadows a person-centred approach. Thinking that all clients must follow the same rules is flawed. Applying rigid discipline is not only a barrier to restraint prevention; it can also precipitate aggression (Curran, 2007).

Consider a client who wants to have a warm shower before bed as a way to relax and cope with intense feelings. He is told that showers are only permitted in the morning. The client is adamant about the need for a shower and starts to shout, scream and bang on the locked bathroom door, while the staff remains focused on enforcing the rule. Eventually the client's distress and behaviour escalate to a point where other clients become distressed and, in trying to contain the situation, staff find themselves involved in a physical altercation. The client challenges the rule and the situation escalates into an aggressive episode resulting in the use of restraint. This scenario highlights how what staff often perceives as a simple rule can lead to a power struggle. Staff members may have been unaware that it was the power struggle and rule enforcement that precipitated or caused the aggression. Instead, they simply focused on the aggression itself. Enabling the client to have a warm shower would have been therapeutic and empowering. Instead the power struggle resulted in the use of restraints, which likely traumatized the client and negatively affected his therapeutic relationship with staff.

Shifting the Focus to Restraint Prevention

An organization begins its transformative journey toward restraint prevention with simple actions to initiate a complex change process. As a result of various factors and events, including recommendations from an internal task force,[1] the Centre for Addiction and Mental Health (CAMH) in Toronto

---

1. Visit www.camh.ca and search for "Restraint minimization taskforce." Also, see the jury recommendations from the Jeffrey James inquest at www.sse.gov.on.ca/mohltc/PPAO/en/Documents/sys-inq-jam.pdf.

shifted its focus from restraint reduction to restraint prevention. To guide the prevention journey, CAMH in 2008 articulated its vision: "CAMH aspires to provide safe therapeutic care and services in a restraint and seclusion free environment" (internal corporate website, 2008). A clear vision and goals act as a reminder and motivator to integrate practice change. At CAMH, the following goals were established and communicated to all stakeholders at the beginning of the journey:

- to develop strategies, systems and processes to promote a least-restrictive environment and respect for client rights
- to safely reduce or replace the use of restraint and seclusion and increase the use of alternatives
- to improve quality of care for clients and quality of work life for the care teams.

Reviewing Current Practices

Guided by a trauma-informed approach, the process of developing a restraint and seclusion prevention initiative involves an in-depth reflection and review of values and commitment to quality care and safety and how these are lived in day-to-day practice. The organization must identify gaps between the current context and future aspirations.

In Ontario, the Psychiatric Patient Advocate Office (PPAO) completed a review of seclusion and restraint practices in Ontario provincial psychiatric hospitals in October 2001. The review indicated that many clients who were restrained did not know why they were restrained and did not even know how they needed to behave in order to be released from restraints. This experience parallels that of abusive situations, in which people who have been abused do not know what they did or what they need to do to make things "okay," which leaves them feeling powerless.

Supporting and Advocating for Clients

CAMH addressed this lack of clarity around restraint use early in our restraint prevention journey by revising the policy and building supports and capacity to better inform clients of the reason for restraint and the behavioural criteria for release. We developed a focused strategy to help staff discuss issues around restraints with clients. This strategy included encouraging clients to share and communicate their feelings while being restrained and debriefing the experience after they were released from restraint. A brochure, "Partnering to Prevent the Use of Restraint and Seclusion" (corporate internal website, 2010), was developed and used with clients and families, highlighting ways to work together to keep everyone safe.

We discussed how best to involve the PPAO in supporting and advocating for clients who experienced a restraint event. Discussions focused on the tension between automatically notifying the PPAO when a client is restrained versus requiring client consent to inform the PPAO. Privacy and confidentiality were at the heart of these discussions. Initially, we decided that privacy and consent were essential; however, we agreed that the threshold for consent was low, as PPAO involvement carried little risk and offered potential benefits to the client in terms of access to advocacy and support. Clients at the time of the restraint event would be asked, several times if needed, if they would like to speak to a PPAO advocate; if they said yes, staff informed the PPAO. Toward the end of the initiative—and following many ongoing discussions on the importance of providing client support and advocacy—we implemented an automatic notification policy. Automatic notification addressed the issue of staff needing to spend time dealing with the complex and emergency needs surrounding the reason for the restraint event, which often affected PPAO notification. When the restraint event is entered in the client's electronic health record, the PPAO is notified of the event. The PPAO advocate then meets with the client and explains the advocate role and obtains consent to act on the client's behalf based on his or her needs and wishes. As well as respecting client rights, this process has strengthened CAMH's relationship with the PPAO, which is a key stakeholder in contributing to our progress.

Supporting clients also involves creating a debriefing procedure to learn what happened, how to prevent future restraint episodes and to re-establish the therapeutic relationship. In the process of developing a client debriefing procedure, we debated who should conduct the debriefing. We explored several options: creating a peer support "debriefer" position; dedicating a staff position involving specialized skills to conduct all debriefings; and asking clients to identify with whom they felt most comfortable having this important discussion. We were not able to identify best practices in the literature about this aspect of client debriefing. Given our value of client involvement, we felt that their comfort and relationships were key aspects in making the debriefing process effective. Therefore, as an organization, we opted to have clients identify the team member with whom they felt they had the best relationship to conduct the debriefing. Another key aspect that we struggled with was when to approach the client to initiate the debriefing; based initially on feedback from other organizations, we started with three hours post-release, but our clinical observation indicated that this time frame was too early because most clients still felt overwhelmed or unable to participate. The final decision was to offer the debriefing within 24 hours of release from restraint or of administration of a chemical restraint. This time frame has been better received, but for various reasons, most clients decline to participate. Some clients are too ill to participate; in other cases, there were trust and disempowerment issues.

Leadership Explores Best Practices

Leadership plays a key role in shaping the organizational architecture for addressing the gap between current and desired end states for restraint use (Golden, 2006). At CAMH, senior leadership identified the need to explore best practices in reducing the use of restraints. This need arose as a result of several events. There were two sentinel events within a year in which clients died while in or shortly following release from mechanical restraints.

One of the deaths was that of Jeffrey James in 2005, who died shortly after being released from restraints. His death resulted in a coroner's inquest in 2008. The inquest generated increased awareness of the risks associated with restraint use and furthered a commitment to explore strategies to facilitate restraint-free environments. Also, the move from manual to electronic data collection increased the amount of information about restraint use events. The least restraint policy was also due for revision. Leaders questioned this policy's focus on minimizing restraints—when and how to safely apply and care for people in restraints—as opposed to preventing their use. This question served as a catalyst for future work in the areas of policy, education and practice that would focus on how to prevent restraints and how to use alternatives. An environmental scan identified a gap between practice and policy expectations; for example, there were discrepancies around staff members' understanding of what constitutes the use of restraints as a last resort.

Part of the commitment to move forward with identifying best practices to support the use of restraint alternatives involved creating an inter-professional task force to review a broad base of evidence. This included reviewing policies, resources and lessons learned from site visits and telephone interviews in order to recommend effective strategies and approaches for reducing restraint use and suggesting strategies and resources for implementing identified best practices. It was important for task force members to learn from other organizations about the essential components in their restraint reduction journeys. The task force activities and recommendations, along with an extensive literature review on effective strategies on restraint reduction, were summarized in the CAMH Restraint Minimization Taskforce report (Restraint Minimization Taskforce, 2008). A priority recommendation was to invest in a three-year full-time position for an advanced practice nurse to lead, manage and integrate the initiative across the organization.

As part of the task force review, a small group participated in a two-day restraint reduction training program by the National Training Assistance Center (NTAC), a division of the National Association of State Mental Health Program Directors. This training emphasized the importance of creating trauma-informed care environments and provided an overview of the neurobiology of trauma and therapeutic implications. Following one of the task force recommendations, all senior leaders, clinical, finance and human resources staff and security (more than 300 people) participated in the training. Client and family representatives were acknowledged as key stakeholders and were also included.

Full participation by clients and families at all levels within the organization is critical to success in planning and implementing safety initiatives. The lived experiences of clients and families contribute to the breadth and innovation by "thinking beyond the box" and challenging established norms and processes in recommending trauma-informed strategies. Clients and families continuously reminded us of how policies and processes affect clients at the human level and challenged us to remain accountable to our values of client-centred and family-sensitive care.

Communicating Goals

To advance in our journey, we focused on communicating our vision and goals to all staff and clients and outlined for everyone the need for change and the safety benefits for clients and staff. The goals of the initiative comprised a large part of the content included in the initial communication strategy. The expertise of and collaboration with our public affairs department were important to the success of this communication strategy. The public affairs director, who also attended the NTAC training, worked collaboratively to establish a communication strategy and support, which included providing updates on the staff intranet, sharing success stories and increasing awareness of areas for further development or areas requiring accountability.

One example of how this collaboration enhanced our communication strategy and effectiveness is in our Partnering to Prevent Aggressive Behaviour (PPAB) education program. The communication strategy for the program highlighted why we were focusing on building capacity around prevention and alternative strategies rather than de-escalation, crisis and emergency management, given a long-time association between restraint use and safety.

Part of communicating goals is letting people know how our efforts are making a difference. The ongoing use, collection and sharing of data in a timely manner at all levels of the organization are important in furthering the journey of restraint prevention. Data analysis and sharing are often neglected or not consistently done at the team level, despite the fact that data discussions at the team level help to identify improvement opportunities. In December 2010, as we entered the final year of our initiative, we communicated an overview of activities and achievements through an article on CAMH's internal website. We shared that since 2008, there was a substantial reduction in the percentage of clients in all types of restraints: more than a 50 per cent reduction in the percentage of clients in restraint and a 37 per cent reduction in the percentage of clients in seclusion (internal corporate document, 2010). The Canadian Institute of Health Information (CIHI) data pertaining to mechanical and chemical restraint events during a three-day period following admission was also shared (see Table 1). In this report, CAMH compared favourably to other psychiatric facilities and various mental health facilities in Ontario.

TABLE 1

CIHI Restraint Data for Three-Day Period Post-admission (2010)

ADMISSION PERIOD DATA	CAMH	PEERS	PROVINCE
Mechanical restraint	1.6%	5.1%	5.7%
Chemical restraint	10.0%	14.7%	16.9%

Over the three years of the initiative, we also achieved substantial decreases in mechanical restraint and seclusion without an increased use of chemical restraint. The number of clients we serve increased by 10.7 per cent; use of mechanical restraint decreased from 4.2 per cent (2008–2009) to 2.2 per cent (2010–2011); use of seclusion decreased from 5.3 per cent to 3.4 per cent; and use of chemical restraint decreased from 4.8 per cent to 3.0 per cent during this same time period.

Revising Policy

The Prevention of Restraint and Seclusion Advisory Committee took the lead in revising our policy. Based on the task force recommendations, best practices and coroner's recommendations in the Jeffrey James inquest, we revised and renamed the least restraint policy to the emergency use of chemical restraint, seclusion and mechanical restraint.

Renaming the policy increased awareness that restraint is to be used only in an emergency situation where there is imminent harm to self or others, and only as a last resort. The revision process involved extensive consultation and dialogue with stakeholders, families, clients, patient advocates and staff.

Even before the policy was revised, such dialogues highlighted the gap between policy expectations and practice and identified areas for policy clarification; for example, some identified gaps—the use of seclusion as therapeutic quiet time, administering chemical restraint as needed and minimal use of alternatives to help clients self-soothe—required further discussion, education and practical support.

Implementing Policy

The issue of restraint reduction brings out many strong perspectives and concerns about safety. As we started the implementation, staff and leadership expressed concern that safety for clients and staff would be compromised. These concerns were particularly challenging at a time of increased focus on workplace safety and violence prevention. Despite many engaging conversations during which important issues were raised, not everyone supported the changes. We responded to these concerns through ongoing communication, reinforcing that we would evaluate and adjust our strategies as needed. We did not wait for unanimous agreement to proceed with our journey; yet we continued to acknowledge concerns and emphasize key concepts such as assumptions that restraints keep people safe and that there are negative consequences to their use.

Strong communication and supports are critical. In our experience, all the concerns, the "what ifs . . . ," did not end up presenting as safety concerns. The increased awareness of criteria for restraint use in complex clinical situations has resulted in intense dialogue regarding the use and non-use of restraints among team members, within various professional disciplines and between departments such as security and clinical teams.

Clinical teams were also engaged in planning discussions that focused on how to minimize the effects of potentially distressing situations for clients that can lead to aggression; for example, informing clients that they will have to remain in hospital involuntarily despite feeling ready to leave. A trauma-informed approach would include upfront discussion about how people cope with bad news and how staff can best support clients and their internal coping mechanisms in these situations.

Sharing our journey and collaborating with other organizations continues to be important to furthering our work. A recommendation from the Jeffrey James inquest was for CAMH to take a leadership role by sharing our revised policy with all psychiatric and Schedule 1 facilities, including provincial and specialty psychiatric hospitals and many general hospitals throughout Ontario in which people can be detained under the Mental Health Act. We continue to share our policy and expertise with other organizations at the provincial and national levels.

Building Capacity

At CAMH, we reviewed the staff development program that at the time focused on crisis intervention and to a lesser extent physical containment. Based on the review, a curriculum committee was formed, with input from diverse stakeholders, including direct care staff, clinical facilitators (new role), client and family representatives and education specialists who developed a new, more targeted and comprehensive education program to meet various staff development needs across the organization.

The new PPAB education program emphasizes prevention and trauma-informed care through core clinical competencies and inter-professional collaboration. It was decided that the focus would be as follows: 90 per cent prevention, eight per cent de-escalation and, when all else fails, one to two per cent restraint and seclusion use with rigorous monitoring and de-restraining attempts. Unlike the previous program delivered over two days, this new program uses modules delivered over the course of a month as in-services in the clinical area throughout the entire organization.

The PPAB modules are designed to optimize team discussion and learning using core competencies and the integration of learning in relevant clinical scenarios. The clinical facilitator, who is a direct care clinical staff member and an informal leader within the team, facilitates the modules and the team discussion. The program comprises nine modules based on core competencies such as team collaboration, trauma-informed care, developing safety plans and using a model of care to guide assessment and interventions. Each module has a key message and a champion to communicate and increase awareness and dialogue among staff and teams. The communication of the theme and messaging for each monthly module was greatly facilitated by active partnership with our public affairs department.

Trauma-Informed Strategies for Inpatient Mental Health Settings

A trauma-informed setting is based on a prevention or upstream approach, whereby root causes or precipitants of aggression and violence are addressed before a situation escalates and becomes a crisis. Such environments begin with a welcoming and open approach where staff members routinely check in with clients around their comfort and listen to their concerns.

Developing a Safety Plan

Part of the education and practice expectations is that staff will work with clients to develop a safety plan. This involves discussing safety with each client and initiating a safety plan upon or as close as possible to admission. Developing a safety plan is essential: it allows clients to identify triggers, emotions and coping strategies to prevent or manage a crisis, giving them a sense of control and empowerment. It also provides staff the opportunity to do a trauma history assessment and understand certain behaviours from a trauma lens. In turn, a trauma lens may inform the use of alternative and self-identified strategies to cope with distressing and overwhelming feelings and symptoms.

Allowing for Flexibility

A main component in creating a trauma-informed environment is to help staff recognize that coercive interventions often cause trauma and retraumatization and must be avoided. One key activity is for each clinical team, with client and family input, to review established norms and rules. Rules that contribute to power struggles between clients and staff must be eliminated as much as possible. This process must include discussing how to achieve and maintain a safe, trauma-informed environment. It may mean doing some things differently; for example, having ongoing access to healthy snacks may replace a practice of having access to food only at specified meal times. Practices that support the establishment of clients' day and night routines are often helpful; however, staff must also be empowered to adjust such practices or rules to meet individual client needs. For example, when clients require access to music outside of established times as a way of helping them self-soothe, staff must be able to assess such needs, take a flexible approach and have the resources to meet the needs.

Providing Alternative Ways to Promote a Sense of Calm and Safety

An "Alternatives to Restraint and Seclusion" booklet was developed to support staff in identifying and using alternatives (corporate internal website, 2011). This booklet includes various activities; for example, art, sensory, relaxation, movement, and reading and writing activities and other calming strategies to help staff work with clients who are experiencing distress, fear or anger. The guide also lists products that are designed to help soothe clients through sensory modalities. Some examples include weighted blankets, stress balls and aromatherapy. Other suggested activities range from instructions on deep breathing and other relaxation techniques to short journaling exercises and ways to facilitate clients' artistic expression. The main benefit of this booklet is that it increases awareness of activities and provides step-by-step instructions, along with a rationale for each activity, making it a readily available and accessible resource for staff. It is helpful to have a guide outlining various activities that help to engage clients in purposeful and meaningful activities that support their comfort, safety and security.

Debriefing with Clients and Staff

Creating a trauma-informed environment requires valuing ongoing learning as part of daily practice. Establishing a debriefing process for care needs, restraint events and crisis situations assists in preventing the future use of restraint, minimizes the negative effects, addresses organizational problems and fosters a trauma-informed environment.

Client debriefing promotes healing, recovery and learning and starts to rebuild the therapeutic relationship with the client. This debriefing is about learning from and with the client, as it facilitates obtaining the client's feedback and perspective. Client debriefings can inform care planning and safety plans by identifying triggers and precipitating behaviour that may have resulted in the restraint or crisis.

Two other components of a comprehensive debriefing process are the immediate post-event debriefings with staff and formal team debriefing with staff and leadership. These debriefings often assist in identifying team, program and organizational themes and patterns in the areas of staff training, culture, hiring practices, policies and support and supervision for staff to create a trauma-informed work and care environment. For these debriefings to be effectively implemented, leadership must be committed to this process. Leadership needs to help staff value the process, primarily by communicating and demonstrating how key learnings from the debriefings have led to positive change.

Providing Staff Development

An organization that aims to provide trauma-informed care and reduce and prevent restraint use must attend to staff development needs. The development of competencies that focus on quality care and interprofessional collaboration are crucial.

Healthy teams are essential to trauma-informed care. This is the main reason for focusing educational strategies on working and learning as teams. Such teams have members that practise together and respect and trust one another. They are aware of one another's roles and offer support, supervision and recognition that promote therapeutic relationships, building on clients' strengths, and minimize coercive practices.

Conclusion

The CAMH journey demonstrates the multi-component nature of developing a restraint prevention policy. It also highlights the need for a long-term sustained commitment to these many components to achieve success. CAMH has developed the systems and processes to support restraint prevention and a trauma-informed approach. Our journey now focuses on continued implementation of these initiatives into daily practice and ongoing reflection and integration of best practices. Trauma-informed care can guide an organization in working through the complexity of providing care in a dynamic health care environment. The journey is complex: there are many side streets and occasional detours, but stay the course. Commit and recommit to the prevention journey!

STRATEGIES TO PREVENT RESTRAINT AND SECLUSION

Help to prevent restraint and seclusion by implementing the following strategies. They are based on good practice principles, and are not exclusive to any one treatment facility:

- Use restraint only for imminent danger of serious bodily harm to self and others (as outlined under Ontario's Mental Health Act).

- Use restraint as a measure of last resort.

- Recognize that coercive interventions cause traumatization and retraumatization and are to be avoided.

- Value and respect the client in all aspects of care.

- Develop individualized, flexible plans and approaches to care.

- Focus on the client.

- Remove both overt and covert expressions of power or control in practices, policies and procedures, especially within the context of unit-based rules.

- Examine and change language that reflects power and control over clients.

- Offer a variety of programming to meet clients' needs.

- Provide staff education on the use of preventive and alternative strategies.

- Work in partnership with clients and families when using the above good practice principles; their ideas, experiences and suggestions are essential for success.

References

Curran, S. (2007). Staff resistant to restraint reduction: Identifying and overcoming barriers. *Journal of Psychosocial Nursing, 45*(5), 45–50.

Cusack, K, Frueh, B. & Brady, K. (2004). Trauma history screening in a community mental health center. *Psychiatric Services, 155*, 157–162.

Golden, B. (2006). Change: Transforming healthcare organizations. *Healthcare Quarterly, 10*, 10–19.

National Association of State Mental Health Program Directors. (2005). *Training Curriculum for Reduction of Seclusion and Restraint: Draft Curriculum Manual.* Alexandria, VA: Author.

Restraint Minimization Taskforce. (2008). *Restraint Minimization Taskforce Final Report.* Retrieved from www.camh.ca

Silas, E. & Fenton, M. (2000). Seclusion and restraint for people with serious mental illnesses. *Cochrane Database of Systematic Reviews, 2000*(1). doi: 10.1002/14651858.CD001163

Teicher, M.H. (2000). Wounds that time won't heal: The neurobiology of child abuse. *Cerebrum, 2*(4), 50–67.

Trauma-informed. (n.d.). Retrieved from www.trauma-informed.ca

Chapter 17

Trauma-Informed Work with Families

Sabrina Baker

Susan's Story

When Susan Brown* was 24 years old, she was brought to the emergency department of the psychiatric hospital in 2010 for beating up her 28-year-old sister, Karen, and threatening to kill her two-year-old nephew at a family brunch. Susan accused Karen of "doing the devil's work" and had left Karen badly bruised before the police responded to the 911 call put out by their mother, Pam.

All the Brown family, including Susan, were traumatized by this event. Susan had reportedly "not been herself" since she was 18. Susan dropped out of her first year of college and spent most of her time "holed up in her bedroom." Pam thought she seemed different—suspicious even—but attributed this to "being depressed, hanging out with the wrong crowd and smoking a lot of marijuana." Pam also thought that Susan was depressed as a result of breaking up with her first serious boyfriend. Pam blamed herself for not realizing earlier that Susan was ill.

After the brunch incident, Susan began displaying noticeable symptoms of psychosis and described having voices telling her not to have anything to do with her family. She was very angry at her family for putting her into hospital,

*"Susan" is based on a composite of clients with whom the author worked.

as she believed there was nothing wrong with her. Pam was designated as Susan's substitute decision-maker during hospitalization.

Gradually, Susan began to make steady progress in the hospital, as she responded to the medication and the protected environment of the inpatient psychiatric department. She was still angry with her family and did not want to have anything to do with them. Pam was still upset by Susan's violence and said that Susan was "not welcome to come home [the two had been living together before the incident] unless she receives a depot injection of her anti-psychotic medication and meets regularly with her treatment team." Pam had decided to take a "tough love" approach with her daughter, believing that this was the only way to "save" Susan and keep the rest of the family safe. She was frightened that Susan would become ill again and feared for her own safety. Susan was not willing to agree to her mother's demands and asked her clinical team not to have anything to do with her mother following her discharge from the hospital.

Pam was referred to meet with the family worker, as she was clearly distressed and needed support, education and counselling in her own right to help her through this crisis.

The Family's Story

Fortunately, Susan's care team included a separate family worker who could provide support to Pam and Karen, while the rest of the team (a psychiatrist and case manager) worked with Susan. Since Susan did not want her family to receive any information about her status, the family worker respected this. The family worker decided that it would be easier for her to support the family and adhere to confidentiality principles by not accessing any information about Susan from the rest of the team and by opening a separate chart for Pam. Pam's hope was to eventually involve the entire family once they were all ready to do this work. In the interim, the work was done separately.

The family worker (a social worker at the hospital) introduced herself and described her role and function as the family worker on the team. She welcomed the family warmly, and invited them to tell their story. Meetings with the family were conducted at an outpatient clinic away from the hospital, reducing any chance of Susan running into her family and creating safety for the family. The worker gave them the time to share their experience in their own way and time, not rushing them or bombarding them with questions. The recent incident with Susan had triggered unfinished business for Pam, as her ex-husband had been verbally abusive to her while they were still married. (He left the family when Susan was 14, and had not had any contact with the family since.)

Pam and Karen said that they felt abandoned by the mental health system, which created stress for them. They recounted examples of taking Susan to various hospitals and asking for help for Susan, only to be told that unless Susan was a danger to herself or others their hands were tied. Pam felt that some professionals were ignoring and blaming her for not being "a good enough parent" to Susan. She also felt that Susan's treatment team perceived her as a "bad" mother for not agreeing to take Susan home from the hospital, regardless of whether Susan agreed to Pam's conditions or not.

The family worker validated Pam's decision to set limits with Susan; this in turn empowered her to feel strong enough to "stay the course" with her daughter. Pam stated that she knew that there was something wrong with Susan but had "no idea how to help her or to make sense of the mental health system and get the necessary help for her." She had hoped that the hospital-ization would allow her daughter to get the care that she needed, but she now realized that Susan's recovery would be more complicated and take longer than she had originally anticipated. Pam realized that she would need to be there for her daughter for a long time, "maybe for as long as she lives." Pam also agreed with the family worker that she would need to take care of herself during this process so she did not "run out of steam and jeopardize my own physical and mental well-being."

Karen was seeing a psychiatrist to address issues that had arisen for her about her parents' separation when she was a child, and felt that it was important that she and her mother receive separate help at this time. For her part, Pam wanted to continue to meet with the family worker for education, support and counselling because she was feeling anxious and frightened about the future. She expressed "not knowing who else to turn to in my time of need." Pam felt isolated and alone and withdrew from her usual support system because she felt it would be disloyal to reveal what happened in the family and felt stigmatized by having a daughter with mental illness. The current crisis was also bringing up unresolved issues about loss and abandonment that Pam preferred to process one-on-one.

Pam was anxious to reconnect with her daughter and to become an ally in her recovery. She hoped that being close before the illness would enable them to eventually get together and "thrive." Pam still believed the team thought she was "a cold and heartless mother for drawing a line in the sand and not allowing Susan to be discharged into my care." However, she maintained her conviction that the only way to "save" Susan was to adopt a tough love approach with her. The family worker supported Pam emotionally during this difficult time and held the hope for Pam that, in time, when Susan availed herself of help, she would start "to reclaim her life" and reconnect with Pam, Karen, her brother-in-law and nephew. In the interim, the family worker helped Pam to grieve, adjust to her current reality and work toward building on her strengths and competencies.

The worker empathized warmly with Pam as she described recent events leading up to Susan's hospitalization. Pam continued to blame herself for not getting help earlier and potentially averting this crisis in her family. She was concerned that her "messy divorce from a verbally abusive man may have caused or contributed to Susan's psychosis." Pam worried that she might be the cause of rather than the solution to her daughter's recovery. Education about etiology, treatment and recovery from psychosis helped to reduce Pam's stress levels and increase her coping skills. Pam benefited from having a safe place to vent her feelings and deal with the sense of loss involved in having a loved one with mental health issues. She said that it was useful to make the connections between the past and present and be reminded of some of the strategies that had been helpful in getting through other difficult times in her life.

Six months after Susan was discharged from the hospital, Pam learned that the police had brought Susan into hospital again. She decided that this was a good time to reach out to her daughter. Susan was responsive to meeting with Pam; she had started to miss having her mother in her life. The family worker and psychiatrist on the unit facilitated brief meetings that had been arranged for the two of them. They ensured that Pam had easy access to a door because she did not feel completely safe with her daughter and wanted to have an escape route should the dynamics between them become heated.

As Susan started to have a positive response to her medication, the former closeness between mother and daughter began to be rekindled. This time, Susan was eager to live with her mother after being discharged and agreed to receive the depot injection and continue to see her treatment team regularly—the terms her mother had set for this arrangement. Susan went home for a few weekends before being discharged, which went well, so Pam was happy to have Susan living back at home, particularly knowing her daughter was receiving medical and psychosocial support from the treatment team. Pam was clear about providing a calm home atmosphere but was adamant that she would continue to set limits with Susan.

The family worker continued to support Pam individually and an additional regular family meeting was scheduled for Pam, Susan, Susan's case manager and the family worker to build on the family's strengths and help to facilitate communication between mother and daughter. Pam is a dedicated advocate for her daughter and is an ally in Susan staying well and eventually re-integrating into the community. As Susan gradually developed a better understanding of her illness, she started to understand her mother's expectations that she accept treatment to "regain her life." Susan was motivated to reconnect with her sister, Karen, and believed that if she demonstrated that she was "stable," this relationship would be resurrected. Reuniting with her nephew provided her with a strong motivation to stay well.

Pam and Susan developed a strong relationship. Initially, Pam noticed that Susan seemed to have "regressed" to a former stage of development and was more dependent on her for help with daily living. Pam's ultimate aim was to help her daughter to become independent and autonomous; she sometimes struggled in determining how involved she should be in Susan's life. Having a separate family worker to speak to about these matters was helpful to Susan. Having a case manager to help Susan achieve her goals helped Pam to feel that she was not alone in caring for Susan.

Today, Susan is taking some college courses and feels hopeful about her future. She is starting to develop friendships and feels "more like my old self." Susan says that "losing mom and Karen was devastating and helps me remember to take my medication every day and do everything that I can not to land back in hospital."

Trauma-Informed Family Work

Family-centred trauma-informed care focuses on meeting the needs of both the person with mental health or substance use issues and his or her family. It builds on the strengths and interconnectedness that exists in families.

A trauma-informed model builds on the core practices of a family-centred approach, which involves listening, responding to and supporting the family's concerns, opinions, values, beliefs and cultural background. A family-centred approach may or may not include the family member being seen for a mental health or substance use problem. Regardless, in no way does the term "family-centred" intend to remove control from the recovering person. A family-centred approach simply recognizes that all family members deserve support, even if the recovering person chooses not to have his or her family members involved. In these situations, families are offered support, whether or not the client chooses to participate. The approach to care and decision-making is collaborative, with each person recognizing the skills, expertise and experience of the other people involved (Baker et al., 2007).

A trauma-informed approach is not simply family-centred: it attends to how the events surrounding the hospitalization of a family member may be traumatizing for others in the family, and how the present events may elicit fears and (mal)adaptive responses to past trauma on the part of family members. Being well supported and listened to, family members can work on their own responses and feel empowered to continue to be allies in their relative's recovery, while also taking care of themselves.

Attending to family members' needs and realizing that they go through their own parallel recovery process is important. This is unlike what has happened historically, when parents, especially mothers, have been blamed for causing mental illness and behavioural problems in their offspring—a perspective that continues to affect the field of psychiatry and traumatize families today. In 1948, Frieda Fromm-Reichmann coined the term "schizophrenogenic mother" to describe what she saw as domineering, overprotective, rejecting mothers, who she believed were causing their children's schizophrenia. This culture of blame persisted until the early 1970s.

In trauma-informed family work, the family worker acknowledges this legacy of blame. Most family members express how helpful it is to explore this matter, as they have often been affected by family-blaming theories and can think that they are the cause rather than part of the solution for their relative's recovery. Shame can affect family members' interest in accessing professional and peer support and their ability to get past feelings that the illness is somehow their fault.

In Susan's situation, the family worker attended to the immediate safety needs of the family, such as Pam's need to be near the door in early meetings with her daughter and setting limits requiring her daughter to be on medication if she were to live at home. Support for Pam's expression of limits was likely critical to her safety and empowering given her history of having an abusive husband. The worker was able to focus on Pam's strengths, resilience and competency and encouraged her to take care of herself during this difficult time. She acknowledged Pam's fears and stress without pathologizing them. Pam started attending a yoga course with a friend and found this beneficial in keeping her stress levels down.

Listening to other families at different stages of the recovery process can be invaluable and provide families with hope for the future. After Pam had five months of individual work, she attended a family psychoeducation group. She worried that other family members would judge her for her "tough love" approach but was pleasantly surprised at how unconditional other participants were toward her. Pam felt supported in the group and other participants shared some of her issues. She expressed that knowing that Susan was experiencing adverse situations in her life and feeling helpless to stop what was happening to her daughter still stressed her. The family worker continued to work with Pam while she participated in the group to help Pam cope with these feelings. Eventually, Pam started to feel calmer and stronger in herself.

Timely trauma-informed care enabled Pam to work through her feelings about her daughter, acknowledge her own experience of violence, mobilize her own strengths and competency and eventually reunite with her daughter. Pam felt that the illness "robbed" her of the daughter she knew but she believes that out of adversity—separately and together—they have both managed to start living their lives in a positive way, appreciative of the family ties they have all developed over a difficult two years.

Susan attributes her current success in large part to her mother's support and help in lobbying for services for her. Pam reports that this experience helped her to re-evaluate her life and make a career change. She is applying to become a social worker as a result of her experiences with Susan.

References

Baker, S., Baker, K. & Collette, E. (2007). *Family Protocol for Early Intervention Programs in Ontario*. Unpublished manuscript.

Fromm-Reichmann, F. (1948). Notes on the development of treatment of schizophrenics by psychoanalytic psychotherapy. *Psychiatry, 11*, 253–273.

Chapter 18

Trauma-Informed Care on a Women's Inpatient Psychiatric Unit

Donna Akman and Cheryl Rolin-Gilman

The Women's Inpatient Unit (WIU) at the Centre for Addiction and Mental Health (CAMH) is a residential service for women who have complex mental health problems and a history of trauma, and who may also have substance use issues. The majority of clients have histories of interpersonal trauma, including but not limited to experiences of sexual, physical and emotional abuse in child- hood and/or adulthood. Further, many of our clients contend with various forms of challenging and oppressive social circumstances, such as social isolation, economic difficulties and discrimination. In recognition of the difficult and often disempowering circumstances of our clients' lives, our model of care is trauma informed and feminist informed, with an emphasis on safety and empowerment through validation, skill development and self-determination. Our program is unique in that it is the only all-women inpatient psychiatric service in Canada dedicated to clients with a history of trauma.

Although a full description of the philosophy and interventions used in the WIU is beyond the scope of this chapter, we describe key practices and policies that reflect our trauma-informed, feminist-informed model of care. These practices and policies include our approach to self-harm and suicidality, substance and alcohol use, admission goals and discharge planning and co-client relationships; and policies regarding locked doors on our unit, the use of physical restraints and managing potentially dangerous clinical situations.

Key Trauma-Informed Principles in the Women's Inpatient Unit

The WIU is an inpatient psychiatric service for adult women who present with complex mental health problems and trauma histories, and who may also have substance use issues. It was developed in response to a recognized need for an all-women psychiatric unit that provides women with a safe community where they could get psychoeducation about the relationship between mental health, addiction, gender and trauma; access a wide range of treatment approaches to reduce distress and increase wellness; and develop and practise skills that support well-being and empowerment. As a feminist-informed, trauma-informed service, the WIU aims to create a therapeutic environment in which women can experience a sense of safety and community, be validated for their strengths and resilience and engage in activities and interactions that promote mastery and empowerment. It is based on the Sanctuary model (Bloom, 1994, 2000), which uses trauma-based and feminist-informed approaches to create a therapeutic community. Within the Sanctuary model, treatment is guided by four aspects of trauma recovery—safety, affect management, grief and emancipation (Bloom, 2000). Within this framework, establishing a safe therapeutic milieu is necessary if recovery is to progress. Affect management refers to the stage of recovery in which people learn to manage their emotional arousal in less destructive ways. Grief refers to the loss, sadness and despair that are components of having experienced trauma, and that must be worked through if recovery is to progress. Emancipation refers to aspects of full recovery, such as social reconnection and the restoration of meaning to one's life through empowerment. These four concepts are guiding features of the principles and practices of the WIU.

Not Just Symptom Reduction, but Wellness

Many of the women who are admitted to the WIU have long-standing difficulties with complex and overlapping symptoms, including depression, suicidality, self-injury, affect dysregulation, flashbacks and dissociation. Our clients typically meet criteria for mood and/or anxiety disorders, including posttraumatic stress disorder, and have received previous treatment in inpatient and/or outpatient settings. Given that a significant proportion of our clients present with past or current suicidality and self-harm behaviours, our population is considered at high risk for safety concerns. Thus, a main treatment priority is to reduce acute symptoms, increase psychiatric stability and improve overall functioning in our clients. However, rather than focusing solely on symptom reduction or psychiatric stability, the WIU aims to help clients move toward wellness by identifying and validating their strengths and resilience and encouraging them to engage in activities and interactions that promote mastery and empowerment.

A Learning and Sharing Environment Embedded in a Treatment Setting

The WIU focuses on helping women identify and harness both internal and external resources in order to increase personal and social empowerment. As such, we use a biopsychosocial approach to reduce symptom distress and increase well-being. In addition to medications and psychotherapy, our approach includes psychoeducation about psychosocial factors that may be influencing mental health difficulties. We aim to create an environment in which women can learn and practise a range of skills and self-care strategies, and we assist women in gaining access to social support and community resources. These features of the WIU are practised within a framework that supports and encourages clients to recognize, value and share their own expertise and wisdom with one another.

A Broad Lens for Trauma

As a trauma-informed program, we use a wide scope in assessing for trauma experiences and related symptoms. We inquire about women's experiences of past or current physical, sexual and emotional abuse, as well as other experiences of physical or sexual violence or intimidation. We assess for childhood experiences of invalidation, neglect and family instability or violence. In addition to inquiring about these more overt forms of traumatic experiences, we consider the many ways that women's daily lives may be affected by unsafe, destabilizing and disempowering experiences, such as low status and low-paying jobs, various forms of harassment and discrimination and gender role expectations that pressure women to assume a disproportionate amount of caretaking responsibilities, meet rigid standards for female attractiveness and adhere to social dictates against anger expression in women. Given our knowledge of each woman's unique history of abuse and violence and of the ways in which all women can be subjected to marginalizing and disempowering social and interpersonal experiences, the WIU uses trauma-informed interventions and policies.

Service from a Trauma-Informed Lens

The program itself is semi-structured and emphasizes group interventions as a way of providing clients with opportunities to develop skills in a supportive, validating environment, where women can learn about and from other women. A variety of groups are offered each day, and while clients are expected to attend groups, it is up to the client, ideally in collaboration with her treatment team, to determine which groups she would find the most beneficial. Thus, each client decides for herself, in collaboration with her treatment team, what her treatment goals are and how best to achieve them while on the WIU. Clients also meet individually with their psychiatrist, primary nurse and other members of the treatment team. They are offered opportunities to engage in a variety of leisure and physical activities on the unit and/or on community outings.

Safety, Coping and Sharing Wisdom

The group interventions that are offered on the WIU are wide-ranging and often comprise psychoeducation, skill development and support. The interventions aim to promote safety, self-care, contextualization of women's experiences, self-determination, validation of women's experiences and expertise, opportunities for women to connect with and learn from other women and self-advocacy. Some groups are more skills-based and focus on developing cognitive, emotional and behavioural skills and strategies to promote safety and increase distress tolerance and affect regulation. There are also groups that have a psychoeducational focus in which clients learn about biopsychosocial factors that are related to their health and well-being. Other groups use the group setting as a venue for women to discover commonalities with other women and share knowledge and information about resources and strategies for wellness and coping. Still other groups are directed more toward enhanced self-awareness. In all of the groups, regardless of the content or focus, women are invited to recognize and value their individual and collective wisdom and resilience.

Trauma-Informed Policies and Practices

Agency in Determining Admission Goals and Treatment Planning

Women learn of the WIU primarily through our emergency department, other CAMH programs and community psychiatrists. Often women know little about the WIU, other than that it is a women-only psychiatric service. Thus, once a woman is seen for potential admission to the WIU, she receives information about our program and how it may be able to meet her needs. She is provided with an overview of the groups offered, the focus of individual sessions, what she can expect in terms of contact with the various members of the team and, if possible, a tour of the unit. Regardless of whether a woman is referred through the emergency department, another CAMH program or the community, she is invited to consider how the WIU can meet her needs, and she is asked to identify goals for her admission. As a woman's stay on the WIU progresses, her treatment goals are likely to be revisited and revised, in collaboration with the treatment team.

A Focus on Keeping Safe: Addressing Self-Harm and Suicidality

From the perspective of the WIU, self-harm is a coping strategy that women develop to manage distress; somewhat paradoxically, in many cases it has helped women survive. With that in mind, psychoeducation is provided to clients about the link between trauma, emotional distress and self-harm. While clients are validated for their resilience and creativity in finding ways to manage their distress and survive in the face of often extremely challenging circumstances, a main focus of treatment is to help them develop other, more effective coping skills. Women on the unit are asked to make a commitment to not engage in self-harm behaviour, and instead to practise using the skills they are learning as part of their treatment. However, clients do sometimes engage in self-injury while on the unit; when that happens, it is viewed as an opportunity to explore the possible precipitants of the behaviour and consider factors that may have prevented the woman from using alternative strategies.

Individualized safety plans, developed to help women identify factors that precipitate distress, cues of distress and strategies for coping with distress that do not include self-injury or suicide, are created within 72 hours of admission and are continually revised and adapted as clients develop new awareness and skills. Each client creates her safety plan in collaboration with her primary nurse, other members of the treatment team and in a group called Keeping Safe, which focuses on teaching women skills to incorporate into their safety plans. Within the group, women are encouraged to share with one another what they have learned about themselves with regard to their own distress signals and strategies for coping. This is encouraged to help women recognize and solidify their capacity for growth and to reinforce women's value to one another through shared experiences and knowledge.

Substance Use Issues

Similar to our approach to self-harm, alcohol and other forms of substance use are seen as a way of coping with distress. Women are asked to make a commitment not to use alcohol or other drugs during their admission to the WIU. However, if they do engage in substance use, their experience is used as an opportunity to consider the precipitants for the use, the consequences of the behaviour and the development of alternative more effective coping strategies. Part of the discussion often revolves around how substance use may have affected the other women on the unit, particularly if clients have been noticeably intoxicated in the presence of other clients. In that case, the safety and stability of the therapeutic community can be negatively affected. It is also explained to clients that continued use of alcohol or other substances is likely to interfere with prescription medications and the ability to take part in group programs. Thus, while each situation is assessed on an individual basis, if it is determined that a woman is not able to abstain from substance use during her admission, she may be asked to leave and invited to return when she can. It may be that the client would be better suited to a program that is primarily addiction-oriented, or one that relies less extensively on the role of a safe and stable therapeutic community.

Self-Awareness and Learning through Co-client Relationships

For many women who attend the WIU, establishing healthy interpersonal relationships can be challenging. Histories of abuse and neglect, along with gender-related socialization to assume responsibility for relationships and to prioritize others' needs ahead of their own, often lead women to have difficulty developing secure and healthy relationships with family, friends and intimate partners. Recognizing, asserting and respecting the need for appropriate boundaries in relationships is often part of the treatment goals for women in our program. For many of our clients with little social support, the WIU offers an opportunity to develop connections with other women that sometimes transform into ongoing friendships. While we aim to support the opportunities for women to reduce social isolation and establish valued relationships with other women, we also strive to help them identify and assert their own needs in the connections they make with one another. This can lead to challenging interpersonal situations in which the goals of one client to establish connections with other women may clash with the goals of another client to set interpersonal boundaries. For this reason, as well as to promote safety and community on the unit, sexual and/or exclusive relationships between clients are discouraged.

However, with regard to co-client relationships, as with other situations that arise, staff takes into account the context of each circumstance in determining how best to approach a complex clinical matter. Clients are encouraged to engage in open discussions among themselves and with members of the treatment team to explore possible advantages and disadvantages of establishing co-client relationships. The perspective of the WIU is that clients have the right to make their own decisions about the relationships they establish, and that if the choices made lead to problems, those situations are opportunities for further learning and self-awareness. The goal of the WIU is not to protect women from making what some may consider to be bad decisions, but to help women make informed decisions and empower them to deal with the outcomes of the choices they make.

Safety and Empowerment through Open Doors

Whereas many psychiatric units tend to be locked, the WIU is an open-door unit, offering women the freedom to come on and off the unit as they wish. Our trauma-informed perspective holds that for many women, being in an inpatient psychiatric setting can lead to numerous situations in which there is actual or perceived disempowerment. Thus, we try to establish policies and practices that support women's self-efficacy and empowerment. Having a locked unit, in which permission to enter or exit must be requested, can be experienced as retraumatizing and/or disempowering. The philosophy of the WIU is that all members of the therapeutic community are responsible for establishing a sense of safety for themselves and the community. Women are therefore encouraged to determine for themselves how best to use the therapeutic milieu in a way that promotes safety. This includes encouraging them to assess their comfort level with leaving the unit for outings. Clients who may be experiencing suicidal ideation or engaging in self-injury or substance use are encouraged to work with their treatment team to evaluate their readiness to leave the unit and establish alternative self-soothing strategies. There are times when the WIU is locked for brief periods as a way of assisting clients who feel significantly at risk and who identify that locking the unit may be helpful, and at times when staff members have identified a client who is considered at acute risk. It is recognized that having locked doors, even for short periods, may be anxiety provoking for other clients, and this is acknowledged and discussed whenever possible.

De-escalating Potentially Dangerous Situations

In most psychiatric inpatient settings, there are times when clients may respond or behave in ways that may require de-escalation in order to maintain safety for all involved. A range of interventions can be used in these situations, from verbally interacting with clients to using physical restraints. At times, staff from other units within the hospital may be called in to assist ("code white"). These interventions, while sometimes necessary, can be retraumatizing and disempowering for clients who are likely already experiencing a loss of control. From a trauma-informed framework, interventions should be chosen with the aim of promoting safety while minimizing the potential for retraumtization and disempowerment. With this in mind, physical restraints are rarely used on the WIU, and a code white is called when other attempts to intervene have been ineffective or when there is a recognized need for immediate support. When a code white is called on the WIU, staff who come to assist are guided to stay in the background in order to reduce the potential for retraumatizing the client, who may have a trauma history. Staff members are educated on ways to intervene that are as collaborative as possible. This often includes helping staff understand the importance of taking the time to negotiate with clients, rather than relying on strategies such as the use of restraints, which may be more efficient, but are also more disempowering. Within this framework, crises are viewed as opportunities to help clients use skills they have learned in treatment, rather than react in familiar but unhelpful, and sometimes dangerous, ways.

Conclusion

As illustrated throughout this chapter, working within trauma-informed and feminist-informed frameworks has helped us to identify how residential psychiatric services can offer women opportunities for safety and empowerment. The practices and policies we have described have been developed over many years of collaboration between WIU staff and clients. These practices and policies are continuously revisited, reconsidered and sometimes revised in order to be responsive to the multiple and sometimes competing needs of clients, staff and the WIU community as a whole.

References

Bloom, S. (1994). The Sanctuary model: Developing generic inpatient programs for the treatment of psychological trauma. In M.B. Williams & J.F. Sommer, Jr. (Eds.), *Handbook of Posttraumatic Therapy: A Practical Guide to Intervention, Treatment, and Research* (pp. 474–491). Westport, CT: Greenwood Press.

Bloom, S. (2000). Creating sanctuary: Healing from systematic abuses of power. *Therapeutic Communities: The International Journal for Therapeutic and Supportive Organizations,* 21(2), 67–91.

Chapter 19

Trauma-Informed Primary Care with Immigrant, Refugee and Non-status Women Living with HIV/AIDS

Mercedes Umaña

At Women's Health in Women's Hands, a Toronto-based community health centre, we use a trauma-informed framework to facilitate each woman's journey living with HIV/AIDS. Working with immigrant, refugee and non-status (IRN) black women and women of colour,[1] we recognize that each woman comes from particular social locations, which create their own challenges and strengths, depending on the complexity of their circumstances.[2]

This chapter discusses how Women's Health in Women's Hands implements a trauma-informed primary health care model for IRN women living with HIV/AIDS—both in the wake of an HIV-positive test result and as part of chronic management of this condition.

Services for these women include general health monitoring by family physicians and nurse practitioners, psychotherapy, nutritional counselling, HIV-related health literacy and prevention, and community development

---

1. Women's Health in Women's Hands Community Health Centre provides services for black women and women of colour from the Latin American, Caribbean, African and South Asian communities within the Greater Toronto Area. Throughout this chapter, for the sake of brevity, we use the term "IRN women living with HIV/AIDS" to refer to women from the priority populations served at the centre, many of whom are immigrants, refugees or women with precarious immigration status.
2. *Social location* refers to intersecting identities based on factors such as ethnoracial background, socio-economic status, immigration status, age, gender, (dis)abilities, sexual orientation and spirituality. Social locations are an important element for understanding the differential impact of the social determinants of health.

initiatives/programs. Some clients seek our services shortly after getting a positive test result from an anonymous testing site; others have known about their HIV status for a long time, having contracted the virus while fleeing their countries of origin and seeking refuge in Canada.

Living with HIV/AIDS may or may not be the central health concern for the women we see, because determinants of health—the impact of unemployment, homelessness, under-housing, settlement difficulties and other social and economic concerns—may create more pressing problems for the client. In other words, issues such as securing immigration status in Canada or finding ways to support children being bullied at school may appear to be a greater priority for clients than trauma-related issues. Critically examining determinants of health is crucial when providing trauma-informed services for any client, but particularly for IRN women living with HIV/AIDS.

A Trauma-Informed Approach

The centre has integrated a trauma-informed framework during two crucial stages of working with IRN women living with HIV/AIDS: during or immediately after a positive HIV test result and throughout ongoing care (chronic management).

Providing Safe and Welcoming Services

Dissociation, sadness, intense fear, confusion, anger and powerlessness are all normal responses to receiving a positive HIV test result, just as they are for all traumatic experiences, as has been extensively documented in the literature (Herman, 1992). Stigma associated with HIV/AIDS remains a distinct element that amplifies the potential traumatic nature of receiving an HIV-positive diagnosis and living with the virus. HIV/AIDS stigma is linked to misunderstanding of the illness; misconceptions about how the virus is transmitted; lack of access to treatment; irresponsible media reporting on the epidemic; the incurability of AIDS; and prejudice and fears relating to issues including sexuality, disease, death and drug use (Joint United Nations Programme on HIV/AIDS, 2005). As a result of stigma, discrimination and shame, people living with HIV/AIDS often do not seek or are not offered treatment, care and support, making them vulnerable to blame, depression, suicidality and self-imposed isolation (African and Caribbean Council on HIV/AIDS in Ontario, 2006; Joint United Nations Programme on HIV/AIDS, 2005).

It is crucial for services to be welcoming to people with HIV/AIDS, recognizing how stigma, cultural beliefs, discrimination and trauma may interact, making it difficult for immigrant, refugee and non-status women to access help.

Taking Time and Promoting Agency and Empowerment

Given the serious life-changing implications of a positive HIV test result, it is important for service providers to understand that clients may need extra time to process the information and may require assistance in establishing a plan of action. Health care providers should allocate the time and space necessary to help IRN women living with HIV/AIDS assimilate the information and express any emotions or reactions to such news.

This kind of support is crucial not just at the time of hearing the diagnosis, but at any point in a woman's journey with HIV/AIDS. A nurse from the centre describes how she extended her appointment time to respond to questions an HIV-positive client had about her difficulties taking an iron supplement. In this conversation, the client tearfully commented on how taking one extra pill in addition to the anti-retroviral medication reminded her of her HIV status and her fears of death, stigma and community rejection. This conversation opened new avenues for the client to continue processing her emotions and building resilience, and for the nurse to be able to provide her with reassurance and empathic understanding.

Interdisciplinary Support That Acknowledges the Many Layers of Trauma

Implementing a trauma-informed framework also involves understanding that a positive HIV test result may bring up traumatic content associated with the circumstances that resulted in the client becoming infected. Unravelling other layers of trauma can be acknowledged by setting up sufficient time for the appointment, not rushing into providing detailed biological explanations about HIV and being open to assisting the client in processing her most immediate reactions or questions.

In our experience, discussing sensitive issues related to HIV/AIDS care and prevention in addition to disclosing new positive HIV test results has required more effective interdisciplinary work, with physicians regularly consulting and collaborating with psychotherapists and community health promoters to facilitate the client's journey living with HIV/AIDS. For example, community health promoters and psychotherapists may sit in with family physicians during any appointment where a positive test result will be communicated to help the client process her most immediate reactions to the diagnosis and to let her know of any other community initiatives from which she could benefit. This collaborative linkage helps to break the stigma and isolation that often result in further revictimization.

Providing immediate referrals to psychotherapists reaffirms the availability of resources to support the client. However, referrals are offered cautiously, specifying to the client that psychotherapy is available as a resource to support her in continuing to process her new reality if she feels the need to talk to someone about the diagnosis or any other current life circumstance. Because some people still believe that psychotherapy and other mental health services are for people who are "crazy," it is crucial to take the time to explain how emotional distress is a normal reaction to a new HIV-positive diagnosis or other critical issues in living with HIV/AIDS and how psychotherapy or counselling services can help women cope.

To enhance access to mental health services, Women's Health in Women's Hands has established a policy where any woman seeking mental health services gets immediate access to counselling and psychotherapy services. Reassuring clients about confidentiality is another important aspect in providing trauma-informed services for IRN women living with HIV/AIDS at all stages, given how small some communities are and the need to prevent stigma. In some African and Caribbean communities in Toronto, for example, being in certain areas or attending certain community events is perceived as affording little privacy, which can contribute to fear of disclosure (African and Caribbean Council on HIV/AIDS in Ontario, 2006). As a result, IRN clients who are HIV-positive may appear to resist referral for ethno-specific counselling or psychotherapy services out of fear that their privacy could be compromised.

Supporting Women's Priorities

Service providers need to understand clients' social locations and how determinants of health might influence treatment planning and outcomes. They may want to consider the following issues in their conversations with newly diagnosed HIV clients:

- **Immigration status:** Treatment planning will usually require community and legal referrals if the client is dealing with precarious immigration status or a refugee claim process, being sponsored or waiting for a humanitarian and compassionate grounds application or a pre-removal risk assessment. In many instances, primary health care providers need to be available to help lawyers document evidence in support of refugee claims, as the traumatic nature of the narratives often requires therapeutic support to deal with clients' traumatic symptoms immediately after discussing their life histories.
- **Family relations:** Is there a member of the client's family or immediate support network on whom she can rely to help her maintain focus on the here and now, and into the future? Connecting with the woman's broader support network can be extremely delicate, as women newly diagnosed as HIV-positive are required to disclose information about anyone whom they could have exposed to the virus. This procedure is usually managed collaboratively by public health officers and physicians who contact third parties so they can be directed to the appropriate services. Service providers need to take necessary measures to screen for any potential circumstances that could lead to HIV-positive women being revictimized in the process of disclosing their new status: for example, disclosure of HIV by women who are in an abusive relationship or who have precarious immigration status could result in increased violence, deportation and even forced separation from their children.
- **Pregnancy and breastfeeding:** Service providers need to follow guidelines around reducing mother-child HIV transmission via breastfeeding and pregnancy: this includes helping women who are newly diagnosed as HIV-positive to access support as they cope and make decisions about their

diagnosis and treatment choices while continuing to fulfil their roles as mothers and caregivers.

- **Dissociative symptoms:** At the time a client receives a positive diagnosis, health providers should understand that dissociative responses may result in her struggling to stay present, to listen or even to figure out a way to get back home. Sometimes clients who appear to be "unco-operative" are in reality expressing normal dissociative responses. At Women's Health in Women's Hands, one of the main priorities at this stage is securing continuity of care through an interdisciplinary approach.

With the development of more effective drugs to treat HIV/AIDS, trauma-informed care has become crucial to chronic management of the disease. For IRN women living with HIV/AIDS, this new reality involves understanding the complexities in women's lives, as certain emotional reactions to living with the virus may also become chronic. What may appear as chronic depression— with catastrophic or fatalistic thinking patterns, fear and chronic feelings of hopelessness—may be the natural reactions to a traumatic event that turned chronic, such as living with the HIV virus and the potential collapse of the immune system over time. Service providers need to understand and support IRN women living with HIV/AIDS in accepting the difficult challenge of continuing to resist the virus, while reclaiming their entitlement to building a fulfilling future as women.

Building a Greater Sense of Community and Empowerment

Another important element that the centre has incorporated in its trauma-informed framework relates to the Greater Involvement of People Living with HIV/AIDS (GIPA)[3] and health literacy/capacity building with women living with HIV/AIDS.

After organizing several workshops and educational activities for IRN women living with HIV/AIDS, the centre acknowledged the requests from a large group of community members for leadership by women who are HIV-positive

---

3. GIPA is a guiding principle that refers to the need for active and meaningful participation of people living with HIV in the inception, development, implementation, monitoring and evaluation of policies and programs (International HIV/AIDS Alliance & Global Network of People Living with HIV, 2010).

in initiatives geared toward building skills and HIV/AIDS health literacy. As a result, the centre developed a program where HIV-positive women play a central role in setting the agenda and bringing speakers of interest. Through this initiative, women who are HIV-positive provide peer support to newly diagnosed women, strengthening their leadership and creating a greater sense of community and empowerment. This effort has crystallized in monthly skills-building/HIV health literacy gatherings, where attendance has reached more than 100 IRN women living with HIV/AIDS from the Greater Toronto Area.

Conclusion

Much work and research remain to be done in broadening our understanding of how determinants of health, along with structural and institutional practices of exclusion, negatively affect certain populations. Research, policy and programming still need to be developed to ensure that health care services respond to the specific needs of diverse populations who experience acute or chronic traumatic reactions.

Our journey in developing a trauma-informed model of care with IRN women living with HIV/AIDS started with community member demands for primary health care services, research and health promotion initiatives addressing HIV/AIDS. Over the last 11 years, Women's Health in Women's Hands has implemented changes in its primary health care model for HIV-positive women, making it more accessible by reducing wait times, enhancing our interdisciplinary model of care by incorporating an understanding of the role of traumatic stress in living with HIV/AIDS, hiring HIV-positive staff dedicated to facilitating skills-building programs with HIV-positive women, engaging in partnerships with organizations that deliver services for this population, conducting community-based research and engaging in knowledge translation initiatives. Our organizational process has resulted in a significant increase in the number of women who are HIV-positive being served at the centre, development of community partnerships creating synergy in program delivery, increased satisfaction from HIV-positive clients and client involvement in leadership roles in the broader community.

It is our hope that more primary health care service providers and community members will use some of the insights shared in this chapter to create and expand trauma-informed models to their specific contexts.

References

African and Caribbean Council on HIV/AIDS in Ontario & HIV Social, Behavioural and Epidemiological Studies Unit, University of Toronto. (2006). *HIV/AIDS Stigma, Denial, Fear and Discrimination: Experiences and Responses of People from African and Caribbean Communities in Toronto*. Toronto: Author. Retrieved from www.accho.ca/pdf/ hiv_stigma_report.pdf

Herman, J. (1992). *Trauma and Recovery: The Aftermath of Violence—From Domestic Abuse to Political Terror*. New York: Basic Books.

International HIV/AIDS Alliance & Global Network of People Living with HIV. (2010). *Greater Involvement of People Living with HIV: Good Practice Guide*. Brighton, UK: International HIV/AIDS Alliance. Retrieved from www.aidsalliance.org/includes/Publication/ GPG-GIPA-English.pdf

Joint United Nations Programme on HIV/AIDS. (2005). *HIV-Related Stigma, Discrimination and Human Rights Violations: Case Studies of Successful Programmes*. Geneva, Switzerland: Author. Retrieved from http://data.unaids.org/publications/ irc-pub06/jc999-humrightsviol_en.pdf

CHANGING THE SYSTEM THROUGH EDUCATION AND INNOVATION

PART 3

CHANGING THE SYSTEM
THROUGH EDUCATION
AND INNOVATION

Introduction

Part 3 looks specifically at the opportunities in the mental health and substance use treatment systems to become more trauma informed. The processes of change differ depending on a range of factors, such as setting, social determinants of health and health equity, as discussed in Part 2. However, solid processes of change rest on education and innovation. The chapters in Part 3 provide examples of the training and education involved in building trauma-informed services and systems and describe innovative programs that are putting this approach into practice.

Section 1: Education

In Chapter 20, Peck and Capyk describe how they came to recognize their leadership role in providing education on trauma-informed practice with community-based agencies that work with girls and women. A service such as theirs, with its mandate of healing, education and prevention of sexualized violence, can play an important role in helping other women-serving agencies at the community level understand trauma and avoid becoming overwhelmed by girls' and women's need for counselling around trauma-related issues. Peck and Capyk describe their introduction of training to community support workers in youth-serving agencies, including the processes and structures involved in creating advisory committees to collaboratively build tailored training on trauma-informed practice. They also advocate the application of a trauma lens at the organizational level to identify potential changes to managerial and administrative processes and systems that might lessen the chances of traumatizing or retraumatizing clients in a range of settings.

Covington, in Chapter 21, describes curricula to develop trauma-informed practice for working with women who have substance use issues. Her work is based on international findings that women experience poor responses to their substance use issues for reasons such as shame, stigma, fear of losing their children and a general lack of well-funded and well–co-ordinated women-centred services. Taking these issues into account, Covington describes why women-specific services are needed and what they would look like. She pays particular attention to retraumatizing practices and behaviours, such as restraints, seclusion, body searches, incarceration and yelling. Covington's work reminds us of the importance of gender and how developing women-specific approaches is especially important when trauma, violence and substance use issues coexist. Covington identifies the critical need for training in trauma-informed practice and explains how the curricula used in service delivery can also serve as a basis for practitioner training.

Dell addresses a trauma-informed approach with a group of incarcerated women who have self-harmed. In Chapter 22, she describes a women-centred perspective on self-harm and views the behaviour through a trauma lens. Dell describes the process of community-based research that identified prison responses to women who self-harm. These ideas led to the development of videos and other products to assist in educating, training and setting the foundation for future research in creating trauma-informed community and correctional systems. Dell highlights the need for education to address how women have been unfairly stigmatized for self-harming and how the act of self-harming has been misunderstood. Training for service providers should include information about the influence of trauma in these women's lives.

In Chapter 23, MacKenzie and Druker describe an emergent practice stemming from a pilot study in Toronto with women who had lost custody of their children to child welfare services. They review the literature on the grief and bereavement associated with child apprehension, noting that apprehension itself can be traumatic. This trauma can lead to self-blame, guilt, shame and anger and can engender substance use. These issues underlie the goal of the Grief and Loss Education and Action group in Toronto, co-sponsored by a community health centre and a women's substance use treatment centre. The 15-week pilot group, which is now in its third cycle, has created a venue for women who have experienced loss to come together and share their stories. The women who have participated in this pilot are acting on their identified interest in educating child welfare and other service providers about this form of trauma through public speaking.

Section 2: Innovation

The chapters in Section 2 feature initiatives that have created new approaches to providing trauma-informed care as a way to rectify problems in programs or services when trauma was not considered a potential part of the women's experiences.

In Chapter 24, Smylie and Ussher describe a more open and client-centred collaboration between child welfare and substance use treatment services. In Canada, these sectors have historically been divided, leading to further traumatization for women, as their respective practices and goals conflicted with one another. Smylie and Ussher stress the importance of linking services in a seamless manner, establishing three-way communication between the parents, substance use services and child welfare agencies, as well as advocating for and supporting mothers. The program at the Jean Tweed Centre grew out of the observation that trauma was affecting the women accessing the centre's substance use treatment services. The centre's response was a highly collaborative initiative in Toronto that engaged five agencies. Together, they developed a common agenda aimed at prevention in a strengths-based trauma-informed program that has evolved over two decades. This innovation breaks through the silos of child welfare and substance use treatment by moving toward a cross-sectoral system aimed at understanding more fully the trauma-related experiences of the families in their care.

Chambers describes development of an empowerment council for clients and patients at the Centre for Addiction and Mental Health (CAMH) in Toronto. When CAMH defined trauma-informed care as a priority, Chambers recognized that assessing the organization's own internal culture was a priority. In Chapter 25, she describes the debates surrounding the evolution of the Empowerment Council. After an extensive consultation process, the council created the CAMH Bill of Client Rights. While the rights do not guarantee appropriate practice, they do outline what clients can expect and what they are entitled to. The document also outlines a set of boundaries that helps clients to defend their integrity and agency within a psychiatric hospital environment. This aspect is particularly important for people with trauma histories.

Brown discusses integrated screening as a component of trauma-informed care in Chapter 26. The development of a trauma-informed screening tool was based on the experience of people working in mental health and substance use services at the state level in California. This tool includes questions about mental health, substance use and trauma and violence histories. A second innovation is a tool assessing a woman's priorities for change, which she is asked to rank in four main areas. Brown addresses the comprehensive training required at the agency level, involving everyone from receptionists to kitchen staff, from managers and supervisors to clinical staff. She argues for a paradigm shift that is transformative—not one more feature of the service, but rather a new approach informed by positive, strengths-based, safe and respectful elements that permeates every interaction and development of the service.

In Chapter 27, Dechief and Abbott provide another example of a transformative process in the evolution of trauma-informed, harm reduction–oriented supportive housing services for women in British Columbia. The clientele accessing the shelter-related services at Atira Women's Resource Society includes women who are homeless, pregnant and mothering and who are dealing with many issues, such as mental health and substance use problems and violence. Dechief and Abbott describe the agency's transition from its abstinence-oriented policy for admission to transitional housing services to a more realistic and honest approach, where a woman can open up about any issues she might have, without fear of being refused treatment. The shift also involves creating an ever-evolving organizational culture that reflects this new approach. Indeed, through experience and practice, the agency intuitively developed trauma-informed principles and applied them in its various shelter service locations as they began to deal directly with substance use and mental health issues. The shift was organic and highly informed by values of respect, equality, responsiveness and empowerment.

Poole and Lyon, in Chapter 28, describe efforts to introduce tobacco treatment services at the Aurora Treatment Centre, a women's residential addiction recovery program. The introduction of tobacco treatment into addiction programs has had a rocky history, despite compelling scientific evidence linking smoking and other types of substance use problems. Poole and Lyon link this evidence to trauma and violence in women and make a compelling case for this innovation. Nonetheless, the introduction of tobacco treatment into addiction treatment required a paradigm shift, calling into question criteria for admission, measures of success and staff and client receptivity. Referral networks were also implicated in this innovation, as they, too, had to address the new paradigm, prepare their clients and assess their own attitudes toward tobacco use. Again, the success of this program integration is based on respect, rapport and relational collaboration, with an emphasis on empowering clients through choice, all of which are elements of trauma-informed care.

Finally, Greaves and representatives of YWCA Toronto discuss how the organization brought trauma-informed principles and practices into its shelter services for women with complex violence-related and mental health issues. The trauma-informed approach was first applied to the development of the ARISE shelter model in 2000. It was extended to other existing violence against women shelters and is now guiding the development of a large new residence on Elm Street for women living on low income and with mental health and substance use challenges. Chapter 29 provides excellent practical examples of changes made in daily operational rules and practices, in relational support for women, in building multidisciplinary staff teams and in providing community-level support in the achievement of trauma-informed goals. YWCA staff members eloquently describe the ongoing challenges and the many rewards of trauma-informed practice in the course of this work.

This part of the book on education and innovation captures a range of activities in progress, as practitioners and services work out new approaches to care, service and system design that are trauma informed. These examples illustrate some of the enormous commitment, insight and energy associated with these changes and provide a strong basis for moving forward.

PART 3

SECTION 1: EDUCATION

Chapter 20

Building Community Capacity for Trauma-Informed Practice

Barbara K. Peck and Stephanie R. Capyk

At the 1998 conference of the American Psychological Association, then-president Philip Zimbardo challenged the psychological community to "give psychology away," to take the insights and practices of their discipline and share them with the broader community to enhance the human condition. The Trauma-Informed Practice and Support training (TIPS)[1] at the Victoria Women's Sexual Assault Centre (VWSAC) in British Columbia was created in an effort to "give away" what we know, and thereby increase the community's capacity to respond with support and skill to survivors of sexualized violence and trauma.

The VWSAC has a mandate of healing, education and prevention of sexualized violence and has provided intervention and prevention services since 1982. These services have included various educational initiatives with partner organizations that provide a large range of community services, such as housing, youth services and reproductive health services, but that do not provide trauma counselling per se. Education sessions have focused on raising awareness of the prevalence and societal context of sexualized violence, describing the many ways a survivor may be affected and clarifying the referral process to our services. We do not provide in-depth information about trauma counselling, as it is a specific type of work requiring specialized skills and organizational capacity. The target audience for this training is people who work in human

---

1. For more information about the TIPS training curriculum, contact the Victoria Women's Sexual Assault Centre at reception@vwsac.com.

services and provide support for a range of issues, some of which may be trauma related. Community support workers are sometimes relieved when we tell them that their role is to be trauma informed in interactions with clients and to refer them to trauma counselling services, rather than to provide trauma counselling.

As awareness and understanding of trauma have increased in recent years, more complex questions have emerged, with corresponding requests for a greater depth of information. Whether or not it is the focus of their work, community support workers are often present with clients struggling with the complex interweaving of traumatic responses that include triggers, flashbacks and overwhelming emotions. Workers may support clients who disclose histories of abuse but who are neither interested in, nor ready for, trauma counselling, as well as clients with addiction or mental health issues that seem to have roots in traumatic experiences. Providing general support and information about referrals has become insufficient to address the complex and urgent issues that community support workers face with trauma survivors.

Our work at the VWSAC is structured around the three-stage model of trauma healing (Herman, 1992). The focus of the first and foundational stage of healing is to educate survivors about the effects of trauma on the whole self and to increase their safety and stability. In early 2008, with funding from Human Resources and Social Development Canada and the United Way of Greater Victoria, we formed an advisory committee with members from a range of youth-serving agencies, including a friendship centre, a child abuse prevention and counselling agency, a children's hospital and an alternative school. We chose to focus on youth-serving agencies because youth are at a critical stage of development where the "right" support can make a huge difference, yet they are least likely to access trauma-specific counselling.

This advisory committee created a curriculum for community support workers that would help them to develop "first stage" support skills and learn how trauma, substance use and mental health issues and challenging behaviours or responses may be interconnected. In providing this training to seven youth-serving agencies, we hoped that youth in our community would receive trauma-informed care in as many places as possible, with support that consistently integrated an understanding of trauma into every interaction.

The committee generally met monthly and provided guidance regarding training content and methods.

In 2010 we received a grant from the Victoria Foundation to offer the training to local agencies that provide services to people experiencing poverty, homelessness, addiction and marginalization. This has allowed us to expand and adapt our TIPS curriculum to be relevant for community support workers who interact with a wider variety of people in different life situations. Like the original TIPS training for youth-serving agencies, working with diverse community agencies has infused our work with a greater understanding of our clients and the web of community agencies that provide critical support services in greater Victoria.

The TIPS Training

"We'd like to begin by inviting you to take a nice deep breath. Notice your feet on the floor. . . "

And so we start the TIPS training, just as we begin our groups for survivors of sexualized violence. The purpose of beginning with this type of exercise is fourfold:

• to provide an example of how to guide clients through a grounding activity
• to allow workers to experience how their clients might be affected by the activity
• to convey that the skills and tools we are teaching are applicable to both clients and workers
• to help participants to be more present for the workshop.

This simple starting point reflects our appreciation of experiential learning and the importance of the well-being of both client and worker and our emphasis on developing safety skills, which we do throughout the training. We use an exercise that facilitates self-regulation because trauma can disrupt this ability (Van der Kolk & Saporta, 1991). Encouraging workers to use this tool for themselves supports the information presented later in the training that witnessing trauma can have similar effects as experiencing trauma directly (Pearlman & Saakvitne, 1995).

The full TIPS training currently runs for two days. One of its strengths is the integration of information in three main areas:

- the survivor (effects of trauma, context of survivors' lives, etc.)
- the helping relationship (skills for safely supporting survivors, integrating TIPS into the workplace)
- the worker (positive and negative effects of working with survivors, ways to mitigate negative effects).

We also emphasize that the training builds on information and skills that community support workers already have and encourage them to modify the tools and information according to their context.

Program Evaluation

As each agency underwent the training, the advisory committee member from that agency provided feedback about how the training was received, as well as its subsequent impact on their co-workers' practice over time. The committee also discussed the overarching goal of building community capacity.

We hired an external research and communications consultant to further evaluate the project. She played an important role, not only in creating the evaluations and analyzing the data, but also in guiding the content and pedagogy. Using an iterative process of curriculum development, participant feedback from each training session informed us about how to shape subsequent training. With each new round of training, the curriculum underwent significant modifications in format, content and/or ways of teaching, based on feedback from previous trainings. Some of the modifications were agency specific, depending on the populations served, and many were general improvements.

The most consistent feedback was that there was not enough time for all of the content and participation that was planned. As we experimented with various formats, the curriculum evolved to have flexible units of training that can be reorganized or excluded based on participants' needs. Written materials for each unit continued to be provided for self-study.

Components of TIPS

Various models of trauma-informed practice have been proposed, each emphasizing somewhat different components or key messages. Different models are described in Harris and Fallot's 2001 special journal issue, *Using Trauma Theory to Design Service Systems,* and Jennings' (2004) report on trauma-informed care, as well as work by Yoe et al. (2007). Based on these models and our own extensive experiences working with survivors of trauma, we found it helpful to group the aspects of trauma-informed practice into four overarching components: trauma competence, understanding the client/survivor, client empowerment and safety (see Table 1). TIPS training addresses factors from each of these components.

TABLE 1

Components of Trauma-Informed Practice and Support

TRAUMA COMPETENCE	UNDERSTANDING THE CLIENT/SURVIVOR	CLIENT EMPOWERMENT
• Be aware of prevalence of trauma. • Recognize effects of trauma on whole person. • Understand that behaviours and responses may reflect attempts to cope with effects of trauma. • Minimize possibilities of retraumatization. • Be aware of the impact on workers and how it may influence their work.	• See client as a whole person. • Use strengths perspective. • Recognize the context in which the survivor lives (family, social, community, cultural, sociopolitical). • Collaborate with supporters.	• Maximize choices. • Give voice to clients (at individual and organizational levels). • Allow client control where possible. • Treat clients with respect. • Validate client experiences and responses. • Collaborate on goals. • Foster client self-advocacy skills.

SAFETY

• Understand safety as fundamental to healing.
• Recognize need for safety in all realms (physical, spiritual, mental, emotional).
• Foster trust between service provider and client.
• Have and teach tools for building safety.
• Recognize difference between trauma-informed and trauma-specific practice and support.

Trauma competence is largely about understanding what trauma is and how it can affect people in various areas of their being and their lives, including understanding the potential impact of secondary exposure to trauma, which involves hearing about a traumatic experience through another person's story. We provide a broad definition of trauma based more on how it affects the person than on the details of the trauma story, and include such concepts as colonial trauma, intergenerational trauma and developmental trauma (attachment disruption). Also necessary for trauma competence is the knowledge that traumatic experiences are not rare and unusual events. Recognizing the prevalence of trauma, particularly among certain populations, does not mean making assumptions about clients' experiences; rather, it means being aware that the experience of trauma is a very real possibility. One does not need to know whether or not particular clients have experienced trauma to provide trauma-informed services.

Understanding the client/survivor is rooted in the strengths perspective that is woven into the TIPS training. We do not elaborate on this concept because the agencies and support workers we encounter are already working from this perspective. Instead, we allot more time to increasing awareness of how the context of people's lives may interact or intersect with their experiences of trauma. That is, systemic and contextual factors may influence a person's likelihood of experiencing or witnessing trauma, the nature of the trauma, the responses of the survivor to the trauma and how others respond to the trauma survivor. Contextual factors include family, culture, socio-economic status, ethnic background, gender, sexual orientation and historical context of country of origin. Although many workers have been exposed to these ideas in varying degrees, direct service work is often narrowly focused on the individual. A trauma-informed perspective requires that we recognize that trauma does not happen in a vacuum.

Client empowerment is another concept that support workers are familiar with; yet the practical application of empowerment can conflict with safety issues. For example, empowerment would suggest that clients have the right to make their own choices about exposing themselves to a risky situation. But from the perspective of safety, this may mean that the client makes a choice that puts him or her in harm's way. The TIPS training explores these challenges. In one exercise, for example, participants consider the costs of too much control in the supportive relationship (e.g., resistance, loss of connection, reinforcing negative beliefs of incompetence, little sense of agency, undermining confidence) and the costs of too little control (e.g., not providing a safe container or secure base, lack of safety, staff feeling disempowered). The trainers acknowledge how tricky it can be to achieve the right balance.

Safety is key to working from a trauma-informed perspective. Because trauma can affect people in all aspects of their lives, safety must be considered holistically. Support workers are often more familiar with attending to external safety issues; therefore, the training focuses more on tools related to internal safety (e.g., deep breathing, grounding, containment, safe place, mindfulness, self-compassion), which can be used with a range of clients, whether or not they have experienced trauma. We do not want survivors to open up about the specifics of their trauma when they do not have the safety to do so, for example, when they are with a worker who is not trained to provide trauma-specific services or when there is no organizational or program infrastructure to provide appropriate support. Some workers struggle with the concept of how to honour a client's story while providing containment and safety. The history that many survivors and groups of marginalized people have of being silenced is a legitimate concern; thus, careful attention is paid to this issue in the TIPS training. Table 1 summarizes some differences between trauma-informed and trauma-specific services. We are very clear that the TIPS training is not trauma specific.

We introduce many of these ideas through an opening story in which the same scenario is presented from two perspectives, the second being more trauma informed. (The story we choose can be modified to reflect the clientele the workers are likely to encounter.) The group then discusses how each approach might affect the client, the worker's understanding of the client, the relationship between the client and worker, the outcome and the worker. As a starting point, this approach is well received and provides a tangible framework for people to grasp a number of key messages about trauma-informed practice in a short time.

TABLE 2

Differences between Trauma-Informed and Trauma-Specific Services

TRAUMA-INFORMED PRACTICE AND SUPPORT (TIPS)	TRAUMA-SPECIFIC PRACTICE
A **perspective/lens** that can be integrated at all levels of the organization.	A **kind of therapy** designed to treat the actual sequelae or aftermath of trauma. Conducted by a person with specific training in trauma treatment.
Applicable to any client, whether or not he or she has a trauma history, and whether or not that history is known.	The client has acknowledged her or his trauma history.
Main focus of practice: Increasing safety through development of self-management skills (e.g., grounding and containment) for current distress. Building on client strengths. Recognizing that some "problematic" behaviours may reflect coping strategies that were intended to increase survival. Supporting clients in reducing harm that may arise from unintended consequences of coping strategies.	**Main focus of practice:** Addressing the three phases of trauma treatment: safety and stabilization; remembrance and mourning (trauma processing); and reconnection. Using specific techniques for trauma processing, such as EMDR, somatic experiencing, art therapy or other modalities that allow the client to explore, come to terms with and integrate traumatic experiences.
The worker does not solicit or go into details of the trauma with the client. The focus is not on a diagnosis or on the specific nature of the traumatic event(s).	The counsellor may go into the details or specifics of the trauma with the client in a paced and contained way.
The client has not consented to trauma counselling.	The client has given informed consent for trauma counselling.
Trauma-informed practice and support does not include trauma-specific practice (and may involve a referral to trauma-specific practice).	Best practices indicate that all trauma-specific work should also be trauma informed.

Applying a Trauma Lens to an Organization

To provide safe and effective services, employees at all levels of human service organizations, not only front-line workers, should be trauma informed. The full TIPS training asks participants to apply a trauma lens at a program or organizational level. As most participants are front-line workers, the consistent feedback has been that many want practical tools and skills for working directly with clients, along with clear direction on when and how to apply the tools. The training, therefore, evolved to have a greater practical emphasis. An experiential approach increased both acceptance of the tools and confidence in using them. The desire for direct-service tools, while not surprising from a practical perspective, may also reflect a sense of powerlessness that workers feel when they are exposed to trauma through their clients. Part of our learning process has been to clarify our target audience and to make sure the curriculum applies to them. A TIPS training for management and administration is one of our hopes for the future.

At this stage, the TIPS training is ready to be shared more broadly as a package with facilitator and participant workbooks. VWSAC has begun to offer fee-for-service training for agencies beyond the greater Victoria area. We have learned that one of the core strengths of this training is the intrinsic partnership between the trainers and the learners. TIPS is not intended as a new way of working; it is a lens that can be shared and integrated into all facets of supporting people wherever they seek help.

References

Harris, M. & Fallot, R.D. (2001). Envisioning a trauma-informed service system: A vital paradigm shift. In M. Harris & R.D. Fallot (Eds.), Using Trauma Theory to Design Service Systems [Special issue]. *New Directions in Mental Health Services, 89,* 3–22.

Herman, J.L. (1992). *Trauma and Recovery: The Aftermath of Violence—From Domestic Abuse to Political Terror.* New York: Basic Books.

Jennings, A. (2004). *Models for Developing Trauma-Informed Behavioural Health Systems and Trauma-Specific Services: An Update of the 2004 Report.* Cambridge, MA: Abt Associates. Retrieved from www.theannainstitute.org/MDT2.pdf

Pearlman, L.A. & Saakvitne, K.W. (1995). *Trauma and the Therapist: Countertransference and Vicarious Traumatization in Psychotherapy with Incest Survivors.* New York: W.W. Norton.

Van der Kolk, B.A. & Saporta, J. (1991). The biological mechanisms and treatment of intrusion and numbing. *Anxiety Research, 4,* 199–212.

Yoe, J.T., Conway, K., Hornby, S., Goan, H. & Teirnan, C. (2007). *Development of a trauma-informed system of care assessment tool* [PowerPoint slides]. Retrieved from www.maine.gov/dhhs/QI/Florida_Conference-SKG-handout.pdf

Chapter 21

Curricula to Support Trauma-Informed Practice with Women

Stephanie Covington

Over the past 30 years, we have greatly improved our understanding of the treatment needs of women with substance use problems. Research reveals that the vast majority of these women have experienced violence and other forms of abuse and that a history of serious traumatic experiences plays an often-unrecognized role in a woman's physical and mental health problems (Felitti & Anda, 2010; Felitti et al., 1998; Messina & Grella, 2006). A history of being abused drastically increases the likelihood that a woman will develop substance use problems.

In 2004, the United Nations Office on Drugs and Crime published a monograph on treating drug addiction among women around the world. In the course of developing the monograph, it was discovered that many of the issues with which women with addiction struggle are universal. These include:

- shame and stigma
- physical and sexual abuse
- relationship issues
  - fear of losing children
  - fear of losing a partner
  - needing a partner's permission to obtain treatment
- treatment issues
  - lack of services for women
  - lack of understanding of women's treatment

- long waiting lists
- lack of child care services
• systematic issues
  - lack of financial resources
  - lack of clean/sober housing
  - poorly co-ordinated services (Covington, 2008a, p. 378).

Helping professionals around the world report an association between addiction and all forms of violence and abuse (physical, sexual and emotional) in women's lives (United Nations Office on Drugs and Crime, 2004).

Recent research also demonstrates that addiction treatment services for women and girls need to be based on a holistic, female-centred approach that acknowledges women's psychosocial needs (Grella, 1999; Grella et al., 2000; Orwin et al., 2001). In my writing, gender-responsive/woman-centred services refers to creating an environment—through site selection, staff selection, program development and program content and materials—that reflects an understanding of the realities of women's and girls' lives and that addresses and responds to their challenges and strengths.

This chapter discusses the rationale for gender-responsive trauma-informed practice and describes five evidence-based and best practices curricula that service providers may find helpful when advocating for and designing adaptations to programming.

Responding to Gender Differences in Experiences of Violence and Trauma

Risk for abuse is gendered. Both female and male children are at relatively equal risk from family members and people known to them. However, as males age, they are more likely to be harmed by enemies or strangers, whereas women are more likely to be harmed by their intimate partners (Covington, 1999, 2003a; Kendall-Tackett, 2005).

In adolescence, boys in the United States and many other white majority countries are at risk if they are gay, young men of colour or gang members.

Their risk comes from people who dislike or hate them. For a young woman, the risk is in her relationship with an intimate partner. For an adult man, the risk for abuse comes from being in combat or being a victim of crime. His risk is from "the enemy" or from a stranger. For an adult woman, the primary risk is again in her relationship with an intimate partner. To generalize, this may account for the higher rate of mental health problems among women: it is more confusing and distressing to have the person who is supposed to love and care for you do harm to you than it is to be harmed by someone who dislikes you or is a stranger (Covington, 1999, 2003a; Kendall-Tackett, 2005).

Women have different responses to violence and abuse. Some women may not be traumatized by abuse because they have coping skills that are effective for a specific event. Sometimes trauma occurs but is not recognized immediately because the violent event is perceived as normal. Many women who used to be considered "treatment failures" because they relapsed are now recognized as trauma survivors who returned to alcohol or other drugs to medicate themselves from the pain of trauma. By integrating trauma services with addiction treatment, we reduce the risk of trauma-based relapse.

Trauma can skew a woman's relational experiences and hinder her psychological development. Because it can affect how a woman relates to staff members, her peers and the therapeutic environment, it is helpful to ask, "Is this person's behaviour linked to her trauma history?" However, traditional addiction and/or mental health treatment often does not deal with trauma issues in early recovery, even though trauma is a primary trigger for relapse among women and may underlie their mental health issues. Many treatment providers do not know what is needed in order to do this work. Here are three important things that can be done in treatment programs to address trauma issues:

1. Educate women about what abuse is, what trauma is and how abuse can sometimes—though not always—cause trauma. Women often do not know that they have been abused—and they often do not understand posttraumatic stress disorder.

2. Normalize women's reactions. It is important that women learn that their responses are normal, given their experiences. Trauma responses are normal reactions to abnormal or extreme situations.

3. Provide coping skills. There are grounding and self-soothing techniques (e.g., breathing exercises) that women can learn to help themselves cope with their traumatic experiences (Covington, 2003a, 2011).

Avoiding Revictimization and Retraumatization

A woman who has experienced a traumatic event feels more vulnerable. She may have difficulty tolerating, expressing and/or modulating her emotions. This results in what is called emotional dysregulation. An example of this is when she over-responds to neutral cues and under-responds to danger cues. Therefore, traumatized women are at increased risk of similar, repeated revictimization. Retraumatization refers to the psychological and/or physiological experience of being triggered. A single environmental cue related to the trauma—such as the time of year, a smell or a sound—can trigger a full fight-or-flight response. Often, providers of substance abuse treatment hesitate to provide trauma services for women in their programs because of the fear of retriggering them. Although triggers in the environment cannot be completely eliminated, it is important to create a safe environment in which women can learn coping skills. This is the reason that the therapeutic environment is so important for women. They must feel safe.

Understanding the impact of trauma and the issue of triggers is particularly important when working with women in the criminal justice system. Unfortunately, standard management practices—such as searches, seclusion and restraint—may traumatize or retraumatize many women. Experiences in the criminal justice system can trigger memories of earlier abuse. It can be retraumatizing when a survivor of sexual abuse has a body search or must shower with male correctional officers nearby. It can be retraumatizing when a battered woman is yelled at or cursed at by a staff member. Incarceration can be traumatizing in itself, and the racism and class discrimination that are characteristic of the criminal justice system can be even more traumatizing.

As the understanding of traumatic experiences increases among clinicians, mental health theories and practices are changing. It is important for service providers to understand trauma theory as a conceptual framework for clinical practice and to provide trauma-informed services for their clients. According to Harris & Fallot (2001), trauma-informed services:

- take the trauma into account
- avoid triggering trauma reactions or retraumatizing the woman
- adjust the behaviour of counsellors and staff members to support the woman's coping capacity
- allow survivors to manage their trauma symptoms successfully so that they are able to access, retain and benefit from the services.

The Trauma-Informed Environment

In women's treatment programs, sensitivity to trauma-related issues is critical for creating a healing environment. A calm atmosphere that respects privacy and maximizes the choices women can make promotes healing. Staff members should be trained to recognize the effects of trauma, and clients should have a clear understanding of the rules and policies of the program. A trauma-informed environment includes various features:

- Attention to boundaries—between staff members and participants, among participants and between participants and visitors. For example, clients should be given permission to say "no" to hugs. Hugging may be an expression of positive emotion for some women, but for those who have been traumatized it could represent an undesired intrusion into their personal spaces.
- Language that communicates the values of empowerment and recovery. Punitive approaches, shaming techniques and intrusive monitoring are not appropriate.
- Staff members who adopt the "do no harm" credo to avoid damaging interactions. Conflict is dealt with through negotiation.
- A feeling of safety for staff. Women often work in environments where they feel harassed and/or disrespected. Many female staff members also have histories of abuse.

Assisting Service Providers with Trauma- and Gender-Informed Practice

The recurring theme of the interrelationship between substance use problems and trauma in women's lives indicates the need for a multi-focused approach to services. I have developed the Women's Integrated Treatment model, which is based on:

- the definition of gender-responsive services provided in an earlier section
- a theoretical foundation that integrates the theories of addiction, psychological development (relational-cultural theory) and trauma
- multi-dimensional therapeutic interventions.

This model is unique from most other trauma programs that do not have a gender-specific focus and use a unidimensional cognitive-behavioural approach.

Three completed studies (Messina et al., in press; Messina et al., 2010; San Diego Association of Governments, 2007) and the final report to the National Institute on Drug Abuse on a randomized-control-group study in drug court (Bond et al., 2010) show positive results for the Women's Integrated Treatment model.

Curricula have been developed that help service providers bring this theoretically and evidence-based approach into the delivery of trauma-informed and trauma-specific services.

Five Gender-Responsive, Trauma-Informed Curricula

In developing gender-responsive services, the curriculum or material used is a crucial ingredient to the success of treatment. The following are five manualized curricula I have designed for working with women and girls. They are theoretically based and trauma informed, each with a facilitator's guide and a participant's workbook. Each curriculum uses cognitive-behavioural, relational and expressive arts techniques. These materials not only help to provide services, but can also be used to educate staff.[1]

1   Helping Women Recover: A program for treating addiction

This newly revised resource provides a comprehensive, 17-session curriculum that includes the information and tools that counsellors, mental health professionals and program administrators need to implement an effective program for women's recovery in varied settings. *Helping Women Recover* (2008b) is organized into four modules that address key areas that women in treatment identify as triggers for relapse: self, relationships, sexuality and spirituality. The material addresses self-esteem, sexism, family of origin, relationships, domestic violence and trauma. The curriculum is built upon the integration of theories of women's psychological development, trauma and addiction.

A step-by-step facilitator's guide and a participant's workbook, entitled *A Woman's Journal*, is filled with self-tests, checklists and exercises to enable each participant to create a personalized guide to recovery. The Helping Women Recover program can be implemented by helping professionals with a range of training and experience (Covington, 2008b).

Helping Women Recover is widely used in addiction treatment programs, mental health clinics, eating disorder programs and domestic violence services. There is also a special edition for women in the criminal justice system. This version provides specific information about women in correctional settings to staff working in these programs.

2   Beyond Trauma: A Healing Journey for Women

Beyond Trauma: A Healing Journey for Women is designed for practitioners to use in any setting (outpatient, residential, therapeutic community, criminal justice or private practice) to help women understand trauma and its impact and to develop coping strategies. It includes a facilitator's guide and a workbook for women, as well as facilitator training videos and a client video.

---

1. More information on the curricula described in this chapter, as well as other gender-responsive and trauma-informed materials for women, can be found on two websites: www.stephaniecovington.com and www.centerforgenderandjustice.org.

The curriculum's 11 sessions cover topics such as the connections between violence, abuse and trauma, reactions to trauma, grounding skills, the mind/body connection and healthy relationships.

The curriculum draws upon psychoeducational, cognitive-behavioural, expressive arts and relational therapeutic approaches to support a strengths-based framework responsive to women's gender-specific needs for healing and support.

This Beyond Trauma curriculum is designed to be used alone or along with the Helping Women Recover curriculum to expand and deepen the trauma work in the Helping Women Recover curriculum.

3   Healing Trauma: Strategies for abused women

This five-session intervention is designed for women who have been abused. There is introductory material on trauma for the facilitator and detailed instructions (specific lesson plans) for the group sessions. The session topics include the process of trauma, power and abuse, grounding and self-soothing and healthy relationships. There is a strong emphasis on grounding skills.

Healing Trauma is an adaptation of Beyond Trauma. It is particularly designed for settings requiring a shorter intervention: short-term addiction treatment, domestic violence agencies, sexual assault services and jails.

The materials (facilitator guide and participant handbook) focus on the three core elements that both staff and clients need to know: an understanding of what trauma is; its process; and its impact on both the inner self (thoughts, feelings, beliefs and values) and the outer self (behaviour and relationships).

4   Voices: A program of self-discovery and empowerment for girls

Voices was created to address the unique needs of adolescent girls and young women (Covington, 2004). It encourages them to seek and celebrate their "true selves" by providing a safe space, encouragement, structure and the support they need to embrace their journeys of self-discovery. The program includes modules on self, connecting with others, healthy living and the journey ahead, which can be delivered in 18 group sessions. Each session has an opening section, a teaching on a topic, an interactive element (discussion of issues, questions, etc.), an experiential component (exercises to try out new skills and learning) and a closing section to facilitate reflection. The program has theoretical foundations in gendered psychological development, attachment, resilience, addiction and trauma. Trauma is addressed in the program both explicitly and implicitly through attention to such issues as self-esteem, connections with others, body image, emotional wellness and good decision-making.

The Voices program is used in many settings (e.g., outpatient and residential substance use treatment, schools, juvenile justice, private practice). It includes a facilitator's guide and a participant's workbook. The participant's journal uses a research-based process called Interactive Journaling. In the context of girls' lives, structured journaling provides an outlet for creativity, personal expression, exploration and application of new concepts and skills.

5   A Woman's Way through the Twelve Steps

A Woman's Way through the Twelve Steps (2003b) includes the original self-help book based on interviews with recovering women about their experiences and understanding of the 12 steps, plus a participant's workbook, a facilitator's guide and a DVD for clients, family members and facilitators who want to learn how women and girls can use the 12 steps in a safe, nurturing way. (Covington, 1999, 2003b, 2009).

When offered as a 13-session program, A Woman's Way through the Twelve Steps includes an opening session followed by one session for each of the 12 steps of Alcoholics Anonymous. It uses interactive exercises to help women understand the principles or themes in each step. Practitioners who participate in A Woman's Way training groups are able to develop a deeper understanding of the basic tools for living that are embedded in the steps.

Learning the Curricula: Staff Development

If a program uses a specific curriculum with women, one of the best ways to train staff, supervisors and administrators is to have them participate in the curriculum themselves as a group. This has been done in a variety of settings, including residential, outpatient and correctional programs. An hour or an hour-and-a-half session can be conducted in a weekly staff meeting or over lunch, with a different staff member facilitating each week. For the program director, these sessions offer a team-building tool and also help to reveal staff members' strengths and challenges.

When planning to implement this process, it is important to be able to explain the differences between a therapy group and the learning (training) group.

TABLE 1

Differences between Training Groups and Therapy Groups

TRAINING GROUP	THERAPY GROUP
Focus is on:	**Focus is on:**
• learning as a group • using the group for experiential learning by means of activities • having support from outside the group (for individual issues) • sequential learning	• individual growth • using the group to recreate family-of-origin dynamics • using the group for support for individual issues • process

Conclusion

Historically, substance use treatment programs were designed for the needs of a predominantly male client population. Over the past three decades, researchers and treatment providers have begun to identify the characteristics and components of successful treatment programs for women. A solid body of knowledge has now been developed that reflects the needs of women in treatment, and there is both a definition of and principles for the development of gender-responsive treatment. Women's exposure to violence has emerged as a critical factor in treatment. Therefore, it is imperative that substance use treatment services become integrated, incorporating what we have learned from relational-cultural theory (women's psychosocial development), addiction theory and trauma theory. A gender-responsive and trauma-informed program can provide the safe, nurturing and empowering environment that women need to find their inner strengths, heal and recover. For both service providers and the women survivors who access services, it is important to understand what trauma is, its process and its impact on thoughts, feelings, beliefs, values, behaviour and relationships. Structured curricula and client workbooks can be helpful in providing such integrated treatment and support.

References

Bond, K., Messina, N. & Calhoun, S. (2010). *Enhancing Substance Abuse Treatment and HIV Prevention for Women Offenders: Final Report*. (Report to the National Institute on Drug Abuse, Grant No. 1 R01 DA022149-01). Unpublished manuscript.

Covington, S. (1999). *A Woman's Way through the Twelve Steps*. Center City, MN: Hazelden.

Covington, S. (2003a). *Beyond Trauma: A Healing Journey for Women*. Center City, MN: Hazelden.

Covington, S. (2003b). *A Woman's Way through the Twelve Steps: Workbook*. Center City, MN: Hazelden.

Covington, S. (2004). *Voices: A Program of Self-Discovery and Empowerment for Girls*. Carson City, NV: The Change Companies.

Covington, S. (2008a). Women and addiction: A trauma-informed approach. *Journal of Psychoactive Drugs* (Suppl. 5), 377–385.

Covington, S. (2008b). *Helping Women Recover: A Program for Treating Addiction* (rev. ed.). San Francisco: Jossey-Bass.

Covington, S. (2009). A Woman's Way through the Twelve Steps: Facilitator Guide and DVD. Center City, MN: Hazelden.

Covington, S. (2011). *Healing Trauma: Strategies for Abused Women.* [CD-ROM]. Center City, MN: Hazelden.

Felitti, V.J. & Anda, R.F. (2010). The relationship of adverse childhood experiences to adult medical disease, psychiatric disorders and sexual behaviour: Implications for healthcare. In R. Lanius, E. Vermetten & C. Pain (Eds.), *The Effects of Early Life Trauma on Health and Disease: The Hidden Epidemic* (pp. 77–87). New York: Cambridge University Press.

Felitti, V.J., Anda, R.F., Nordenberg, D., Williamson, D.F., Spitz, A.M., Edwards, V. et al. (1998). Relationship of childhood abuse and household dysfunction to many of the leading causes of death in adults: The Adverse Childhood Experiences (ACE) study. *American Journal of Preventive Medicine, 14,* 245–258.

Grella, C. (1999). Women in residential drug treatment: Differences by program type and pregnancy. *Journal of Health Care for the Poor and Underserved, 10,* 216–229.

Grella, C., Joshi, V. & Hser, Y. (2000). Program variation in treatment outcomes among women in residential drug treatment. *Evaluation Review, 24,* 364–383.

Harris, M. & Fallot, R. (Eds.). (2001). Using Trauma Theory to Design Service Systems [Special issue]. *New Directions for Mental Health Services, 89.*

Kendall-Tackett, K. (2005). Introduction: Women's experiences of stress and trauma. In K. Kendall-Tackett (Ed.), *Handbook of Women, Stress and Trauma* (pp. 1–5). New York: Brunner-Routledge.

Messina, N., Calhoun, S. & Wanda, N. (in press). Enhanced drug court treatment for women offenders: A randomized experiment. *Criminal Justice and Behavior.*

Messina, N. & Grella, C. (2006). Childhood trauma and women's health outcomes: A California prison population. *American Journal of Public Health, 96,* 1842–1848.

Messina, N., Grella, C., Cartier, J. & Torres, S. (2010). A randomized experimental study of gender-responsive treatment for women in prison. *Journal of Substance Abuse Treatment, 38,* 97–107.

Orwin, R., Francisco, L. & Bernichon, T. (2001). *Effectiveness of Women's Substance Abuse Treatment Programs: A Meta-Analysis.* (NEDS contract no. 270–97–7016). Arlington, VA: Substance Abuse and Mental Health Services Administration, Center for Substance Abuse Treatment.

San Diego Association of Governments. (2007, April). Beyond trauma: Providing trauma-informed services to women in drug treatment. *CJ Bulletin,* 1–11.

United Nations Office on Drugs and Crime. (2004). *Substance Abuse Treatment and Care for Women: Case Studies and Lessons Learned.* New York: United Nations Publications. Retrieved from www.unodc.org/pdf/report_2004-08-30_1.pdf

Chapter 22

Responding to Women's Self-Harm
A 10-Year Reflection on the Need for Trauma-Informed Care

Colleen Anne Dell

> One of the first artworks that Darcie made was a small, stitched train cast in wax; and all around the train there were delicate, red threads sticking out of the wax. She said that when she stopped self-harming, she would remove the threads. Darcie has passed on now, and the train with the threads is still here. . . . She taught us all that we have so much to learn about how to care for each other.[1]

Trauma-informed work with women who need opportunities for healing requires additional considerations when they are engaged in self-harming behaviours. Historically, there has been limited awareness about self-harm. It was not until the 1990s that the media, research studies and the experiences of front-line service providers began to bring awareness to the issue of self-harm, mainly among women and girls. It was around the same time that the need to account for the impact of trauma on women's healing and well-being began to gain attention.

Our current understanding of self-harm is situated for the most part as an individualized problem, reflective of the majority of "cases" having been

---

1. This is a dedication to Darcie Hall from Edith and all the girls and women in the Crossing Communities Art Project and the Elizabeth Fry Society of Manitoba Self-Harm Research Project team. This quote appears in *Community Mobilization for Women and Girls Who Self-Harm: An Environmental Scan of Manitoba Service Providers*, available from http://socserv.socsci.mcmaster.ca/ihrktn/ihrkt-images/Community%20 Mobilization.pdf.

276 Becoming Trauma Informed

encountered within the health care system. The criminal justice system has also notably dealt with self-harming behaviours, particularly among female prisoners. Given that self-harm among women and girls is a recent acknowledgment, and alongside growing understanding about trauma-informed care, there is much to be considered about how the two areas intersect, so that supportive and effective responses are available. A beginning point is prioritizing the wisdom offered from the complex lived experiences of women and girls. Service providers need to consider a women-centred perspective and their own interpretations of trauma in order to better understand self-harming behaviours.

Understanding Self-Harm

In the past decade, self-harm has often been used interchangeably with terms such as self-injury and self-mutilation. Conventionally, this language has imparted descriptions of individuals inflicting visible, physical harm onto their bodies, including slashing, cutting, head banging and bone breaking. There has been misunderstanding about the intent of the behaviour, with people often believing it to be the result of a weak or failed suicide attempt. In response, women's self-harm has historically been met with shock, even repulsion. It has also been widely characterized as manipulative, attention-seeking behaviour. This kind of judgment has translated into disempowering forms of care emphasizing control and punishment, particularly within the medical and criminal justice fields: it leaves clients feeling isolated, stigmatized and shameful, and is contrary to current approaches to trauma-informed care.

Self-injury, as listed in the *Diagnostic and Statistical Manual of Mental Disorders* ([DSM-IV-TR], American Psychiatric Association, 2000), is commonly seen as a symptom of borderline personality disorder. It is also linked with diagnostic categories, including depression, anxiety and addiction —all common diagnoses for women who have experienced DSM-IV-TR–diagnosed trauma. Emerging research over the past decade has challenged solely individualized, medical-based definitions of self-harm. There is also a growing concern that self-harm is increasingly being identified as a symptom of a mental health issue, instead of being viewed primarily as a coping strategy (Kilty, 2006).

A trauma lens recognizes self-harm as a sign of emotional distress, defining it as any behaviour, be it physically, emotionally, socially or spiritually founded, that a woman commits with the intention to cause herself harm. This ranges from physical injury to self-destructive behaviours, including problematic substance use and sexual risk-taking (Adams et al., 2005; Fillmore & Dell, 2001; Huntington, 2001; Kilty, 2006). Self-harm is seen as a coping and survival mechanism for dealing with emotional pain and distress, isolation and oppressive conditions in women's lives, including childhood and adult experiences of abuse and violence (Adams et al., 2005; Fillmore & Dell, 2005; Groves, 2004; Hyman, 1999; McCreary Centre Society, 2006). Although it is unhealthy, self-harm provides women with identifiable coping responses, including a sense of release and cleansing, a means to feel, a sense of control and a way to communicate internal pain (Adams et al., 2005; Fillmore & Dell, 2001; Hyman, 1999; Snow, 2002).

Women who self-harm may have experienced trauma as children or adults: from family substance use problems, dysfunctional family relationships, parental death, partner violence or childhood experiences of abuse and violence (Abrams & Gordon, 2003; Babiker & Arnold, 1997; Borrill et al., 2005; Gladstone et al., 2004; Noll et al., 2003; Turell & Armsworth, 2003; Van der Kolk et al., 1991; Wichmann et al., 2002). Marginalized women, such as those who are incarcerated, may encounter additional factors, including the fear of losing child custody, poor relations with staff and other prisoners, confinement in segregation and general stressful living conditions (Arbour, 1996; Boritch, 2000; Kilty, 2006; Martel, 1999). Contributing factors to self-harm can vary, and are not necessarily rooted in what health care and other practitioners conventionally conceive of as traditional forms of trauma (e.g., direct experience of abuse and violence).

The personal experiences of women I have worked with who self-harmed revealed a breadth and depth of contributing factors. In a course on addictions that I recently taught at the University of Saskatchewan, a student, Jo-Anne [a pseudonym], challenged the traditional conceptualization of self-harm, commenting that her self-harming behaviours were not connected to a brutal act in her childhood or adulthood, but rather, that she was traumatized by her distress and struggle with feelings of disconnection from herself as a teen. She explained:

> Most people ask[ed] me why I would cut myself and my response was that it was the way I could deal with intense emotions, it made me feel better. When you cut yourself, your physiological reaction is that you get a rush of endorphins, like an adrenaline high. I was using the cutting as a coping method to deal with what I later found out to be panic attacks.

The fact that Jo-Anne responded by self-harming stridently communicates the traumatic effects of her lived experience with anxiety, and cutting as a means to cope with her feelings of "going crazy."

The clear message here is that Jo-Anne's experience was traumatic, but not in the way many service providers traditionally conceive of it. Just as the DSM-IV-TR can be criticized for focusing on extreme traumatic events in an individual's life, so too can interpretations of self-harm. Adler and Adler (2007) discuss their research with primarily adult women, commenting how "most people discussed past verbal, physical, or sexual abuse, and some traced their current emotional distress or pain to the relatively common traumas of adolescence, such as peer rejection or parent–sibling favoritism, but others insisted that their childhood had been basically happy" (pp. 541–542). We need to recognize the inherent limitations of our current conceptualizations of what trauma is in women's lives, its relationship to self-harm and its subsequent influence on our responses.

Conceptualizing Trauma

A women-centred perspective recognizes that trauma can occur with less acute/dramatic or direct experiences, such that individual experiences of trauma defy a traditional DSM-IV-TR definition. Recent work on self-harm has highlighted that many "believe or feel that the traumas [experienced in their lives] were not that severe" (Marsh, 2010, p. 3) and conversely that "simply learning about traumatic events carries traumatic potential" (Marsh, 2010, p. 2). First Nations, Métis and Inuit women have experienced historical trauma through a loss of culture as a result of devastating colonial government policies and practices in Canada. These include residential schooling; the "Sixties Scoop," during which Aboriginal children were apprehended and fostered or adopted by middle-class white families; and the Indian Act.

Locust (2000) explains that residential schools and their associated trauma have been a "de-feathering process" that has stripped Aboriginal Peoples of their knowledge, spirituality, physical and emotional well-being and sense of community.

It is necessary for service providers to integrate the historical and contemporary social contexts of women's lives in their conventional perceptions of traumatic life experiences. They need to account for the complexity of women's lives, particularly among those who are marginalized, and address whatever concerns are most immediate for them, whether this be finding employment or housing or coping with child care issues. Problems such as these may present a greater urgency for women than treating *the* traumatic event in their lives. For example, deprivations in housing, nutrition and child care are common in the lives of criminalized women; a criminalized woman is typically young, a mother, poorly educated, under-employed, single or involved in an unstable relationship and a survivor of childhood and/or adult violence.

Adler and Adler (2007) identify physical forms of self-harm as most prevalent among socially vulnerable groups, including youth who are homeless or in foster care, prisoners and individuals who are structurally disadvantaged in society. A 2010 study in the United Kingdom found that young black women were most likely to self-harm, and noted the link between their self-harming and a preponderance of social problems, such as being more likely to be unemployed and report housing problems (Cooper et al., 2010). It is difficult to identify *the* traumatic precursor to women's self-harming behaviour. Trauma may be experienced as a culmination of an individual's direct and indirect lived experiences.

It follows that a woman-centred perspective of self-harm differs from a DSM-IV-TR definition of self-injury, in that the focus is not centred on the perceived threat of death or other serious injury. Current research disputes the long-standing perception that self-harm and suicide attempts are one and the same. It suggests that self-harm and suicide attempts have different intents, etiologies, bodily harms, frequency and methods (Fillmore & Dell, 2005; Harris, 2000; Paul et al., 2002; Vanderhoff & Lynn, 2001; Wichmann et al., 2002). Suicidal acts are oriented toward ending pain and suffering by ending life, while self-harm is viewed as a behaviour that enables women to cope within their lives, albeit in an unhealthy manner (Borrill et al., 2005; Burstow, 1992; Fillmore & Dell, 2001; Vanderhoff & Lynn, 2001).

Controlling and Punitive Responses to Self-Harm and Trauma

In 2001 and 2005, I co-led two research studies in collaboration with Cathy Fillmore of the University of Winnipeg and the Elizabeth Fry Society of Manitoba. These studies emerged from the Elizabeth Fry Society identifying an urgent need to better understand the alarming increase it saw in the number of women involved in the criminal justice system who identified as engaging in self-harm. We examined the supports available to criminalized women who engaged in self-harming behaviours and the responses—both helpful and unhelpful—of service providers in correctional institutions and community settings (Fillmore & Dell, 2001, 2005). We concluded that non-controlling and non-punitive responses were most helpful.

Recent literature and practices on trauma-informed care highlight the need to emphasize empowerment, choice, readiness and prevention planning when working with women with substance use problems (Covington, 2008). However, it is well known that health and correctional staff often continue to respond to women's self-harm with judgment and confusion. Such stigmatization invokes feelings of guilt and shame in the women, which in turn decreases their likelihood of accessing required medical and therapeutic attention, particularly for pregnant and parenting women. A 2007 study of 115 women in Regina, Saskatchewan, who injected drugs concluded that the women had an ongoing fear of having their children apprehended and felt they needed to hide their injection drug use and not access essential health and social services in order to maintain custody of their children (Stadnyk et al., 2007).

In correctional institutions, women's reluctance to disclose physical forms of self-harm is compounded by the fear of punitive responses, such as segregation, as well as being assigned a higher risk-assessment score, which may result in their being housed within a higher security level (Canadian Association of Elizabeth Fry Societies, 2003; Faith, 1993; Fillmore & Dell, 2001; Kilty, 2006; Martel, 1999). Presse and Hart's (1999) study of 26 patients admitted to the Intensive Healing Program at the Prairie Regional Psychiatric Centre in Saskatchewan found that 73 per cent of women engaged in self-injurious behaviour before being admitted and 50 per cent continued afterwards. A more recent study of federally incarcerated women in Canada concluded that the vast majority had engaged in physical self-harming behaviours prior to incarceration and had also attempted suicide (Power, 2010).

A 2010 community forum hosted by the Forensic Behaviour Science and Justice Studies initiative at the University of Saskatchewan addressed prison responses to women's physical self-harm. Correctional, community and academic attendees agreed that increasing security (e.g., restricting visits with children) and isolation (e.g., placement in segregation) among prisoners who self-harm contributes to deterioration in their mental, physical, emotional and spiritual health. Nonetheless, while this meeting was taking place, only a few kilometres away, an imprisoned woman was being restrained to a body board for her 32nd consecutive day because of her self-harming behaviours. She was identified as a threat to the correctional facility and herself. Two interrelated considerations are allowing for such a response—continued misunderstanding of self-harm, which contributes to overly controlling and punitive responses, and the consequent impact of shame associated with self-harming behaviours.

The destructive effects of controlling and punitive responses—based on a misunderstanding of self-harm—is illustrated in *Pictures of Self-Harm*, a film produced by the Crossing Communities Art Project in Winnipeg, Manitoba ([CCAP], 2008). CCAP is a not-for-project organization where artists meet with women and youth on the margins of society to create art for social change. In *Pictures of Self-Harm*, women used video cameras to reflect on their substance use, cutting, the sex trade/sexual exploitation and eating disorders. They interviewed artists, sociologists, prison guards, community members and medical practitioners to explore why women self-harm, how it is responded to and what can be done to help.

The film shares Tonya's experience of the impacts of others' unhelpful responses to her self-harming, especially within the health field. Tonya describes in the film how she felt abandoned and punished in a hospital emergency ward where she went after physically harming herself: "I sat there for three hours. No one was there to help me. They just glared at me like I was taking up space for more important illnesses. I eventually left," she says.

"The only thing I wanted was for someone to put their hand on my head or on my hand and say, 'You know what, you are going to be OK.' That's all I wanted."

A guard with the Winnipeg Remand Centre shared the practice of controlling with physical restraints women who self-harmed:

> It is just this huge plethora of self-harm, and here is me thinking, oh, keep her isolated, keep her safe, you know, put her in the zute suit, to, you know, so she doesn't hurt herself. You know, if we can get all the counsellors kind of trained and understanding of you know, what the whole concept of self-harm is, then I mean at least that is a baby step in the right direction. It's a long way to go from the institutional level.

Jo-Anne's story has a similar controlling theme. She comments,

> In January 2002, I had a complete mental breakdown. I cut my arm up worse then ever before. I looked down and realized that if I did not get help, I may kill myself. I packed a bag and had my friend drive me to the hospital. The doctor didn't want to admit me, but [wanted] to [instead] send me to my original psychiatrist in the morning. I told him he could admit me now or I'd come back in half an hour and he could give me a blood transfusion because I would slit my wrists. By law he had to admit me.

Accounting for the effects of trauma within the women's lives, whether defined narrowly in terms of a violent experience or more broadly and linked with social determinants of health, is overlooked in controlling and punitive responses to women's self-harm. No further explanation is required than consideration of the potential retraumatizing effects of physical restraints on an individual with a history of victimization and who is searching for control through her self-harming behaviour.

Overcoming Misunderstanding:
A Trauma-Informed Approach

Women who self-harm desperately need medical and allied health professionals to understand why they are harming themselves and acknowledge the etiological role of trauma in their coping responses. Client-centred responses are increasingly being recognized in trauma-informed approaches to care. A client-centred approach can assist women who self-harm to overcome internal stigma (e.g., based in feelings of shame and guilt) and external stigma (e.g., based in controlling and punitive responses). For Aboriginal women in Canada, stigma needs to also be understood in the context of women disowning their cultural reality via internalized shame because of external governmental actions (Niccols et al., 2010).

Practitioners also need to abandon patriarchal attitudes that involve punishing women as a way to control what they see as "unfeminine" self-harming behaviours (Dell et al., 2009). This is especially true of the corrections environment, in which punishment is the cornerstone of regulating the institution. It is critical that service providers' responses do not further stigmatize women's behaviour, but that they instead promote acceptance, understanding, compassion, care, respect and support for women's empowerment.

A three-minute stop-motion film, *Stigma, Barriers, Change* (Crossing Communities Art Project, 2009), produced at the 2009 International Custody and Caring Conference workshop, "Implications for Women's Healing from Problematic Substance Abuse," provides some insight. Created under the guidance of the Crossing Communities Art Project, the film made by conference attendees illustrates how stigma, steeped in misunderstanding, acts as a barrier to women accessing services. Key messages included not judging others, caring for everyone, having hope, listening to others, caring for children, loving, overcoming barriers and creating individualized responses.

Another recent project examined the role of stigma and the important skills and traits of treatment providers who work with Aboriginal women healing from illicit drug use. They concluded that treatment providers need to:

- relay empathy for women's struggles
- be accepting of their past behaviours
- inspire them through role modeling
- recognize the role of trauma in their healing
- support non-hierarchical communication with them
- show they care
- support the linkage to spirituality in their healing
- assist them in moving toward the future while acknowledging but not staying "stuck" in the past (Dell et al., 2010).

These skills and traits speak to the need to guide individuals along their healing journeys and not direct and attempt to control them. Service providers also need to support women in the face of the stigma they commonly experience in accessing services.

There are three key ways that service providers can work to understand self-harm, conceptualize trauma and respond in an integrated way.

First, there needs to be increased educational opportunities and training around self-harm for community service providers, hospital personnel and correctional staff. Particular attention should be paid to debunking the myth that self-harm is strictly a form of manipulation or indicative of suicidal intention. Emphasis should also be placed on increasing understanding about the underlying issues associated with self-harm and women's lived contexts. This requires an inclusive understanding of the role of trauma, based on women's understanding. For Aboriginal women, this also requires recognizing intergenerational trauma and culture-based ways of knowing and healing.

Second, research should be undertaken that evaluates access to self-harm treatment and healing approaches, interventions, programs, supports, policies and services, with particular emphasis on those accessed by criminalized women. For example, it would be useful to study the impact of adopting a women-centred policy in correctional facilities that would not "isolate women during crisis and would strive to recognize the voices of the individual women to secure a more individualized approach to 'intervention'" (Kilty, 2006). A study by Messer and Fremouw (2008) affirms the need for models, or integrated models, to best understand and respond to youth self-mutilation.

Finally, as discussed, there is a need to address the destructive impact of stigma on women's access to integrated self-harm and trauma-informed health and social services. Women-centred approaches need to be adopted that recognize the connections between women's experiences of marginalization and disenfranchisement (e.g., poverty, abuse, sexism, colonization) and how these relate to women's criminalization, self-harm and trauma. Multidisciplinary therapeutic approaches that identify self-harm as a sign of emotional distress and contextualize the client as a trauma survivor should be examined. Responses should be directed based on women's readiness and position.

Conclusion

Ideally, addressing these three components will allow us 10 years from now to reflect back on progress we have made toward understanding and effectively responding to women's self-harm. Applying a trauma-informed approach to self-harm would help women deal with the roots of their self-destructive behaviours in non-threatening ways and ultimately live healthier lives. Attention to a trauma-informed approach is particularly important in our current governmental context of increased control and punishment of marginalized individuals in Canada, including women prisoners.

References

Abrams, L. & Gordon, A. (2003). Self-harm narratives of urban and suburban young women. *Affilia, 18,* 429–444. doi: 10.1177/0886109903257668

Adams, J., Rodham, K. & Gavin, J. (2005). Investigating the "self" in deliberate self-harm. *Qualitative Health Research, 15,* 1293–1309. doi: 10.1177/1049732305281761

Adler, P.A. & Adler, P. (2007). The demedicalization of self-injury: From psychopathology to sociological deviance. *Journal of Contemporary Ethnography, 36,* 537–570. doi: 10.1177/0891241607301968

American Psychiatric Association. (2000). *Diagnostic and Statistical Manual of Mental Disorders* (4th ed., text rev.). Washington, DC: Author.

Arbour, L. (1996). *Commission of Inquiry into Certain Events at the Prison for Women in Kingston* (Catalogue No. JS42-73/1996E). Ottawa: Solicitor General of Canada. Retrieved from www.justicebehindthewalls.net/resources/arbour_report/arbour_rpt.htm

Babiker, G. & Arnold, L. (1997). *The Language of Injury: Comprehending Self-Mutilation*. Leicester, UK: British Psychological Society.

Boritch, H. (2000). Women in prison in Canada. In B. Schissel & C. Brooks (Eds.), *Marginality and Condemnation* (pp. 309–328). Halifax, NS: Fernwood.

Borrill, J., Snow, L., Medlicott, D., Teers, R. & Paton, J. (2005). Learning from "near misses": Interviews with women who survived an incident of severe self-harm in prison. *Howard Journal of Criminal Justice, 44*(1), 57–69. doi: 10.1111/j.1468-2311.2005.00355.x

Burstow, B. (1992). *Radical Feminist Therapy: Working in the Context of Violence*. Newbury Park, CA: Sage.

Canadian Association of Elizabeth Fry Societies. (2003). *Submission of the Canadian Association of Elizabeth Fry Societies (CAEFS) to the Canadian Human Rights Commission for the Special Report on the Discrimination on the Basis of Sex, Race and Disability Faced by Federally Sentenced Women*. Retrieved from www.elizabethfry.ca/submissn/specialr/4.htm

Cooper, J., Murphy, E., Webb, R., Hawton, K., Bergen, H., Waters, K. et al. (2010). Ethnic differences in self-harm, rates, characteristics and service provision: Three-city cohort study. *British Journal of Psychiatry, 197*, 212–218. doi: 10.1192/bjp.bp.109.072637

Covington, S. (2008). Women and addiction: A trauma-informed approach. *Journal of Psychoactive Drugs, 40*(Suppl. 5), 377–385.

Crossing Communities Art Project. (Producer) & Regier, E. (Director). (2008). *Pictures of Self-Harm* [video]. Winnipeg, MB.

Crossing Communities Art Project (Producer). (2009). *Stigma, Barriers, Change* [video]. Retrieved from http://lookinginspeakingout.com

Dell, C.A., Fillmore, C.J. & Kilty, J.M. (2009). Looking back 10 years after the Arbour Inquiry: Ideology, policy, practice, and the federal female prisoner. *Prison Journal, 89*, 286–308. doi: 10.1177/0032885509339506

Dell, C., Kilty, J., Fillmore, C., Grantham, S., Lyons, T., Clarke, S. et al. (2010). *Turtle Finding Fact Sheet: The Role of the Treatment Provider in Aboriginal Women's Healing from Illicit Drug Abuse* (Community-Engaged Scholarship for Health, Product ID No. Z3KNXKHD). Retrieved from www.ces4health.info

Faith, K. (1993). *Unruly Women: The Politics of Confinement and Resistance*. Vancouver: Press Gang.

Fillmore, C. & Dell, C. (2001). *Prairie Women, Violence and Self-Harm*. Winnipeg, MB: Elizabeth Fry Society of Manitoba. Retrieved from www.pwhce.ca/pdf/self-harm.pdf

Fillmore, C. & Dell, C. (2005). *Community Mobilization for Women and Girls Who Self-Harm: An Environmental Scan of Manitoba Service Providers*. Winnipeg, MB: Elizabeth Fry Society of Manitoba. Retrieved from http://socserv.socsci.mcmaster.ca/ihrktn/ihrkt-images/Community%20Mobilization.pdf

Gladstone, G., Parker, G., Mitchell, P., Malhi, G., Wilhelm, K. & Austin, M. (2004). Implications of childhood trauma for depressed women: An analysis of pathways from childhood sexual abuse to deliberate self-harm and revictimization. *American Journal of Psychiatry, 161,* 1417–1425.

Groves, A. (2004). Blood on the walls: Self-mutilation in prisons. *Australian and New Zealand Journal of Criminology, 37*(1), 49–64. doi: 10.1375/acri.37.1.49

Harris, J. (2000). Self-harm: Cutting the bad out of me. *Qualitative Health Research, 10,* 164–173. doi: 10.1177/104973200129118345

Huntington, A. (2001). Childhood maltreatment and adult self injury: A woman's account. *Practice: Social Work in Action, 13*(2), 31–42. doi: 10.1080/09503150108411509

Hyman, J.W. (1999). *Women Living with Self-Injury.* Philadelphia: Temple University Press.

Kilty, J. (2006). Under the barred umbrella: Is there room for a women-centred self-injury policy in Canadian corrections? *Criminology and Public Policy, 5*(1), 161–182. doi: 10.1111/j.1745-9133.2006.00107.x

Locust, C. (2000). Split feathers: Adult American Indians who were placed in non-Indian families as children. *Ontario Association of Children's Aid Societies Journal, 44*(3), 11–16.

Marsh, T. (2010). *Enlightenment Is Letting Go! Healing from Trauma, Addiction, and Multiple Loss.* Bloomington, IN: AuthorHouse.

Martel, J. (1999). *Solitude and Cold Storage: Women's Journeys of Endurance in Segregation.* Edmonton, AB: Elizabeth Fry Society of Edmonton.

McCreary Centre Society. (2006). *Self-Harm: Pain from the Inside Out.* Ottawa: Canadian Health Network. Retrieved from www.canadian-health-network.ca

Messer, J. & Fremouw, J. (2008). A critical review of explanatory models for self-mutilating behaviors in adolescents. *Clinical Psychology Review, 28,* 162–178. doi: 10.1016/j.cpr.2007.04.006

Niccols, A., Dell, C. & Clarke, S. (2010). Treatment for Aboriginal mothers with substance use problems and their children. *International Journal of Mental Health and Addiction, 8,* 320–335.

Noll, J.G., Horowitz, L.A., Bonanno, G.A., Trickett, P.K. & Putnam, F.W. (2003). Revictimization and self-harm in females who experienced childhood sexual abuse: Results from a prospective study. *Journal of Interpersonal Violence, 18,* 1452–1471. doi: 10.1177/0886260503258035

Paul, T., Schroeter, K., Dahme, B. & Nutzinger, D.O. (2002). Self-injurious behavior in women with eating disorders. *American Journal of Psychiatry, 159,* 408–411.

Power, J. (2010). *Preliminary Results from the Women's Self-Injurious Behaviour Study* (Emerging Research Results, No. 10-1R). Ottawa: Correctional Service of Canada. Retrieved from www.csc-scc.gc.ca/text/rsrch/smmrs/err/err10-1/docs/err10-1-eng.pdf

Presse, L.D. & Hart, R.D. (1999). Variables associated with parasuicidal behaviors by female offenders during a cognitive-behavioral treatment program. *Canadian Psychology, 40*(2a), 108.

Snow, L. (2002). Prisoners' motives for self-injury and attempted suicide. *British Journal of Forensic Practice, 4*(4), 18–29.

Stadnyk, B., Kennedy, K. & Smith, C. (2007). *Women Who Inject Drugs, Who We Are: The View from Here.* Regina, SK: AIDS Programs South Saskatchewan. Retrieved from http://edocs. lib.sfu.ca/projects/chodarr/documents/chodarr1178.pdf

Turell, S.C. & Armsworth, M.W. (2003). A log-linear analysis of variables associated with self-mutilation behaviors of women with histories of child sexual abuse. *Violence against Women, 9,* 487–512. doi: 10.1177/1077801202250961

Vanderhoff, H. & Lynn, S.J. (2001). Assessment of self-mutilation: Issues and considerations. *Journal of Threat Assessment, 1*(1), 91–109. doi: 10.1300/J177v01n01_07

Van der Kolk, B.A., Perry, J.C. & Herman, J.L. (1991). Childhood origins of self-destructive behavior. *American Journal of Psychiatry, 148,* 1665–1671.

Wichmann, C., Serin, R. & Abracen, J. (2002). *Women Offenders Who Engage in Self-Harm: A Comparative Investigation* (Catalogue no. PS83-3/123E-PDF). Ottawa: Correctional Service of Canada. Retrieved from http://dsp-psd.pwgsc.gc.ca

Chapter 23

A Mother's Loss

The Unacknowledged Grief of Child Apprehension for Women Who Use Substances

Tammy MacKenzie and Amy Druker

A mother's experience of loss, grieving and trauma from having a child apprehended by child welfare authorities often goes unrecognized and unresolved. While grief is the expected emotion following loss and is generally viewed as a "normal" and healthy reaction, little research and few resources exist to help mothers deal with the devastating effects of losing custody of their children to child welfare authorities.

Many women accessing the Pathways to Healthy Families program at the Jean Tweed Centre in Toronto feel a devastating sense of grief when they lose custody of a child to child welfare. This loss is complicated by feelings of shame, helplessness, anger and emotional numbness. The fact that this form of grief is rarely acknowledged as legitimate traps women in their experience of loss and heightens their isolation. The apprehension of a child, while it may be necessary, alters a woman's sense of self and can result in many of the symptoms we have come to recognize as trauma and posttraumatic stress. As noted by Cantwell-Bartl (n.d.), yearning, searching and loneliness are the hallmarks of the anguish of separation. This often runs concurrent with the experience of numbness, disbelief, distrust, anger and a sense of futility about the future.

This chapter describes our experience with "complicated" and potentially traumatic grief with mothers who have lost custody of their children to child welfare. We discuss the gap in services, emerging themes and practical strategies to support these women. We also highlight the effect this work can have on service providers and describe an emerging practice that is based on feedback from bereaved mothers.

Unresolved Grief as Trauma

Unresolved grief as trauma is a new concept in clinical practice. Bringing a trauma-informed perspective to services for women who have lost custody of their children should start with a more formal acknowledgment that the woman may be struggling with parallel manifestations of both grief and trauma. It is also important to recognize that women with trauma histories are more likely to experience subsequent grief as complex trauma (Cantwell-Bartl, n.d.). This is particularly relevant to our work, since more than 80 per cent of the women we see at the Jean Tweed Centre for help with substance use have also experienced trauma.

According to Jacobs (1999), the criteria for traumatic grief must include the death of someone close to the mourner. The apprehension of a child may be seen as a logical extension of this criterion, as a series of losses that have a cumulative effect rather than as a single defining event. Further, we know that people who have experienced grievous loss feel varying degrees of anger, guilt, sadness, depression, hopelessness and numbness (Doka, 1989). In cases of "disenfranchised grief"—that is, when the grief is connected with a loss that cannot be openly acknowledged, publicly mourned or socially supported— these feelings can persist for a very long time.

Unlike a "normal" profound loss, such as the death of a loved one, there are no rituals or rites to facilitate and validate the maternal grieving process involved in a loss of custody: there is no announcement of the loss of custody, no recognition of the loss of the child's place in relation to others, no allowance for public expression of grief, no opportunity for community members to come together to offer empathy and support. Mourners who feel alienated from their community and lack recognition of their loss often experience grief more intensely than they might otherwise have done (Robinson, 2001). Indeed, when feelings are denied, especially when they are cemented in place by shame and fear, they can become more powerful.

In recent years, our Toronto-based community partners have identified gaps in services for women dealing with custodial loss. The participation of bereaved mothers in research conducted by the South Riverdale Community Health Centre (Bannerman et al., 2009), has deepened our understanding of common themes that underline the ways in which women's grief mirrors trauma responses.

In 2006, the Young Parents with No Fixed Address Committee of Toronto commissioned a study on service interventions and gaps in services for women who have lost custody of their children. A literature review and interviews with health practitioners found that women who experience custody loss/apprehension are likely to be vulnerable and disadvantaged mothers, often marginalized because of poverty, socio-economic status, race, mental health and substance use problems and immigration status (Novac et al., 2006). Perhaps not by coincidence, the women who experience this type of unacknowledged and often unresolved grief are primarily an invisible population of women whose voices are often silenced. In Canada, poor women, Aboriginal women and women of colour are the most vulnerable to arrest, child apprehension and poor health outcomes (Boyd & Marcellus, 2007).

Mirroring Trauma Responses

The need for a trauma-informed perspective to support women through and beyond the loss of child custody is highlighted by the women's descriptions of their feelings and behaviours. The following common trauma-like responses emerged from the stories shared in research conducted on grief and loss with women who experienced child custody loss (Bannerman et al., 2009).

Numbing/self-punishment: As a coping strategy, women increased their drug use to manage feelings of shame, guilt, "dead aloneness" or isolation, loneliness, hopelessness, pain and anger. Self-punishing behaviours, including unsafe drug use and lifestyles and even deliberately putting oneself in harm's way, were common responses to the shame and pain associated with child apprehension. In the words of one woman:

> It f***** me up for years [when my child was taken into care]. I was on another planet for the next five years. I was devastated. I pretty much tried to kill myself for the next five years. No one checked on me afterward.

Powerlessness: Feeling powerless was associated with many situations, including the absence of supportive services for bereaved mothers. Women also described feeling separate from the legal process after their children were apprehended. Court dates come and go, and some mothers are left feeling like they were not involved in the process. According to another woman:

> We are ants facing an elephant. We are women who have survived abuse, poverty, lack of parenting role models and have been negatively labelled by society.

Betrayal: Women reported having confided in their child welfare worker, only to have the information used in proceedings against them. This leaves them wondering who "their worker" is.

Silencing: The vast majority of women whose children have been apprehended are assigned a legal aid representative. While some of these lawyers may be very committed, they are not always informed or able to meet with clients before their first appearance in court to explain the legal proceedings and to ask for their directives. As a result, women feel they do not have a voice in legal proceedings, which determine, among other things, the nature and extent of access to their children.

Shame: As discussed earlier, society continues to judge some mothers as not fit to parent. The court process of custodial loss can be very humiliating; not only are the women's parenting skills being called into question, but also their lifestyles. These judgments may be internalized and women begin to doubt their ability to parent.

Unrealistic expectations: For mothers to regain custody, they must respond to a barrage of expectations (e.g., urine screens, hair strand tests, mental health assessments, substance use treatment, supervised access visits). They may be required to attend programs; however, lengthy waitlists, lack of transportation and other barriers associated with poverty make it more difficult for women to meet all of the requirements. In the process, they likely do not feel in control of what is happening and feel excluded from decisions about what it is they actually need.

Feeling "dead alone": These were the words a woman used to describe her experience of losing custody of her child. When a child is made a Crown ward with no access for the purposes of adoption, the mother will often ask for photographs and updates. However, once a child is adopted, the adoptive parents are under no legal obligation to provide any information. Birth mothers are often left feeling alone, isolated, angry, confused, ashamed and utterly devastated.

Strategies to Minimize the Trauma of Apprehension

Schachter et al. (2009) developed nine principles of sensitive practice for health care practitioners supporting adult survivors of childhood sexual abuse. These principles parallel support strategies for women who have lost custody of their children to child welfare.

1. **Nurture respect:** Mistrust of professionals is common. It is important to acknowledge and validate this response; in so doing, trust may develop.

2. **Take time:** Spend time listening. Women want to feel genuinely heard and valued. Offer your time to participate in meetings with child welfare workers, doctors, nurses and other professionals as a support/advocate. Help women obtain a legal aid certificate; accompany them to court/legal appointments if they think this is helpful.

3. **Establish rapport:** This is a very difficult time for a mother; she can often feel alone and like she is "just another client." Stay connected to her, even when she finds it hard to connect. Many service providers withdraw support when there is no longer a child involved. It is important to stay involved with the woman before, during and after she gives birth, regardless of whether the child is in her care.

4. **Share information:** Provide practical, non-judgmental information about substance use, pregnancy and parenting. With pregnant women, explore what they want in terms of their birth plan and substance use (whether it is abstinence, safer use or reduction) and parenting goals. Provide information and referrals to community resources. It is important to help women feel they have choices. Demonstrating your belief that they know best what they need may be the most helpful service you provide.

5. **Share control:** When a referral to child welfare is deemed necessary, it is important, whenever possible, to involve the mother in a discussion and support her in making the call herself where possible. If the woman is pregnant (especially if she has had previous child apprehensions), ensure that a plan is in place before the birth. If an apprehension is going to happen, explore how the woman would feel best supported through the process. Who should be present when the baby is taken into care? How soon after the apprehension will she have access to her child? If this is an apprehension at birth and the mother has identified parenting as her goal, advocate with hospital staff and child welfare authorities a plan that supports the bonding of mother and child immediately following birth. Explore alternative parenting arrangements as appropriate. Does the mother have family or friends who might be willing to care for the child as an interim measure, or longer if necessary?

6. **Respect boundaries:** Women must be aware of your limits to confidentiality and how their information may or may not be shared. Giving women some choice at the outset about how information is shared will go a long way in building trust and minimizing feelings of betrayal.

7. **Foster mutual learning:** This will be a difficult time for both the woman and you as a helping professional. Every woman's experience is different and support needs will vary. Being honest about your knowledge of the process and your potential areas for learning can help to foster a relationship with the mother in which she feels like she has a "partner" in the process.

8. **Understand non-linear healing:** Just as women's experiences of losing child custody will be different, so will their healing processes. Women will have varying degrees of tolerance for support and treatment. Support women to share with you how they are feeling, if they are ready and interested in treatment and what type of services they feel would be most beneficial.

9. **Demonstrate knowledge about interpersonal violence:** Promote a collaborative and trauma-informed response with other service providers involved with the mother and child.

Effects of Child Apprehension on Service Providers

According to Novac et al. (2006), service providers who work with women whose children have been apprehended are often affected by the intensity of this work and the implications of their actions, sometimes triggering their own experiences with grief, loss and trauma. This has sometimes been referred to as vicarious trauma (McCann & Pearlman, 1990). Service providers may face various challenges:

Tension/role conflict: Service providers who work with mothers face their own stress, including a tension between service provision and the duty to report harm to a child. They often report feeling conflicted about when to refer to child welfare services. This situation is always difficult and may affect the relationship mothers have with service providers.

Uncertainty/lack of clarity: There are definite grey areas involved when working with mothers whose children have been apprehended. One of these can be the range of responses from child welfare in relation to substance use. The use of cannabis is one example where views differ; alcohol use is sometimes treated differently than illicit use of other drugs, and prescription drug use may also be viewed differently.

Stress: Role conflict between service providers can cause tension and stress. Although child welfare and support workers hope to work collaboratively, differences in mandate sometimes make it difficult to achieve a collaborative response.

Stretched: With limited funding and resources, many service providers, including child welfare workers, are dealing with increased caseloads and more onerous documentation requirements. They may feel stretched by these demands, which may be reflected in their interactions with mothers, other service providers and their own families.

Emotional response: When there is a close working relationship with a woman and she loses her child, we empathize with her pain and may feel the loss of our own relationship with the child. Service providers who are not aware of their own emotional response and who do not have access to clinical supervision may become cynical, harsh or burned out. This may manifest itself in stress-related illness (Schmid, as cited in Novac et al., 2006, p. 30). Schmid recommended that service providers address the following questions to prepare them to deal with their clients and their own grief:

- How do I help my clients recognize their pain and work through this?
- How does their pain affect me?
- Is there grief and loss for me as a support worker, and what do I do about it?
- What is our agency doing to enable and equip me to deal with my response to the losses our clients have encountered?

Creating a Space for Women to Use Their Voices

The catalyst for a new partnership program between the Jean Tweed Centre and the South Riverdale Community Health Centre was a 2009 research project, in which women were invited to share their experiences of losing child custody. Women said that this project marked the first time they had been invited to share their stories about apprehension. It was also their first opportunity to explain how they felt during and after the loss and what they needed now to carry on. One participant described having searched for services to address her grief and trauma for the past 16 years. Almost all of the women spoke of a critical need for programs in this area and said that they would participate if such programs existed.

After extensive study of the women's responses, a 15-week pilot group was proposed—the Grief and Loss Education and Action Group. The goal was to provide an opportunity for women to speak and to be heard and acknowledged around experiences of grief, loss and resilience—one mother to another. The group was organized around the central themes of telling stories, building on and learning new coping strategies, consciousness-raising, creating art and taking social action, which included engaging in a dialogue with child welfare representatives to support a shift in practice toward a harm reduction philosophy (Kenny & Druker, 2011).

The Grief and Loss Education and Action Group recently completed a third cycle and is into the fourth cycle. Women from the first, second and third groups continue to meet once a month to support one another and advance their work on action-oriented goals. In response to women's ideas of wanting to raise awareness among service providers about this under-recognized form of grief, women were trained in public speaking and have used this new skill to educate service providers, social work students and women living in the shelter system who may have had similar experiences.

Conclusion

Given the judgment that pregnant and parenting women who use substances face in society, it is not surprising that the grief/trauma response to child apprehension is complicated for both the mothers and those who work with them. Service providers have much work to do to bring attention to this under-recognized form of grief. We must shift how we engage women who use substances toward an approach that respects and acknowledges women's grief and expertise—the skills and knowledge they have gained in their lives in responding to the effects of trauma. Women need to feel understood and that they are valued collaborators. In this way, service providers and women together can turn angst into action.

Many thanks to the women whose life experiences inspired this chapter.

References

Bannerman M., Kenny K. & Judge C. (2009). *Women and CAS: Experiences of Grief and Loss.* Toronto: South Riverdale Community Health Centre.

Boyd, S.C. & Marcellus, L. (Eds.). (2007). *With Child: Substance Use during Pregnancy. A Woman-Centred Approach.* Halifax, NS: Fernwood.

Cantwell-Bartl, A. (n.d.). *Is This Person Suffering Grief or Trauma or Traumatic Grief?* Retrieved from www.cismfa.org.au/pdf/CantwellBartl.pdf

Doka, K.J. (1989). *Disenfranchised Grief: Recognizing Hidden Sorrow*. Lexington, MA: Lexington Books.

Jacobs, S. (1999). *Traumatic Grief: Diagnosis, Treatment and Prevention*. New York: Bruner/Mazel.

Kenny, K. & Druker, A. (2011). "Ants facing an elephant": Mothers' grief, loss, and work for change following the placement of children in care of child protection authorities. In D. Barrett (Ed.), *Children of the Drug War: Perspectives on the Impact of Drug Policies on Young People* (pp. 151–170). New York: International Debate Education Association.

McCann, I.L. & Pearlman, L.A. (1990). Vicarious traumatization: A framework for understanding the psychological effects of working with victims. *Journal of Traumatic Stress, 3*(1), 131–149.

Novac, S., Paradis, E., Brown, J. & Morton, H. (2006). *A Visceral Grief: Young Homeless Mothers and Loss of Child Custody* (Research Paper 206). Toronto: Centre for Urban and Community Studies, University of Toronto.

Robinson, E. (2001). *Adoption and loss: The hidden grief*. Retrieved from www.ccnm-mothers.ca/English/articles/Robinson.htm

Schachter, C.L., Stalker, C.A., Teram, E., Lasiuk, G.C. & Danilkewich, A. (2009). *Handbook on Sensitive Practice for Health Practitioners: Lessons from Adult Survivors of Childhood Sexual Abuse*. Ottawa: Public Health Agency of Canada.

PART 3

SECTION 2: INNOVATION

Chapter 24

Collaboration between Child Welfare and Substance Use Services

Diane Smylie and Carolyn Ussher

Traditionally, the mandates of child welfare services and services for women with substance use problems have been viewed as competing, with child welfare focusing on the children and the substance use sector focusing on the women, making the two services incompatible. For the many women[1] and children who have had traumatic experiences and who are involved with both sectors, this polarization can contribute to further traumatization.

This chapter explores how collaboration between the child welfare and substance use fields is a trauma-informed practice. A broader, interconnected understanding of child safety and the impact of trauma on parents can lead to better outcomes for both children and women involved with substance use and child welfare services. The chapter focuses on what this collaboration means for service delivery and policies in both sectors and on the corresponding need for collaboration at the practitioner, organizational and system levels.

The Context

The link between a history of trauma and problematic substance use has been well documented in the literature and is captured in other chapters in this book. However, this link is often not reflected in service responses for women

---

1. While this chapter focuses on collaboration as it relates to services for mothers, there is also a need to think about how services can respond to the needs of fathers or male partners with a history of trauma.

who are involved with child welfare and substance use services. In the Canadian Incidence Study of Reported Child Abuse and Neglect, Trocme et al. (2005) noted that in substantiated child maltreatment cases, alcohol and other drugs were identified in 14 to 18 per cent of cases involving female caregivers and 17 to 30 per cent of cases involving male caregivers. In the United States, it is estimated that 50 to 80 per cent of parents involved in the child welfare system have substance use problems (Child Welfare League of America, 1998, as cited in Marsh & Cao, 2005, p. 1262). Given this situation, it is important to understand the links among trauma, substance use and involvement with child welfare and find ways to support multi-burdened women as they negotiate these two systems of service and attempt to provide a healthy environment for their children.

A growing body of literature illustrates the connection between early childhood trauma and changes in brain development. "Research suggests that too much negative stimulation (in the form of abuse) or too little positive stimulation (in the form of neglect) can both upset the delicate balance between higher and lower regions in the young brain" (Perry, 1997, p. 13). This imbalance contributes to various problems, including difficulties coping with environmental stressors (Mustard & Cynader, 1997). Neglect and abuse put the child on a "chronic alert for danger," and "as that child grows older, any perceived threat in the environment, however slight, may cause a powerful surge of stress hormones through all body systems, which greatly reduces the individual's capacity to cope with challenges" (Mustard & Cynader, 1997, p. 13). People who experience childhood trauma are at a higher risk of adopting unsafe coping behaviours, which include problematic substance use (National Executive Training Institute, 2005).

Parents—both mothers and fathers—may have had child welfare involvement over the course of their lives. A traumatic experience, such as having been removed from their own parents' care as children, can increase the complexity and stress of their current interactions with child welfare and should be considered by both child welfare and substance use service providers when developing service responses. This is an example of how retraumatization in the course of interactions with child welfare has the potential to increase the risk of unsafe substance use, which may in turn affect child safety and well-being. For many people who have experienced trauma, the very presence of child welfare, no matter how well-intentioned, can trigger shame and humiliation when they feel that their parenting and lifestyle are under investigation, and they may respond aggressively in response to these feelings (National Executive Training Institute, 2005). Such responses are often misunderstood by child welfare workers and can be seen as "resistance" or "lack of insight," further complicating the situation and increasing stress.

Overall, the real or perceived threat of losing custody of a child creates a situation of "power over" parents that would be very difficult for most people to manage, and for those with histories of trauma, can trigger responses related to past situations over which they had no control and were overwhelmed. The stress that parents experience in their interactions with child welfare may result in a return to previous or more risky patterns of substance use that can in turn undermine their parenting capacity and custody goals. Acknowledging the power imbalance and the related potential for retraumatization is a central step in developing approaches that are supportive rather than coercive or punitive.

Issues related to trauma and child welfare are compounded for mothers. Not only are women more likely to have frequent child welfare involvement related to their substance use, but also the stigma directed to pregnant and parenting women who have problems with substances remains firmly entrenched (Greaves & Poole, 2005). The presence of child welfare, combined with a trauma history and a fear of losing children, places women at high risk for acute trauma responses and more chaotic substance use (Greaves et al., 2004).

It is because of this context that the child welfare and substance use services must collaborate in a way that ensures that the mother (parental)/child relationship remains at the centre of service planning and communication. However, despite this clear need for collaboration, achieving it has often been challenging (Drabble & Poole, 2011).

Collaboration as a Trauma-Informed Approach

Family preservation, child safety, healing from trauma and trauma prevention are interconnected goals for women accessing both child welfare and substance use services. While these two sectors have historically operated separately, some jurisdictions are now moving to a more collaborative, integrated approach.

Through collaboration, dialogue and knowledge exchange, substance use and child welfare service systems can work toward integrated service delivery that minimizes the risk for further trauma and promotes healing for parents with trauma histories. This is key to helping parents meet their custody goals and support the development of safer family environments for their children.

Implications for Direct Service in the Substance Use Field

Three-way communication: When working with a woman seeking assistance for a substance use problem, the service provider can discuss the benefits of three-way communication among the client, the substance use counsellor and the child welfare worker. Two benefits are the opportunity to report strengths and progress to child welfare rather than only reporting child-related risks as required by legislation, and to support and advocate for the parent throughout the child welfare process. While it may be difficult at the outset to explain the concept of open communication between the sectors, this is an important step toward service co-ordination that can improve outcomes for both child and mother. In some cases, child welfare may contact the substance use clinician first and, with signed consents, discussion can inform the substance use assessment and service planning. Child welfare often has a wealth of information that can help to support caregivers and children.

Support for parenting: Mothers involved in child welfare are often understandably anxious about their children and the threat of losing custody. Understanding this anxiety and working collaboratively to support parenting that enhances safety and well-being of the children gives parents a sense of competence. The service provider has an opportunity to help normalize parental reactions and educate parents about how trauma responses may be playing a role in coping and parenting. It is important for substance use counsellors to be open to hearing about child functioning and safety and how the parent's substance use and other coping behaviours may affect parenting and hence the child's safety.

Seamless, supportive planning: When service plans are co-ordinated and inform one another, care and support is neither disjointed nor adversarial. Safety plans for both mother and child can be negotiated in a way that minimizes fear and shame and supports the mother's engagement. Conversely, lack of communication among child welfare, substance use services and the client can result in blind advocacy for the mother (or child), which reinforces maternal feelings of powerlessness, limits healing and compromises safety for both mother and child.

Reducing the potential for retraumatization through advocacy: Professionals working in the substance use sector can act as allies in the child welfare journey by attending case conferences and helping the client to process child welfare information. If there is concern about the child having been exposed to potentially traumatic situations, child welfare may recommend a trauma assessment for the child and a co-ordinated approach with the parent. In some situations, trauma may affect attachment and development, and service providers can lend their expertise to encourage interventions that collaboratively support the mother and child.

An example of this trauma-informed, collaborative work in action is the Pathways to Healthy Families program based at the Jean Tweed Centre in Toronto. A comprehensive day program, specifically for women and their children, is offered, as well as various outreach components. Representatives from child welfare agencies in Toronto were consulted during the development of the seven-week day program. The program provides an opportunity to address attachment, parenting and substance use concerns. One objective that was identified through the development process is improved relationships between child welfare and participating women. Two program components promote this objective: a mid-point meeting between participants and their child welfare workers, where women are encouraged to speak about their progress; and a workshop with a child welfare staff member, where women can consult with someone other than their worker and question policies, options and rights without discussing their specific relationships and history with child welfare. This program has extremely high satisfaction and retention rates.

System-Level Collaboration for Trauma-Informed Child Welfare and Substance Use Services

Although trauma-informed service planning and policy developments have not always been the stated goal underlying collaboration, the corresponding shift away from a siloed approach has promoted a range of trauma-informed services. The following section describes how child welfare and substance use service systems in Toronto have built collaborative bridges that have expanded and strengthened trauma-informed practice.

For more than 25 years, the Jean Tweed Centre has been providing substance use programming for women. In the course of the agency's development, it became apparent that women seeking assistance with their substance use were often dealing with a history of trauma and child welfare involvement. In response, the centre began designing a trauma-informed service that focuses on supporting mothers and their children. This has involved ongoing learning about the effects of trauma, particularly women's concerns about their parenting abilities as the consequence of growing up in unsafe and non-nurturing environments themselves.

A growing awareness of the relationship between trauma, substance use and mothering became the impetus to connect with local service providers in the allied fields of children's mental health, child development and child welfare. Dialogue between these stakeholders about the need for more integrated ways of working in partnership led to the development of Breaking the Cycle, a program for substance-using pregnant women and new mothers and their children in downtown Toronto.

When funding became available through the province's Early Childhood Development Addictions Initiative (ECDAI), stakeholders worked with the Jean Tweed Centre to develop an expanded model of service, which included forming an outreach counselling service in partnership with various community-based agencies and child development and child care services. Through this initiative, the centre also began to work closely with the child welfare sector in a service co-ordination capacity and provide training to child welfare workers on topics such as problematic substance use, harm reduction, trauma, parenting and stigma. To support cross-sectoral training, regular consultation sessions were arranged with two local child welfare agencies. Every six weeks, supervisors from the Children's Aid Society of Toronto and the Catholic Children's Aid Society of Toronto provided consultation to staff working with mothers involved in child welfare. These consultations yielded insights into the concerns and perspectives of child welfare and served as a front-line forum for dialogue that encouraged a better understanding of sector-specific mandates and how these shaped service delivery.

Knowledge exchange was further supported by ECDAI funding of an annual conference for Ontario service providers, featuring speakers and workshops on issues related to substance use, parenting and child development. Another initiative developed through the ECDAI was the collaborative development of *Practice Guidelines between Toronto Substance Abuse Treatment Agencies and Children's Aid Societies* (Working Group, 2005). This marked the first time that representatives of all four of the city's child welfare agencies worked collaboratively with staff from five substance use service agencies to develop a policy document.

A significant contribution to embracing a collaborative climate was the intro-duction of the Transformation Agenda 2005 (Ministry of Children and Youth Services, 2005) to the child welfare sector in Ontario. This policy supported a move away from service delivery that focused primarily on risk and deficits to a system that supports a flexible approach to child welfare and linkages across systems. Key in this approach is the differential response model that emphasizes focusing on strengths and needs, identifying community resources and engaging families voluntarily in supportive child welfare service. It strengthens the working relationship between the child welfare and substance use service sectors and sets the stage for improved collaboration and service provision, consistent with a trauma-informed approach. In taking a more holistic approach to supporting and engaging women with substance use problems, this approach facilitates improved understanding of how trauma may be shaping current interactions with child welfare, parenting and substance use services. This understanding is the foundation of a more compassionate and helpful approach on the part of all systems of care in a position to assist parents.

Funding to achieve the goals of the Transformation Agenda supported the Jean Tweed Centre and the Centre for Addiction and Mental Health to work with child welfare to deliver Strengthening Families for the Future,[2] a prevention program for families affected by substance use and/or mental health issues. This collaboration has provided a unique opportunity for child welfare staff to co-facilitate a strengths-based, trauma-informed drug prevention program with service providers from the substance use treatment sector.

More recently, the Ministry of Children and Youth Services has funded a three-pronged initiative that supports:

1. the introduction to children's aid societies (CAS) of a Jean Tweed Centre substance use consultant who accompanies child welfare staff to client meetings in the community and provides case consultation and team-based training to intake staff

2. the collaborative development of child welfare practice guidelines for intake

3. provincial online training on substance use problems and addiction for child welfare service providers.

In all three projects, trauma-informed care in a child welfare context has been identified as a central theme. It was included as a module in the online training and a principle in the practice guidelines and was integrated throughout consultations and training for CAS intake.

The collaboration in Toronto has been the product of many people and organizations understanding the need to move toward a shared philosophy and values to better serve women and their families. It has led to a cross-sectoral system that is much more responsive, staffed by managers and service providers who have a far deeper understanding of how trauma often affects the families with whom they work. Moreover, the collaboration has equipped front-line workers with the tools to increase child safety in a way that values and supports healing for parents who themselves grew up in unsafe environments. This movement has occurred slowly over the past two decades. It has required all those involved to stretch and challenge themselves,

2. Strengthening Families for the Future is a 14-week manualized program, updated with input from Ontario treatment agencies from the original Strengthening Families program designed by Karol Kumpfer. See www.camh.ca/en/education/about/camh_publications/Pages/strengthen_families.aspx

to be willing to engage in dialogue, to find ways of building bridges to connect and support mandates that were once deemed incompatible. Further progress requires continued commitment and expanded implementation of trauma-informed practices.

Conclusion

When trauma-informed support for women with substance use problems and safety for women and their children are understood to be interconnected, service responses can avoid contributing to further traumatization. When services, program design and policy practices recognize how traumatic experiences can shape interactions with the child welfare and substance use systems, we can not only reduce risks to women and children, but also promote opportunities for attachment and healing.

The efforts made in Toronto are a model of how trauma-informed practices can bridge the seemingly disparate mandates of child welfare and substance services for women. While the model may not be replicable in other jurisdictions with different community contexts, it can provide ideas and inspiration for improving trauma-informed collaboration between these two sectors.

References

Drabble, L. & Poole, N. (2011). Collaboration between addiction treatment and child welfare fields: Opportunities in a Canadian context. *Journal of Social Work Practice in the Addictions, 11*, 124–149.

Greaves, L., Pederson, A., Varcoe, C., Poole, N., Morrow, M., Johnson, J. et al. (2004). Mothering under duress: Women caught in a web of discourses. *Journal of the Association for Research on Mothering, 6*(1), 16–27.

Greaves, L. & Poole, N. (2005). Victimized or validated? Responses to substance-using pregnant women. *Canadian Woman Studies, 24*(1), 87–92.

Marsh, J.C. & Cao, D. (2005). Parents in substance abuse treatment: Implications for child welfare practice. *Children and Youth Services Review, 27*, 1259–1278.

Ministry of Children and Youth Services. (2005). *Child Welfare Transformation 2005: A Strategic Plan for a Flexible, Sustainable and Outcome Oriented Service Delivery Model.* Ottawa: Author.

Mustard, F. & Cynader, M. (1997, Spring). Brain development, competence and coping skills. *Entropy, 1*(1), 5–6.

National Executive Training Institute. (2005). *Training Curriculum for Reduction of Seclusion and Restraint. Draft Curriculum Manual.* Alexandria, VA: National Association of State Mental Health Program Directors, National Technical Assistance Center for State Mental Health Planning.

Perry, B.D. (1997). Incubated in terror: Neurodevelopmental factors in the "cycle of violence." In J.D. Osofsky (Ed.), *Children in a Violent Society.* New York: Guilford.

Trocme, N., Fallon, B., MacLaurin, B., Daciuk, J., Felstiner, C., Black, T. et al. (2005). *Child Incidence Study of Reported Child Abuse and Neglect–2003: Major Findings.* Ottawa: Minister of Public Works and Government Services.

Working Group for Practice Guidelines between Toronto Substance Abuse Treatment Agencies and Children's Aid Societies. (2005). *Practice Guidelines between Toronto Substance Abuse Treatment Agencies and Children's Aid Societies.* Retrieved from www.jeantweed.com/ LinkClick.aspx?fileticket=iHuc39ECglQ%3D&tabid=107&mid=514

Chapter 25

What Do Client Rights Have to Do with Trauma-Informed Care?

Jennifer Chambers

Abuse and other experiences of trauma are about violations: of our bodies, our minds, our basic human needs, our choices. There is considerable evidence that most people attending mental health facilities are survivors of abuse (Cusack et al., 2003; Firsten, 1991; Rose, 1991; Weaver et al., 1994) and that abuse survivors have a high likelihood of developing an addiction (Bryer et al., 1987; Rose, 1991). One might reasonably expect that mental health services would be structured to acknowledge and address this reality. Yet mental health service providers typically ignore people's trauma histories (Firsten, 1991; Frueh et al., 2001; Weaver et al., 1994). This is particularly true of people labelled "seriously mentally ill" (Bryer et al., 1987), who are most likely to spend time in a psychiatric institution and for whom a history of trauma is often disregarded, as if they are "too sick" for that to be significant (Grubaugh et al., 2011).

This failure to grasp the need for trauma-informed care has meant that treatment services fail to acknowledge that they themselves can be traumatizing (Cusack et al., 2003; Nibert et al., 1989). As a result, rights that could protect clients from further trauma are often seen as interfering with care. In fact, client rights are essential to any good care, especially trauma-informed service.

Rights are about who gets to exercise power and control over a person or group and the resources they need. People with trauma histories have experienced a loss of control over their own lives, and service providers need to be aware of how their approach to care can be experienced by clients as another traumatizing experience—yet another context where control is not in their hands.

Rights are about boundaries that protect individuals from harm. Recognizing and respecting client rights can be seen as a guide to creating a safe environment, without which nothing good can happen.

For decades, clients and their supporters have been describing how mental health services can be frighteningly coercive. Only now has this reality begun to be recognized. In the systemic overemphasis on the medical model approach to treatment, people's life experiences and how these interact with their environment are often treated as irrelevant. Self-identified needs are eclipsed by the expectation that clients comply with medical instructions, despite evidence that self-identified needs are a better predictor of good outcomes and that empowerment promotes recovery (Crane-Ross et al., 2006; Roth & Crane-Ross, 2002).

The Empowerment Council

The evolution of trauma-informed care at the Centre for Addiction and Mental Health (CAMH) rests on a foundation of client empowerment. Change that affects individuals who access health care services does not occur in a vacuum; it needs support at a policy level, including commitment to an organizational culture that respects client rights and input. To guide the process of creating a healing space, there needs to be an independent voice that both represents and is accountable to the people that services are intended to help. The establishment of the Empowerment Council at CAMH in 2001 and the subsequent development of the CAMH Bill of Client Rights illustrate the convergence of trauma-informed care and fundamental principles promoting informed choice, safety and self-determination.

The Empowerment Council is an independent, client-run organization. Members, the board and staff are current or former clients of mental health and/or addiction services. In the early 1990s, the Ontario government directed all of the psychiatric hospitals in the province to set aside funding to create and sustain their own patient councils. Each council was intended to be a voice for the people on the receiving end of these hospital services. After two mental health and two addiction facilities in Toronto were merged into the Centre for Addiction and Mental Health, CAMH decided that it needed a voice to represent clients at all four sites. (Previously only the Queen Street Mental Health Centre had an organization representing clients, known as the Queen Street Patients' Council.) In March 2001, people with personal experience of the mental health and addiction systems met to decide on the mission and purpose of their new organization and to elect representatives from among themselves to move this mission forward. In time, the organization was named the Empowerment Council.

Historically, the rights of users of health care services and the approach of service providers have seemed to be at odds with each other. The creation of the Empowerment Council was a means for clients to have their own voice. One of the most important things clients have had to say involves the impact of traumatic experience. If this were really heard and understood, it would fundamentally change the way mental health facilities operate.

How Trauma-Informed Care Converged with Client Rights

In 2005, the CAMH Bill of Client Rights was created to "emphasize the rights of clients rather than organizational convenience" (Centre for Addiction and Mental Health, 2005, Preamble). Throughout the three-and-a-half year process of developing it, the Empowerment Council consulted extensively with CAMH clients, negotiated with CAMH on behalf of all of the people who use its services, then went back to clients with the organization's response on each proposed right. Each of the 10 rights is based on actual client experiences: CAMH took seriously clients' rendition of their bad experiences and their suggestions on how to remedy problems through the bill.

The discussion process highlighted the vulnerability of people interacting with a psychiatric institution when it comes to respect for basic human rights. Initially, there was some debate about whether to follow the tradition of many hospitals and create a "rights and responsibilities" document. The Empowerment

Council pointed out that no other oppressed group has responsibilities attached to its rights. Do women get equal pay for equal work only if they also do the dishes? Rights are meant to rebalance inequity; they are not privileges that must be earned. It was particularly important to clarify this point, given that basic human needs have often been treated as "privileges" in the environment of a psychiatric institution. The bill also went beyond the 10 vague "motherhood" statements that often comprise hospital bills of patient rights. Clients stated, and CAMH agreed, that in order to be meaningful, rights need to be specific.

There was lively discussion about such concerns as whether the word "rights" should be changed. It was suggested that the word "rights" is too confrontational (as it supported clients having expectations about how they deserved to be treated), and that this could interfere with staff goals requiring clients to compromise these same rights: for example, a voluntary client gave up her right to go outside because she was threatened with a withdrawal of all services if she did not comply. The Empowerment Council asked whether anyone would find this idea acceptable if it were applied to the rights of another group of oppressed people. Should rights related to racial discrimination be removed in order not to interfere with compromises sought by white people? The question was also asked why patients should have rights when staff does not have rights. A CAMH human resources professional pointed out that this was a ridiculous statement; staff does have rights: it has a collective agreement. It helps to have champions among the powerful.

In another instance, a senior physician said that there was no need to include the right not to be abused "because it never happens." A CAMH manager openly disagreed, observing that abuse does occur, and that is why CAMH needs the Empowerment Council and the bill. "The right to be free from physical, sexual, verbal, emotional and financial abuse" has been enshrined in Right #2: Right to freedom from harm. The development of the bill provided opportunities for these kinds of ethically inconsistent perspectives to come forward and be addressed. Clearly, it is far better that the rights of clients be sorted out in boardrooms than having to be fought for by vulnerable people alone on a ward.

If a mental health facility decides that trauma-informed care is a priority, it must first look to itself and whether it is a source of healing or a contributor to further trauma. While there has been very little attention to the psychiatric hospital as a source of trauma, what research does exist has found that a substantial percentage of people have experienced traumatic events while in the institution (Cusack et al., 2003; Nibert et al., 1989). CAMH adopted a client-driven bill of rights as both a process and an end product, and it has continued to support these rights through ongoing education. Although it is not always possible to ensure that rights are respected in practice, having a common understanding and awareness of their rights grants clients the safety of knowing what to expect, with a means of getting assistance or appealing if their rights are not respected. (At CAMH, individual advocacy is available to clients through the Psychiatric Patient Advocacy Office and the client relations officer, with systemic advocacy by the Empowerment Council.)

Many of the rights endorsed in the bill pertain to self-determination and the opportunity to exercise meaningful choice. A pervasive complaint by users of mental health and addiction services is that choice is meaningless when people are subject to coercion if one particular treatment recommendation (almost always for a psychiatric medication) is not accepted. Thus, Right #4 states: "Every client has the right to a choice of services, and will not be denied other options if the client does not choose one treatment or service." Coercion is not care, and service providers must give up the notion that compliance is a desirable goal.

Trauma-informed care mirrors the concept of individualized care, meaning that a person's self-identified needs, not diagnostic categories or institutional convenience, drive the structure and content of the care plan. One must be wary when implementing changes that the same old ways are not just being repackaged. (For example, a client goal recorded as "he wants to comply with medication" was a clue that a care plan was just a pretense of client self-determination.)

The CAMH Bill of Clients Rights and the Empowerment Council illustrate the need for providers of trauma-informed care to lead by example. Both are designed to maximize client safety, actual and perceived. Rights violations are about the undue imposition of one person's will on another. If people who are supposed to care for others trample their rights and violate their personal boundaries, they are hurting people, not helping them. Clients defending their rights is a sign of self-respect that should be encouraged. Client rights are about being treated as full citizens, even in the mental health and addiction treatment systems. Creating an environment in which these rights flourish is the first step to making a space for real healing.

CAMH BILL OF CLIENT RIGHTS

1: Right to Be Treated with Respect

2: Right to Freedom from Harm

3: Right to Dignity and Independence

4: Right to Quality Services That Comply with Standards

5: Right to Effective Communication

6: Right to Be Fully Informed

7: Right to Make an Informed Choice, and Give Informed Consent to Treatment

8: Right to Support

9: Rights in Respect of Research or Training

10: Right to Complain

For the complete CAMH bill of client rights, visit www.empowermentcouncil.ca or www.camh.ca.

References

Bryer, J., Nelson, B.A., Miller, J.B. & Krol, P.A. (1987). Childhood sexual and physical abuse as factors in adult psychiatric illness. *American Journal of Psychiatry, 144,* 1426–1430.

Centre for Addiction and Mental Health. (2005). *Centre for Addiction and Mental Health Bill of Client Rights.* Retrieved from www.camh.ca

Crane-Ross, D., Lutz, W.J. & Dee, R. (2006). Consumer and case manager perspectives of service empowerment: Relationship to mental health recovery. *Journal of Behavioral Health Services and Research, 33*(2), 142–155.

Cusack, K.J., Frueh, B.C., Hiers, T., Suffoletta-Maierle, S. & Bennett, S. (2003). Trauma within the psychiatric setting: A preliminary empirical report. *Administration and Policy in Mental Health, 30,* 453–460.

Firsten, T. (1991). Violence in the lives of women on psychiatric wards. *Canadian Woman Studies, 11*(4), 45–48.

Frueh, B.C., Cusack, K.J., Hiers, T.G., Monogan, S., Cousins, V.C. & Cavenaugh, S.D. (2001). Improving public mental health services for trauma victims in South Carolina. *Psychiatric Services, 52,* 812–814.

Grubaugh, A.L., Zinzow, H.M., Paul, L., Egede, L.E. & Frueh, B.C. (2011). Trauma exposure and possttraumatic stress disorder in adults with severe mental illness: A critical review. *Clinical Psychology Review, 31,* 883–889.

Nibert, D., Cooper, S. & Crossmaker, M. (1989). Assaults against residents of a psychiatric institution: Residents' history of abuse. *Journal of Interpersonal Violence, 4,* 342–349.

Rose, S. (1991). Acknowledging abuse backgrounds of intensive case management clients. *Community Mental Health Journal, 27,* 255–263.

Roth, D. & Crane-Ross, D. (2002). Impact of services, met needs and service empowerment on consumer outcomes. *Mental Health Services Research, 4*(1), 43–56.

Weaver, P., Varvaro, F.F., Connors, R. & Regan-Kubinski, R.J. (1994). Adult survivors of childhood sexual abuse: Survivor's disclosure and nurse therapist's response. *Journal of Psychosocial Nursing, 32*(12), 19–25.

Chapter 26

Integrated Screening, Assessment and Training as Critical Components of Trauma-Informed Care

Vivian B. Brown

The chapter focuses on the experiences of PROTOTYPES[1], a large non-profit agency in Southern California, in bringing a trauma-informed approach to its services for women and children. The catalyst for offering a more integrated approach to treating women with substance use, mental health and health issues was the agency's involvement in the Women, Co-occurring Disorders and Violence Study (WCDVS). PROTOTYPES was one of the nine study sites. As part of this groundbreaking research, the agency designed and implemented a trauma-informed approach to treatment in its large residential programs in Pomona and Ventura and, later, in its large outpatient program for women and men and its low-cost housing facility for women and their families in Pomona.

The WCDVS was an important study, in that it represented the first federal initiative in the United States to address the failure of existing services to address the complex needs of women with co-occurring substance use and mental health issues and histories of physical and/or sexual abuse. The five-year study, funded by the Substance Abuse and Mental Health Services Administration, found that attending to trauma in addiction and mental health treatment improves the effectiveness of treatment for women (Gatz et al., 2007; Morrissey et al., 2005). The study also showed that women diagnosed with serious mental illness and addiction disorders found trauma-

1. The legal, trademarked name of the agency is PROTOTYPES: Centers for Innovation in Health, Mental Health, and Social Services.

informed, integrated treatment to be more responsive to their needs and those of their children than treatment as usual. Lessons learned from the study included specific steps that were effective in transforming systems from a traditional approach to a trauma-informed one (see www.nationaltraumaconsortium.org).

Through its participation in WCDVS, PROTOTYPES made significant changes in its program policies; integrated trauma with its substance use, mental health, physical health and housing services; and involved consumers in all aspects of service design and research. The agency has also been influential in helping the local service system in Los Angeles County to become more trauma informed. This chapter will outline some of these changes, with a focus on creating the tools and structural support needed to screen and assess for multiple concerns in an integrated, trauma-informed way.

Being "Trauma Informed"

Harris and Fallot (2001) state that to be trauma informed means to know the history of past and current abuse or trauma in the life of the consumer with whom one is working. It involves understanding the role that violence and victimization play in the lives of most consumers of substance use and mental health services and using that understanding to design service systems that accommodate the vulnerabilities of trauma survivors and facilitate consumer participation in treatment. In a trauma-informed system, trauma is viewed as a defining and organizing experience for the survivor.

Facilitating Trust and Safety

In all aspects of trauma-informed approaches to providing treatment, including screening and assessment, safety is key. Programs need to establish an environment that is safe, warm, nurturing and welcoming. This environment gives the women the sense that their recovery matters and that they are worthy of care and respect. Staff members are trained to treat all women with respect and warmth and to avoid behaviours that are shaming or aggressively confrontational.

As part of an environmental scan, programs need to look at all their procedures through a trauma lens to avoid or minimize retraumatization. Trauma survivors may feel vulnerable in situations that might seem non-threatening under normal circumstances. One potentially upsetting aspect of care for consumers is not being fully informed of program rules and procedures. Just as women should be told prior to screening about the kinds of questions to anticipate, once they are in the program, daily activities they are expected to attend should be described in detail. Staff members need to be mindful that the women who may be frightened and overwhelmed may also have difficulty processing even the most basic information. Therefore, it is helpful to have the same information repeated a number of times in non-threatening and non-shaming ways.

An ideal residential treatment program provides the essentials of what Sandra Bloom (1997) has called "sanctuary." Program policies and procedures should provide physical and emotional safety. While seclusion and restraint are obvious examples of practices that consumers often experience as retraumatizing, many other procedures, such as how we ask about the multiple issues women may be facing, need to be similarly examined for their potential to retraumatize.

Discussing these issues is key to an open and genuine collaboration between provider and consumer in a trauma-informed system. Whenever possible, consumers choose where, how and when they will receive services. They help to set service priorities and determine which services will be delivered first.

As Herman (1992) describes, the core experiences of psychological trauma for the survivor are disempowerment and disconnection. Recovery, therefore, must involve empowerment and connection. Yet trauma has affected the survivor's ability to trust. On one hand, the trauma survivor yearns for someone she can trust and depend on; on the other hand, she fears that she will once again be traumatized by any helper.

Trust and safety must be earned and demonstrated over time. By beginning the new service relationship with an open question about what the woman wants and what would make her feel more comfortable and safe, the service provider takes the first step toward establishing safety. Disclosing trauma is not a requirement to receiving trauma-informed services.

In addition, program staff needs to recognize the impact of historical and intergenerational trauma for a number of cultures (e.g., African-Americans, Aboriginal people, people fleeing war-torn countries) and use that understanding to inform services.

An Integrated and Trauma-Informed Approach to Screening and Assessment

All service agencies need to begin by screening the women who enter their programs for trauma histories, as well as for substance use and mental health issues. The screening can be relatively brief and non-threatening, following a sensitive and culturally competent process. Consumers should be told during intake that they will be asked some questions that might be sensitive. If they do not want to answer specific questions, they should have the option to say "I do not want to answer." Historically, we have often taught our clients to "lie" to us when they feel they have to answer questions that are uncomfortable or that may lead to negative consequences. For example, when a program, such as a domestic violence program known not to admit women with substance use problems, asks potential clients about their substance use, the women may lie about their substance use in order to be admitted. If a woman says she does not want to answer a question about domestic violence, we should respect her choice and understand that something may be happening in her life that she is reluctant to disclose. This reluctance to disclose may mean that she fears a negative response; she was told to be silent by her family or her abuser; or she is feeling shame and/ or guilt. And if the woman does disclose, it is important that we validate the disclosure and express empathy and caring.

A brief screening instrument was developed in California under the Co-occurring Joint Action Council (COJAC),[2] a state-wide coalition focused on co-occurring disorders. The COJAC Co-occurring Disorders Screening Tool (Table 1) consists of nine questions: three about substance use, three about mental health and

2. Members of the COJAC screening subcommittee: Vivian Brown, chair; Richard Browne, LA County Alcohol and Drug Program Administration; Carmen Delgado, State of California Alcohol and Drug Programs; Joan Hirose, State of California Department of Education; Rollin Ives, State of California Department of Mental Health; Lisa Melchior, The Measurement Group; Tom Metcalf, Sutter County; John Mills, LA County Mental Health Department; Terry Robinson, Alcohol and Drug Policy Institute; Al Senella, Tarzana Treatment Programs; John Sheehe, LA County Mental Health Department; Karen Streich, LA County Mental Health Department; Wayne Sugita, LA County Alcohol and Drug Program Administration.

three about traumatic events history. The screener was designed to help integrate trauma-informed services into treatment—not to exclude anyone from services.

TABLE 1
Co-occurring Disorders Screening Tool

Step 1: Ask the primary screening questions:

3 Questions for mental health:

☐ Have you ever been worried about how you are thinking, feeling or acting?

☐ Has anyone ever expressed concerns about how you were thinking, feeling or acting?

☐ Have you ever harmed yourself or thought about harming yourself?

3 Questions for alcohol and drug use (Health Canada Best Practice Report):

☐ Have you ever had any problem related to your use of alcohol or other drugs?

☐ Has a relative, friend, doctor or other health worker been concerned about your drinking or other drug use or suggested cutting down?

☐ Have you ever said to another person, "No, I don't have an alcohol or drug problem," when around the same time you questioned yourself and felt, maybe I do have a problem?

3 Questions for trauma/domestic violence:

☐ Have you ever been in a relationship where your partner has pushed or slapped you?

☐ Before you were 13, was there any time when you were punched, kicked, choked or received a more serious physical punishment from a parent or other adult?

☐ Before you were 13, did anyone ever touch you in a sexual way or make you touch them when you did not want to?

Step 2: If participant answers 2 questions with "yes" (1 mental health and 1 substance abuse or 1 substance abuse and 1 trauma):

☐ Use GAIN Short Screener or Modified MINI for further assessment.

Adapted with permission from the Canadian Collaborative Mental Health Initiative, and Co-morbidity Screen, Boston Consortium of Services for Families in Recovery.

In the pilot test of the screener, which involved a number of agencies and participants ranging from high-school age through adulthood, no participant showed resistance to answering the screening questions; the screener identified many individuals who might have co-occurring disorders. After the screener was adopted by COJAC, some counties and service providers throughout California began implementing it across both mental health and substance use systems, as well as in emergency rooms.

PROTOTYPES has implemented an online screening, using the COJAC screener, for anyone seeking information on the agency's website. The individual can answer the questions and is given direction for follow-up; for example, if she answers "yes" to question #3 (harming yourself) or #7 (partner has pushed or slapped you), she is encouraged to call to speak to someone as soon as possible. If she answers "yes" to two or more questions, she is encouraged to arrange an appointment or, if she prefers, someone will call her. If she answers "no" to all questions, but would still like to speak to someone, she gets a message to call for an appointment.

We developed another assessment tool, the Readiness to Change Measure (Brown et al., 2000), based on our work on level of burden for women with multiple needs/problems. The level of burden refers to the findings that most women in PROTOTYPES' substance use treatment programs had four or more needs and that they were not ready to deal with all of those needs at once. The women are asked to complete a simple, non-threatening measure with four ladders. The four ladders represent four common areas of need: substance use, emotional issues, domestic violence and HIV and other health issues. The ladders represent different levels of change, from contemplation to action. The woman is guided through the steps of change and rates where she puts herself on all four ladders. In this way we ascertain which problem she is most ready to start with, which problem to work on next and so on. When we respond to the problem for which the woman rates herself as "most ready," she is more engaged and motivated and feels we are listening to her concerns: we are truly "starting where the client is."

Another area for assessment is de-escalation. In every trauma-informed program, women should be assisted in developing an inventory of triggers, not only for substance use, but also for feeling out of control or overwhelmed. Identifying and learning to recognize triggers restores a sense of safety. After they can recognize triggers that precede feeling out of control, the women should have the opportunity to complete an assessment designed to help them and us identify the strategies that contribute to feeling comforted and in control. This assessment should include the activities that women can do on their own, such as writing or drawing in a journal or taking a walk, as well as activities that require another person, such as talking to a friend or joining a group activity. The Task Force on the Restraint and Seclusion of Persons Who Have Been Physically or Sexually Abused (Carmen et al., 1996) has developed an excellent tool to assess potential trauma triggers and potential calming strategies.

Training

All staff members at a human services agency can benefit from general training in trauma to help them understand that trauma is the expectation, not the exception. This includes receptionists, security personnel and kitchen staff. Training should focus on what trauma is and how it manifests itself in our clients. The purpose of training is to help everyone become more sensitive to issues of trauma and less likely to frighten or retraumatize women seeking services. In the case of non-clinical staff, training also helps them to feel that they too play a significant role in assisting trauma survivors and reduces their discomfort around responding to survivors. In our experience, it is very powerful to have the training co-led by a professional staff member and a survivor staff member.

The trauma training, while not designed to go into traumatic experiences in-depth, may raise unresolved trauma experiences for some staff members. Secondary trauma is an important issue that can be discussed as part of the training. Numerous recovering staff were able to tell us during the trainings that they never dealt with their trauma experiences in their recovery, and that they now would like to take that step. A segment on staff self-care and staff group support should, therefore, be an important part of the training.

A second level of training focuses on trauma-informed care. This training, for managers, supervisors and clinical staff, explores what trauma-informed care is and what it looks like. This begins the journey into looking at all program procedures and practices that may be retraumatizing and leads to changes in policies and procedures. As part of training, specific components of treatment, such as vocational training, are looked at through the trauma lens. Issues are then addressed, such as helping women to learn coping skills for situations where an employer might raise his or her voice and be frightening.

A third level of training, for clinical staff, involves specific modifications for trauma survivors in their program areas, including residential, case management, outpatient and screening/assessment, as well as trauma-specific interventions, such as Seeking Safety.

Conclusion

Often our systems operate with a multitude of services. We talk about integrating services, but are so siloed into disciplines and problem areas that we generally give only token support to service integration. Even when we do organize services around the family, we are still deficiency-oriented; that is, we are primarily interested in the family's needs, deficiencies and diagnoses.

Working in partnership with other services, disciplines and sectors on inter-professional education, integration of screening and services and other forms of collaboration also underpins the transformation of systems of care into trauma-informed systems. This transformation requires a paradigm shift. At first, thinking about trauma seems like one more thing to be considered in the clinical assessment of every client. However, trauma-informed transformation involves a shift in how consumers and their behaviours are viewed, how staff responds to consumers and how services are delivered. Authentic acknowledgment of each client's strengths, rather than her deficiencies or problems, will allow for a true recovery community that values diversity. Co-creating our services in partnership with our clients will lead us to a truly responsive service system focused on safety, respect, skills building and mutual learning.

References

Bloom, S. (1997). *Creating Sanctuary: Toward the Evolution of Sane Societies*. New York: Routledge.

Brown, V.B., Melchior, L.A., Panter, A.T., Slaughter, R. & Huba, G.J. (2000). Women's steps of change and entry into drug abuse treatment: A multidimensional stages of change model. *Journal of Substance Abuse Treatment, 18*, 231–240.

Carmen, E., Crane, B., Dunnicliff, M., Holochuck, S., Prescott, L., Rieker, P. et al. (1996). *Massachusetts Department of Mental Health Task Force on the Restraint and Seclusion of Persons Who Have Been Physically and Sexually Abused: Report and Recommendations*. Boston: Massachusetts Department of Mental Health.

Gatz, M., Brown, V., Hennigan, K., Rechberger, E., O'Keefe, M., Rose, T. et al. (2007). Effectiveness of an integrated, trauma-informed approach to treating women with co-occurring disorders and history of trauma: The Los Angeles site experience. *Journal of Community Psychology, 35*, 863–867.

Harris, M. & Fallot, R. D. (Eds.). (2001). Using Trauma Theory to Design Service Systems [Special issue]. *New Directions for Mental Health Services, 89*.

Herman, J. (1992). *Trauma and Recovery: The Aftermath of Violence—From Domestic Abuse to Political Terror*. New York: Basic Books.

Morrissey, J.P., Jackson, E.W., Ellis, A.R., Amaro, H., Brown, V.B. & Najavits, L. (2005). 12-month outcomes of trauma-informed interventions for women with co-occurring disorders. *Psychiatric Services, 56*, 1223–1232.

Chapter 27

Breaking Out of the Mould

Creating Trauma-Informed Anti-violence Services and Housing for Women and Their Children

Lynda Dechief with Janice Abbott

Atira Women's Resource Society, located in Greater Vancouver, offers 17 supportive housing programs, including emergency shelter, low-barrier independent living and first- and second-stage transition houses for women aged 16 and older, as well as their children.[1] It serves women with a range of needs: women who are homeless; who are pregnant or new mothers; who struggle with mental wellness and/or substance use; who have experienced violence and abuse; or who face additional barriers to securing and maintaining housing due to sexism, racism, transphobia and other forms of oppression. With a commitment to offering services to women from a harm reduction perspective and within a feminist and anti-oppression framework, the organization is uniquely positioned to shed light on trauma-informed practice in anti-violence and housing contexts.

When Atira opened its first transition house—now called Durrant House—in South Surrey in 1987, staff routinely screened prospective clients for alcohol and other drug use and for mental health issues, as was and continues to be the practice at many transition houses. If women admitted to either, they were refused space.

---

1. For more information about Atira Women's Resource Society, visit www.atira.bc.ca.

After Janice Abbott took on the position of administrative co-ordinator in 1992, Atira's screening processes began to change. Abbott remarks that, based on her lived experience and "the lies we were telling each other about women's use of substances and the lies we were forcing them to tell us, we just stopped screening for struggles with mental wellness and substance use."

Abbott admits they didn't really know what they were doing, but they knew women were using substances and hiding it or struggling with their use of prescription or "legal" drugs, which were "allowed," and no one was talking with the women or supporting them around these struggles. Although most of the prescription medication women were taking was to deal with problems such as anxiety and depression, "we were screening for struggles with mental wellness and, in theory, not doing admissions based on women having a diagnosis. It just made no sense and we were missing a golden opportunity to explore options and alternatives with women and unintentionally shaming them with our silence or rather, our requirement they be silent."

Despite the decision to stop screening for mental health, substance use or anything other than an experience with violence/abuse, Abbott still believed Atira needed to provide specialized resources for women struggling with substance use. She started working with other women in the community to establish a case for a new house and funding. By the time Shimai Transition House opened in 1997, Atira was already firmly operating within a harm reduction framework. And although they didn't know the name of it then, they were employing aspects of trauma-informed care in their daily practice. They were focusing on what was wrong with the system and what had happened to the women, rather than on what was "wrong" with the women themselves.

I spoke with Janice Abbott, now chief executive officer of Atira, about the distinctive ways in which Atira is putting trauma-informed care principles into practice today.

Lynda: Janice, one of the key characteristics of trauma-informed services is that they focus on what has happened to the person rather than what is wrong with the person. From this perspective, the use of alcohol or other drugs and the development of mental health issues "are understood not as pathology but primarily as attempts to cope and survive; what seem to be symptoms may more accurately be solutions" (Peck, 2009, p. 6). Tell me how Atira has created services based on this view.

Janice: We recognized long ago that substance use and struggles with mental wellness are often effects of trauma and that women who use alcohol or other drugs and/or have mental health struggles are more vulnerable to ongoing violence and abuse. So we not only don't ban women from services for telling us they struggle with either or both; we actually assume women struggle and our services are informed by that understanding. We then create safety, understanding, acceptance, empathy and space for talking about and exploring options and alternatives to substance use. We offer options for recovery and empowerment and/or for using substances safely. And we are available if and when women want support to stop using, no matter what time of day or night.

Lynda: Isn't it true that you also work with other sectors, like the health care system, to help them to understand and address the links between violence/abuse, substance use and mental health issues?

Janice: Yes. In 2002, we contacted a kindred spirit in the local health authority and started working with a group of community agencies to develop a health centre, day care and housing for pregnant women struggling with their use of alcohol and other drugs. We worked with the community and local and provincial authorities to increase understanding of the relationship between women's experience of violence/abuse and substance use. When the Maxxine Wright Community Health Centre opened in November 2005, it was for women affected by their struggles with substance use and/or violence/abuse.

Services are provided from an understanding that, even if women don't disclose violence or abuse, we have to make every aspect of the program safe for them. Every detail, from the intake form to how we share information among the partners, is scrutinized for how it could potentially retraumatize women affected by abuse or violence.

We recognize that even if women don't disclose violence in their current relationships, many have herstories of violence and abuse. These may be from within their family of origin or within the foster care system, at school, especially if they are not Caucasian, not heterosexual or are differently abled; working in the sex trade (paid or unpaid); or just trying to make ends meet and living in poverty. Our services are designed to assume the possibility that women have been affected by violence/abuse/powerlessness and therefore support women to live as valuable and valued and fully participating members of their communities.

Statistics from 2009 show that 35 per cent of the women accessing services at the Maxxine Wright Community Health Centre report using alcohol or other drugs (but not experiencing violence), 14 per cent report being affected by violence (but not using substances) and 51 per cent report being affected by both issues (Penaloza et al., 2009).

Lynda: Not requiring women to disclose violence and minimizing retraumatization are key to providing trauma-informed care. Another characteristic of being trauma informed is as Fallot (2008) states, taking "an integrated, whole person view of individuals and their problems and resources" (p. 9). Would you say that also happens at the Maxxine Wright Community Health Centre?

Janice: Maxx Wright was developed because pregnant and early parenting women facing these struggles were running all over Surrey to access services. They were going to one doctor for their methadone and another for their prenatal care. They were going to one program for a hot meal and yet another one for free diapers. They were going to mental health services and being told that they needed to get their addiction under control first, then going for addiction counselling and being told that they needed to first deal with the violence in their relationship. They were going to a transition house and being told they weren't allowed to stay if they had recently used alcohol or other drugs. And that's if they had enough bus money and energy to get to all those places.

Maxx Wright recognizes the complexity of women's lives and provides all those services, and more, under one roof. Last year, we opened 12 units of short-term/shelter housing for women on the same site, and this year, we opened 24 units of longer-term housing. It's hard for women to deal with everything they've experienced and are experiencing if they don't have a safe place to live.

Lynda: According to Peck (2009), another tenet of trauma-informed care is that service time limits are determined by survivor self-assessment and recovery and healing needs. How is that enacted in Atira's residential programs?

Janice: Until recently, funding for first-stage transition houses and shelters stipulated that women could only stay for 30 days, so that was the policy at several of our programs. However, instead of asking a woman/family to leave after 30 days, we stretched the rules until the woman had safe, affordable housing. We also created other housing programs that are longer term. For example, at Koomseh, our second-stage transition house, women and their children can stay up to 18 months. However, because we were finding that that still wasn't enough time for some women, we also created housing without time limits, including housing with limited as well as with significant supports. We call it indefinite housing. Finally, a year ago, our funders revised our contracts so we can now work with individual women and families to determine the best length of stay for them based on their circumstances. This is one of the most important changes to our services in years, as every woman has different needs and varying access to community and personal resources.

Lynda: I recently did a workshop with the staff at the Rice Block, one example of "indefinite housing" for women, and when I entered the building for the first time, it wasn't immediately obvious to me who was working there and who was living there. Is that related to the trauma-informed principle of having a "non-authoritarian approach" and "seeing the clients as equals"?

Janice: Yes, it's one of our policies at Atira to compel staff not to dress in ways that create a separation between them and the women accessing our services. And we don't call the women "clients" or "patients": we refer to them as "tenants" or "residents," but only when it's absolutely necessary to make a distinction; mostly we just call them "women." It's more accurate and we don't find that using a language of professionals is helpful in our work, especially if it means diagnosing or labelling women. That can be part of exerting power and control over women, which can be retraumatizing. It's what they are fleeing in their everyday lives, so we work hard not to recreate that dynamic.

We also hire women with lived experience, which means we are the women we work with. And while we encourage our staff to remember where we came from, which creates a place of connection, we also encourage ourselves to remember where we are. We do have jobs and homes and often stability, so we need to acknowledge our points of privilege as well as our points of oppression.

Treating women with respect is key to our work. We do sometimes need to involve the Ministry of Children and Family Development when we see issues with the kids, but we do it in a very transparent way. We explain to women why we think a call to the ministry is important and we encourage women to make the call themselves with our support. Most women will do that. If they don't, we let them know that we need to make that call, and invite them to sit with us while we call. As much as possible, we don't have conversations about women behind their backs, and we don't share information about them without their permission, not even among our own programs. Building trust is very important for women who have been violated by the people in their lives they trusted most.

Lynda: A focus on relationships, or a "relational approach," is important in trauma-informed work. It sounds like aspects of that approach—being "strengths-based," "prioritizing choice and control" and "focusing on empowerment"—are pretty fundamental to Atira's work.

Janice: Absolutely. A good example of that is Wraparound. Most of the women we see are accessing a number of services and the Wraparound model helps to "wrap" a range of services "around" a woman and her child by co-ordinating the support network in her life. But it's different than integrated case management in some fundamental ways. To begin with, the woman herself decides who is her network; networks often include "informal" supports like family and friends, who are going to be there for the long haul when services providers have closed her file or moved on to other jobs. The very first meeting focuses on identifying the woman's strengths. Some women struggle to identify their own strengths and are amazed at what their network members say. For example, a woman may have been accused by other service providers of being conniving or of manipulating the system because she is accessing a number of services for free items, whereas her network will identify her resourcefulness at trying to make ends meet and provide for the needs of her children.

Over several meetings, the support network together comes up with a realistic action plan, with the Wraparound facilitator ensuring that the woman's safety, support needs and voice are central to the process. Again, the network doesn't talk about her or share information between meetings without her knowledge and consent.

Preliminary evaluation of the Wraparound program revealed the principles and processes to be very successful in working with women and their children. In addition to being effective in engaging "hard to reach" families, Wraparound resulted in significant improvements in access to health care, birth outcomes, families' health and well-being, housing and nutritional status of women and their children, reduced risk from the use of substances, improved parenting outcomes, fewer removals of children and an increasing move toward family reunification. For more information and quantitative and qualitative findings, see Cailleaux & Dechief (2007).

Lynda: How do you find staff with the necessary skills to provide trauma-informed services to women and their children?

Janice: As noted earlier, we have a policy of hiring women with lived experience. Some of our staff members have been to college or university, but we see real-life experience as just as valuable, if not more so. We also provide paid training for staff to support them in their work. In addition to undergoing eight hours of basic orientation to Atira's beliefs and practice with respect to supporting women who have experienced violence, staff has over the years been offered training in harm reduction, trauma-informed care, non-violent communication, anti-oppression work, pregnancy-related integrated management of addictions, the 16-step empowerment model, motivational interviewing, relapse prevention and cultural safety. And we are constantly reviewing and embracing best practices based on our own experiences and those of others doing similar work.

We also have a policy to hire staff that reflects the makeup of the women we provide services to, so we actively encourage applications from under-represented groups, such as women of colour, Aboriginal women, women with disabilities, lesbians and women whose sexual orientation is fluid. And more than 28 languages are spoken by Atira's staff; we have Aboriginal women's outreach workers; and women of colour and Aboriginal women are well represented in Atira's management.

Lynda: Peer support and cultural safety/competency are key aspects of trauma-informed care. How do you ensure that staff members themselves are supported around the trauma they may have experienced and don't burn out doing this work?

Janice: We actively encourage women on staff to take care of themselves. We offer semi-annual workshops on collective care and ethics. We value the women who work here and the work they do.

Atira staff are some of the highest paid in the province; they have good benefits, including an employee assistance program where they can access counselling; and they work a nine-day fortnight, which means they work a short four-day week every second week. Having days off in order to have a good work-life balance is important. In addition to the usual statutory holidays, women also get International Women's Day and their birthday off, with pay. And we allow for a week of "special days," so women don't have to lie to us about being sick if they need to stay home for the furnace repair person or because they want to attend their child's school play.

And we look for opportunities to do more. In 2009–2010, we received grants from Worksafe BC and the Women's Health Research Network to conduct a research project that implemented mindfulness-based stress reduction groups for the staff, based on gentle yoga stretching and movement, body awareness and relaxation and understanding the stress-response cycle. The mindfulness-based stress reduction group we implemented was found to significantly improve staff's ratings of their physical health, decrease their emotional exhaustion and symptoms of depression and increase their sense of professional efficacy (Dechief & Pomaki, 2010).

We're not saying we're perfect, far from it in fact, but we're trying hard to provide principled services and to keep evolving as we learn.

Lynda: It certainly sounds as though rather than making women fit into your mould, you're constantly working to expand the mould to include all women who have been affected by violence, abuse and trauma.

HOUSING SERVICES OFFERED BY ATIRA

Housing services offered by Atira are unique in the range of supportive housing models available—and the innovative services provided—to women of all ages, and sometimes their children, many in Vancouver's Downtown Eastside.

Some highlights:

Ama House, a transition house for women aged 55+, is the first of its kind in Canada.

Kye7e House provides housing for 11 women over age 45 in the Downtown Eastside. The women have a communal kitchen and sitting area with a phone, and hot meals are delivered to them once a day.

The **Rice Block** is a 46-unit, single-room accommodation hotel. It has an industrial on-site community kitchen, where women cook for themselves and one another. The Rice Block has a drug and alcohol counsellor on site and offers 16-step and Re-discover Parenting groups. Each resident works one-to-one with a designated staff member. The Rice Block is also home to the Enterprising Women Making Art storefront, a social-purpose business that provides women with an alternative form of employment. A community garden has been created in the abandoned lot adjacent to the building.

Shimai Transition House is a first-stage transition house for women and their children escaping abuse, which is staffed 24 hours a day, seven days a week. Length of stay ranges from a few hours to six months or longer, depending on a woman's self-identified needs. Like all of Atira's programs, Shimai operates within a harm reduction model.

Bridge Women's Emergency Shelter in the Downtown Eastside is staffed 24 hours a day, with employees offering women emotional support, referrals, resource information and advocacy. There is no maximum length of stay and women work actively with a housing outreach worker to find, secure and maintain long-term, safe, affordable housing.

References

Cailleaux, M. & Dechief, L. (2007). "I've found my voice": Wraparound as a promising strength-based team process for high-risk pregnant and early parenting women. *UCFV Research Review*, 1(2), 16–38. Retrieved from http://journals.ufv.ca/rr/RR12/article-PDFs/found.voice.pdf

Dechief, L. & Pomaki, G. (November 2010). *Taking Care of Those Who Care: Assessing Organizational and Individual Stress Management Interventions for Anti-violence Workers.* Richmond, BC: WorkSafe BC. Retrieved from www.worksafebc.com

Fallot, R. (2008, February). *Trauma-informed services: A protocol for change.* [PowerPoint slides]. Paper presented at the Conference of Co-occurring Disorders, Long Beach, CA.

Peck, J.A. (2009, May). *Trauma-informed treatment: Best practices.* [PowerPoint slides]. Paper presented at the Los Angeles County Annual Drug Court Conference, Los Angeles, CA.

Penaloza, D. Stafford, V. & Soberano, L. (2009). *Measuring success at Maxxine Wright CHC.* [PowerPoint slides]. Report prepared for the Fraser Health Authority, Surrey, BC.

Chapter 28

Integrating Treatment of Tobacco with Other Substances in a Trauma-Informed Way

Nancy Poole and Judy Lyon

In mental health and substance use services, we are moving slowly but surely toward the implementation of tobacco-free policies. In the process, we are noticing how critical it is to implement these policies in a trauma-informed way, given how common it is for tobacco to be used by smokers to mediate symptoms of stress and anxiety. This chapter uses the example of one substance use treatment program that has implemented tobacco-free policies to illustrate how the challenges of integrating work on tobacco can be addressed when trauma is taken into account.

In 1998, staff at the Aurora Centre, a women's substance use treatment centre based in Vancouver, on the site of BC Women's Hospital, began to proactively track tobacco use among its clients. Clients were encouraged to consider tobacco as a "drug of problem" alongside other mood-altering drugs commonly used by women, such as alcohol, cocaine, marijuana and benzo-diazepines. They were also asked to rate tobacco's importance as a drug of problem for them. The results were compelling—not only did approximately two-thirds of the women in treatment indicate that smoking was a problem for them, but in each year since this shift to inquire about tobacco, they have rated tobacco as one of their "top three" drugs of problem.

These findings sparked an eight-year process of gradually integrating tobacco treatment into substance use programs at Aurora. In May 2006, Aurora became the first residential treatment centre in Canada to formally treat tobacco along with other substances, and the centre officially became "smoke free." Other programs have begun to examine how they might integrate treatment for tobacco dependence within treatment for other substances (Bobo & Davis, 1993; Orleans & Hutchinson, 1993). In the course of this work, programs have recognized how deeply entrenched is the resistance to this integration, and how important it is to address the many reasons for client and service provider resistance to integration, including the perception that tobacco helps to cope with trauma and related stressors (Hammond & Gregoire, 2011; Ker et al., 1996; Teater & Hammond, 2010).

This chapter examines how Aurora addressed the link between smoking, alcohol and other substance use and the experience of trauma in this groundbreaking programming. We describe the challenges of integrating treatment for tobacco with treatment for other substances and how our commitment to trauma-informed practice supported the process.

The Context: A Mystifying Lack of Recognition of Tobacco and Trauma in Addiction Treatment

It is not easy to explain how support for tobacco cessation evolved separately from treatment for other addictions, particularly given the high rates of overlap between the two. Studies have found that 79 to 82 per cent of women in substance use treatment smoke (Bobo, 2002; Teater & Hammond, 2010) and that there are gender differences in smoking. Women with addiction to other substances are significantly more likely to be smokers than their male counterparts (Husky et al., 2007). Moreover, addiction treatment clients smoke more (Perine & Schare, 1999), start earlier and have more difficulty quitting (Asher et al., 2003). There are also serious interconnected health impacts: smoking-related diseases are the leading cause of death for people previously treated for alcohol and other substance use problems (Hurt et al., 1996). In addition, tobacco use can be a relapse trigger for other substances (Gulliver et al., 2006).

The health risks of smoking are particularly serious for women. Female smokers are twice as likely to develop lung cancer as male smokers of similar age and smoking history (Henschke, 2006). According to the Office of the Surgeon General in the United States (2001), tobacco-related sex-specific and gender-specific risks for women include reproductive health problems, cancers and heart disease. These health risks alone are a compelling rationale for expanded treatment options for women who smoke.

Treatment providers at Aurora were well aware of how the experience of violence and trauma is linked to substance use problems in general. Yet only recently have researchers specifically identified how smoking is more prevalent in women who have a history of violence and trauma than for those in the general population. For example, the smoking rates for women with post-traumatic stress disorder range from 39 to 45 per cent (Fu et al., 2007; Helstrom et al., 2009), to 54 per cent for survivors of sexual assault (Amstadter et al., 2009) and 58 per cent for severely battered women (Weaver & Etzel, 2003). In one study (Lipschitz et al., 2003), 86 per cent of girls of low socio-economic status with posttraumatic stress disorder smoked. In addition to the high prevalence of tobacco use, women smokers with experience of trauma are frequently heavy smokers. Loxton et al. (2006) found that women with a history of intimate partner violence were almost four times more likely than women smokers without trauma to consume a pack or more of cigarettes a day (see also Lemon et al., 2002; Weaver & Etzel, 2003), and 29 per cent of women smokers in trauma treatment have reported smoking a pack or more daily (Helstrom et al., 2009).

Challenges Posed by Integration

While there were many compelling reasons for integrating treatment for tobacco with the treatment for alcohol and other drug addiction, Aurora staff faced a number of challenges. Three of these challenges are of relevance to this chapter.

The first challenge was to enlist the support of referral agents to continue to refer women smokers for treatment, which proved difficult, in part because many continued to operate from the misconception that it is too much to ask clients to stop all addictive substances at once. Referral agents play a critical role in helping women prepare for treatment, including understanding women's readiness and capacity to heal within a group treatment environment. But when Aurora began integrated treatment, surveys showed that only 37 per cent of referral agents strongly supported the change in policy and practice, whereas 65 per cent of clients strongly supported it.

A second challenge was to determine how to approach the use of tobacco within what was traditionally an abstinence-based program. Aurora had typically asked women who relapsed to return to outpatient treatment until they were ready to commit to the abstinence approach of the residential treatment context. But the nature of tobacco addiction, the high likelihood of relapse and use of nicotine replacement therapy provoked the centre to re-examine its policies related to eligibility for treatment, relapse and harm reduction. We decided that clients would not be required to abstain from tobacco for two weeks prior to admission, as they were with other mood-altering substances. And staff realized that its approach to relapse had to be more nuanced for tobacco. It became evident that when a woman relapsed to tobacco use, there were often other treatment issues present that also needed to be addressed, and these were fully explored. All in all, a paradigm shift was required by staff members to factor in the significant change that was being asked of clients in the implementation of the tobacco policy. This shift in paradigm had benefits for increasing flexibility and commitment to trauma-informed and harm reduction practice overall.

Aurora's third challenge was in partnering with clients to increase their awareness that while they may perceive smoking as a beneficial coping mechanism to deal with feelings of fear and anxiety, the actual harms outweigh the perceived benefits. With that in mind, women were encouraged to use the treatment experience as an opportunity to explore ways other than smoking to self-soothe or relax. In order to overcome this challenge, staff required education to allow them to factually respond to women's queries about the health, social and financial impacts of tobacco use. Staff members were also required to support women's stated post-treatment goals for tobacco abstinence, regardless of the women's level of awareness of these impacts.

Trauma-Informed Practice

To address these challenges, Aurora has incorporated the following core aspects of trauma-informed care in the process of integrating tobacco treatment into the treatment of other addictions:

1. Clients are encouraged to exercise *choice* within the treatment context wherever possible.

2. *A joint learning environment* is created, where connections are made between violence against women in general, trauma specifically and the experiences of mental health problems and addictions. Clients learn alternative coping strategies that increase safety and promote health.

3. In their work with women with substance use problems, treatment providers assume a *stance based on respect, rapport and relational collaboration,* rather than exercising their expertise and authority over the treatment process.

4. Treatment providers educate and *work with referral agents* and others in the addiction field from this respectful and rapport-fostering stance.

These four aspects of trauma-informed practice in the context of integrated addiction treatment for women are described here in more detail. Responding to the needs of women who are addicted to tobacco has served to reinforce, clarify and improve the overall trauma-informed practice at Aurora.

Consumer Choice

Abstinence-oriented addiction treatment has often been experienced by clients as rule bound and full of advice from treatment providers who claim to "know best" about recovery because they have often had years of personal recovery experience and/or experience guiding women through the process. Gradually, provider-determined approaches have been supplanted by recovery/ discovery processes and client-directed (Miller et al., 2005) and women-centred approaches, which make women with the substance use problems the experts in their own lives (Payne, 2007).

The first choice that clients at Aurora had to make after tobacco treatment was integrated into the addiction program occurred at intake, when they had to decide what type or level of nicotine replacement they wanted to use—if they wanted to use it at all. Working through this choice with women, especially women who were new to cessation and had quit only to have access to treatment, created an immediate shift toward a more sensitive and client-driven intake process. All Aurora staff were keenly aware of the discomfort and anxiety created by smoking cessation and the need for women to find strategies to relieve these immediate symptoms, as well as longer-term strategies for meeting the functions that tobacco had provided for them, such as mediating trauma symptoms (Greaves, 1996).

The Aurora counsellors facilitate this process by framing tobacco cessation as each woman's commitment to her health and recovery, with staff providing support to help women honour this commitment to themselves. In this way, the overall trauma-informed principle of eliciting compassion and respect for self, others and place is realized. Women are asked about their preferences for how counsellors might support them when they experience fear and anxiety and may be at risk of relapse. Should relapse occur, women are supported to reassess their stage of readiness to abstain, and if they are interested, they are supported in recommitting to tobacco abstinence and continued participation in the treatment program. Choice and self-determination are maximized, and the potential negative experience of authority, domination or traumatization is avoided.

Learning about the Connections

Learning about the impact of smoking on women's health and its relationship to other addictions and trauma is also a key aspect of trauma-informed care at Aurora. Various group educational series have been offered by the centre, each one designed and redesigned, based on input from clients. Over the years, clients have indicated as useful three educational components that are relevant to trauma-informed practice:

1. **Naming the negative physical effects of smoking on women's health and the potential for health improvement with quitting.** The immediate physical health benefits of quitting smoking had been described in Deborah Holmberg Schwartz's *Catching Our Breath* (1997) as "Your body

will forgive you." This linking of the health benefits of quitting with forgiveness and compassion for self is very much aligned with trauma-informed practice and was often cited in program evaluations by clients as a particularly helpful framing of the uncomfortable quitting process. In addition, the focus on positive health improvement was directly linked to and reinforced by other treatment components that support physical health recovery, such as yoga, morning walks and good nutrition.

2. **Naming the links between smoking and victimization, coping and healing.** The educational programming covers the high levels of smoking and experiences of trauma and violence among women in addiction treatment. The programming also offers opportunities for women to discuss how tobacco, similar to other substances, is used to cope with stress, numb feelings and increase energy—thus acknowledging its benefits, while also exploring the serious health risks of smoking. Women often reported seeing tobacco as a reward after a stressful time: instead of shutting down that conversation, the educational programming helps women explore other self-care options they could use to address the perceived benefits and needs that smoking has provided. Again, the focus is brought to the positive—to women's coping mechanisms, resilience and strengths.

3. **Promoting "consciousness raising."** This has been done by addressing how the tobacco industry has targeted and manipulated women by playing on their vulnerabilities, promoting smoking as a way to feel liberated and stay slim. The programming has used media resources to promote and support women's understanding and resistance to these messages, drawing on, for example, Dr. Jean Kilbourne's "Deadly Persuasion" media presentation (1999). As such, the individual experience of tobacco use is linked to structural influences on women's smoking, much in the way that service providers in women-centred treatment programs attempt to help women understand the structural nature of violence against women, to know that it is "not their fault" that they experienced violence.

Collaborative Provider Stance with Clients

The third aspect of trauma-informed practice facilitated by integration of tobacco into addiction programming was a shift in the stance of treatment providers. Counsellors were less confrontational and more collaborative and had greater recognition of women's need for safety and healing. In the process of making the programming change, the counsellors undertook extensive training to learn more about tobacco's effect on women's health, its link to other addictions and the positive impact of smoking cessation on recovery from other substances. In this process, some staff members were provided with support to stop smoking. In becoming learners about nicotine addiction themselves, and in recognizing first-hand how uncomfortable quitting smoking can be, staff members were assisted in developing a less directive treatment stance. The goal was to create a gentler, more supportive atmosphere, where shame about smoking was reduced, and anxiety about relapsing and being asked to leave treatment lessened. The treatment atmosphere shifted toward one that fosters acceptance, reflection and community building.

Collaborative Provider Stance with Referral Agents

This tobacco-related work also afforded treatment providers an opportunity to share their learning about tobacco with the external referral agents to help other treatment providers engage with the importance of integrating tobacco cessation into addiction treatment. This outward-focused, co-learning reduced Aurora's separation from other tiers of care, and helped outpatient counsellors effectively prepare women for integrated treatment. It also prompted these agencies to consider and revise their own practice of providing tobacco cessation support within their services.

Conclusion

The Aurora Centre has courageously undertaken an extended effort to integrate tobacco treatment with the treatment of other addictions. The decision was made based on the high prevalence of smoking among women in treatment for alcohol and other drug addiction, the very serious impact of smoking on women's health, the evidence for an increase in sustained recovery for women when all substances are treated at once, as well as clients' interest in getting enhanced support for smoking cessation. Recognition of how tobacco and other substances are used to mediate the all too common effects of violence and trauma for women was central to the enhanced program design.

Working from a trauma-informed stance in the integration and delivery of tobacco cessation programming had many benefits: clients had more choice in the treatment process; Aurora created a less directive learning environment and considered new approaches to relapse, and retraumatization was minimized through a more collaborative treatment provider approach. In this way the Aurora Centre serves as an exemplar of trauma-informed practice in its work to integrate treatment for tobacco addiction into the treatment of alcohol and other drug addictions.

References

Amstadter, A.B., Resnick, H.S., Nugent, N.R., Acierno, R., Rheingold, A.A., Minhinnett, R. et al. (2009). Longitudinal trajectories of cigarette smoking following rape. *Journal of Traumatic Stress, 22,* 113–121.

Asher, M.K., Martin, R.A., Rohsenow, D.J., MacKinnon, S.V., Traficante, R. & Monti, P.M. (2003). Perceived barriers to quitting smoking among alcohol dependent patients in treatment. *Journal of Substance Abuse Treatment, 24,* 169–174.

Bobo, J.K. (2002). Tobacco use, problem drinking, and alcoholism. *Clinical Obstetrics and Gynecology, 45,* 1169–1180.

Bobo, J.K. & Davis, C.M. (1993). Cigarette smoking cessation and alcohol treatment. *Addiction, 88,* 405–412.

Fu, S.S., McFall, M., Saxon, A.J., Beckham, J.C., Carmody, T.P., Baker, D.G. et al. (2007). Post-traumatic stress disorder and smoking: A systematic review. *Nicotine and Tobacco Research, 9,* 1071–1084.

Greaves, L. (1996). *Smoke Screen: Women's Smoking and Social Control.* Halifax, NS: Fernwood.

Gulliver, S.B., Kamholz, B.W. & Helstrom, A.W. (2006). *Smoking Cessation and Alcohol Abstinence: What Do the Data Tell Us?* Bethesda, MD: National Institute on Alcohol Abuse and Alcoholism.

Hammond, G.C. & Gregoire, T.K. (2011). Breaking ground in treating tobacco dependence at a women's treatment center. *Journal of Social Work Practice in the Addictions, 11,* 1–16.

Helstrom, A.W., Bell, M.E. & Pineles, S.L. (2009). Feeling better and smoking less: The relationship between trauma symptoms and smoking over time. *Cognitive Therapy and Research, 33,* 235–240.

Henschke, C.I. (2006). Women's susceptibility to tobacco carcinogens and survival after diagnosis of lung cancer. *JAMA, 296,* 180–184.

Holmberg-Schwartz, D. (1997). *Catching Our Breath: A Journal about Change for Women Who Smoke* (2nd ed.). Winnipeg, MB: Women's Health Clinic.

Hurt, R.D., Offord, K.P., Croghan, I.T., Gomez-Dahl, L., Kottke, T.E., Morse, R.M. et al. (1996). Mortality following inpatient addictions treatment: Role of tobacco use in a community-based cohort. *JAMA, 275,* 1097–1103.

Husky, M.M., Paliwal, P., Mazure, C.M. & McKee, S.A. (2007). Gender differences in association with substance use diagnoses and smoking. *Journal of Addiction Medicine, 1,* 161–164.

Ker, M., Leischow, S., Markowitz, I.B. & Merikle, E. (1996). Involuntary smoking cessation: A treatment option in chemical dependency programs for women and children. *Journal of Psychoactive Drugs, 28,* 47–60.

Kilbourne, J. (1999). *Deadly Persuasion: Why Women and Girls Must Fight the Addictive Power of Advertising.* New York: Simon & Schuster.

Lemon, S.C., Verhoek-Oftedahl, W. & Donnelly, E. (2002). Preventative healthcare use, smoking, and alcohol use among Rhode Island women experiencing intimate partner violence. *Journal of Women's Health and Gender-Based Medicine, 11,* 555–562.

Lipschitz, D.S., Rasmusson, A.M., Anyan, W., Gueorguieva, R., Billingslea, E.M., Cromwell, P.F. et al. (2003). Posttraumatic stress disorder and substance use in inner-city adolescent girls. *Journal of Nervous and Mental Disease, 191,* 714–721.

Loxton, D., Schofield, M., Hussain, R. & Mishra, G. (2006). History of domestic violence and physical health in midlife. *Violence against Women, 12,* 715–731.

Miller, S.D., Mee-Lee, D., Plum, B. & Hubble, M.A. (2005). Making treatment count: Client-directed, outcome-informed clinical work with problem drinkers. *Psychotherapy in Australia, 11,* 42–56.

Office of the Surgeon General. (2001). *Women and Smoking: A Report of the Surgeon General.* Atlanta, GA: Centers for Disease Control and Prevention.

Orleans, C.T. & Hutchinson, D. (1993). Tailoring nicotine addiction treatments for chemical dependency patients. *Journal of Substance Abuse Treatment, 10,* 197–208.

Payne, S. (2007). In-hospital stabilization of pregnant women who use drugs. In N. Poole & L. Greaves (Eds.), *Highs and Lows: Canadian Perspectives on Women and Substance Use* (pp. 249–255). Toronto: Centre for Addiction and Mental Health.

Perine, J.L. & Schare, M.L. (1999). Effect of counselor and client education in nicotine addiction on smoking in substance abusers. *Addictive Behaviors, 24,* 443–447.

Teater, B. & Hammond, G.C. (2010). Exploring smoking prevalence, quit attempts, and readiness to quit cigarette use among women in substance abuse treatment. *Social Work in Health Care, 49,* 176–192.

Weaver, T.L. & Etzel, J.C. (2003). Smoking patterns, symptoms of PTSD and depression: Preliminary findings from a sample of severely battered women. *Addictive Behaviors, 28,* 1665–1679.

Chapter 29

Responding to the Women

YWCA Toronto Moves Its Practice to a Trauma-Informed Approach

Lorraine Greaves in conversation with Jennie McKnight, Ruth Crammond and Heather McGregor

The YWCA in Canada has a long and rich history of responding to women's social and housing needs in safe and compassionate ways. This article describes the initiation and ongoing evolution of a trauma-informed approach at the YWCA Toronto in response to women's evolving needs. The following captures Lorraine Greaves in conversation with YWCA Toronto staff: Jennie McKnight, clinical director; Ruth Crammond, director of shelter and housing; and Heather McGregor, CEO.

Lorraine: What provoked the transition from a feminist anti-oppression approach to the development of a specific trauma-informed approach?

Jennie: The trauma-informed approach was intended to augment the existing approach, which, among other things, included a commitment to working from an anti-oppression framework. The historical context involves YWCA Toronto being awarded a contract in the early 2000s to re-open a shelter for women and children fleeing violence, which became known as ARISE. In planning for the shelter's opening, the YWCA sought to identify best practices for violence against women (VAW) services and took steps to identify and implement a model that reflected the state of knowledge and practice in the field.

Heather: We were seeing women with more and more complex mental health issues. Providing appropriate services for them increasingly created significant issues for our staff teams and our organization. We wanted to assist women to prepare better for independence and autonomy by enhancing their skills and abilities to support themselves in the community. At the same time, we were being challenged to deal directly and more effectively with the effects of their trauma and violence histories.

Jennie: Research into existing best practice approaches led to a team of YWCA management and staff visiting a VAW shelter in Chicago that had implemented a service model that incorporated elements of a trauma-informed approach. In addition, YWCA Toronto conducted needs assessments in which service recipients and staff of our existing shelters commented on how to improve service delivery. The findings revealed that women with mental health issues were not being well served (they were either being discharged because of disruptive behaviour or self-selecting out of the VAW system), and staff did not feel they were skilled in addressing some of the behaviour related to the impact of trauma. A few years after the new model was implemented at ARISE, the YWCA began to roll the model out to other programs, including our previously existing VAW shelter (the Women's Shelter) and our homeless women's shelter (First Stop, Woodlawn), where we had more mental health and addiction issues among the women. We spent a great deal of effort adapting the model to the unique service mandates, client populations and physical layout of each program site.

Lorraine: How do you define "trauma informed"?

Ruth: We view it as a way of talking about the range of violent and intrusive experiences that women can experience in their lives. This continuum can include histories of chronic or episodic interpersonal violence, like partner abuse, and it also can include the pervasive effects of experiences of social violence, like poverty and racism. Our approach sees these experiences as having an impact on women (and their families and communities), and a critical aspect of our ability to be effective service providers is to see the dynamics of our relationships in service settings through this lens.

An example we often use to describe how we apply a trauma-informed approach has to do with "chores" in our shelters for women fleeing violence.

Part of the communal living context in these settings requires that women participate in some activities that support the maintenance of a clean and healthy environment. Some women struggle with us around this issue for different reasons. In our previous way of working, if a woman consistently did not fulfil her community responsibility by doing her chore, she would be given a series of warnings that could lead to her ultimate discharge. With the focus on trauma, there is a greater effort to understand what might be happening for this woman, both in terms of her relationship to the task itself and to us as the people assigning it to her. Maybe her abuser criticized her housekeeping, which led to violence. Or maybe she has experienced abuse and rejection from parents or others in positions of power. We try to engage with her in ways that might give some clues for everyone involved about how the actions of workers and clients alike are being understood and responded to.

Lorraine: What were some of the operational issues in pushing this philosophy forward?

Jennie: A big focus in the model's development was identifying the staffing resources (skills and capacities) to deliver it. New job descriptions were developed that required knowledge and experience that had a more clinical dimension. Considerable effort also went into operationalizing the model by having subspecialties within the multidisciplinary team approach. For example, case managers handling day-to-day operations were also required to act as a resource to clients and the team in specific areas of practice, such as addiction, mental health or immigration/legal information. The idea was to create a multidisciplinary team that could attend to the range of service needs we were seeing. Since we were operating from the assumption that trauma and oppression can affect all aspects of experience, we wanted to create a staffing model that could identify and meet the broadest range of service needs in an integrated and timely way.

Lorraine: What specific practices did you change in the shelters?

Ruth: We tried not to replicate abusive systems, so we have minimized rules and regulations. We do not control food and always have an open kitchen. There is a natural tendency to revert to rules when things get tricky and to impose structures, which we try to avoid by developing insight in both our workers and clients to understand the impacts of trauma and oppression. Our model did away with a formal warning system in our VAW shelters that would caution women about the consequences of their behaviour. We refused to institutionalize the homes, so there are not a lot of signs and warnings on the walls. We also work with women to make the home seem like a community.

Jennie: It has been a great challenge to create the conditions where women who have experienced trauma can see clear, transparent practice in how the shelter runs, which can reduce their anxiety about staff having power over them, without being either overly rigid or too loose. Either of those conditions can be triggering, so we focus a lot on how our actions affect individuals and the larger community.

Lorraine: How would you describe the decision-making process to make this shift? Were there philosophical and political considerations?

Heather: From a management standpoint, we were certain this model would be an improvement in shelter services for women, but we have a union and we had to take careful steps as we introduced and expanded our new approach.

Shelter workers have traditionally been highly skillful in case management areas—helping women who are in crisis or great danger to navigate complex, multiple systems, such as housing, family and criminal and immigration law, education, health and economics. With the trauma-informed approach, we formally introduced more clinical elements, such as the demonstrated capacity to understand how trauma plays out in women's lives and to respond appropriately. For example, if a woman who has been traumatized seems to be avoiding contact with her worker, what might that say about her experience of vulnerability and her strategies for safety? In the new model, we sought workers who had training and experience in the kinds of reflective and relational practices that render visible the ways trauma is present in the here and now, not just as a historic event. Both case management skills and clinical skills are important; we needed to be more rigorous in our recruitment and retention efforts in making sure we hired for each. This continues to be quite challenging, because these skills are not necessarily taught or acquired in the same ways.

Jennie: At the sites where programs were already running, we had to negotiate new job descriptions that included new qualifications with some existing unionized staff. This was not easy. However, at all the sites, we invested significant resources in training and capacity-building using a trauma-informed model. For some existing staff, we offered additional training opportunities, paid for some professional education and held jobs for those going back to school.

Lorraine: What have been some issues in establishing the new model? Were there any conflicts in practice?

Jennie: We endured some criticisms from the community for professionalizing our staff this way, and there were worries about medicalization and elitism from some of our partners and academic colleagues.

There has also been some tension in our efforts to integrate and apply the analytical frameworks of trauma and anti-oppression. For example, some social workers in residential settings tend to understand systemic issues and power dynamics, whereas other workers coming to us sometimes take a more traditional clinical approach emphasizing individualized behaviour. As we try to incorporate the insights and knowledge of both of these paradigms, we have had to overcome a tendency to polarize them as either social or psychological. In daily practice, where women with complex histories and ways of navigating in the world are sharing space and resources, it is challenging to work in ways that acknowledge the effects of a range of harmful experiences and also promote a climate of mutual respect, safety and responsibility.

We have had some scope of practice issues and still need to work on clarifying the differences between trauma-specific counselling and trauma-informed services. We continue to work to bring team awareness to the dynamics among and between clients and workers, needing to attend to issues of structure, predictability and transparency, so that triggers related to trauma are understood by all. Trauma has an impact on all of us. We strive for a holistic approach that engages mind, body and spirit and creates an environment where people can have experiences of self-efficacy, safety and connection to others, which we believe are essential to recovering from many of the harmful effects of trauma.

Lorraine: How do you see trauma-informed practice/philosophy being integrated into your new 300-unit supportive housing unit at the Elm Centre in downtown Toronto?

Heather and Jennie: The multidisciplinary element was already present in our shelter service model, but Elm will include intensive multidisciplinary supports for the 100 women (one-third of the residents) living with mental health and addiction issues: this will include access to social work, addiction support, nursing, psychiatry, occupational therapy and vocational support. We also plan to integrate some on-site access to primary health care. Adding these elements presents new logistical challenges, but is not a big leap philosophically, since experience with our homeless shelter has indicated that access to both mental health care and primary care is a barrier for homeless women who are also struggling with addiction, mental health issues and trauma-related sequelae. We will have a psychiatrist and a nurse on the staff team.

Another way a trauma-informed approach is evidenced in the service model for Elm is the commitment to a subteam within the larger staff that is specifically focused on community development across the entire community of 300 units. This shift reflects both the specificity of working in a mixed residential setting as well as an acknowledgment that many of the long-term effects of trauma include social and relational challenges. Along with the intensive individual case management services, community developers with subspecialties will support active participation in the community, which we hope will have a beneficial impact on overall well-being, especially as it relates to trauma.

As well, trauma-informed practice has been integrated into our Elm model through our intake process, which is informed by an understanding of trauma. We include trauma screening in our intake process and ensure that our intake workers are flexible and skillful in helping women through those difficult portions of the conversation. We haven't required that applicants have pre-existing formal mental health diagnoses, and in fact have broadened the types of formal mental health diagnoses beyond what would ordinarily have been prioritized for assertive community treatment team (ACTT) support. In practice, the impact of the trauma these women experience gets codified under a wide variety of diagnostic categories, and we wanted to be sure we were responding to how trauma and mental health actually affect women's homelessness.

Lorraine: How do you measure the success or impact of this new model?

Heather: Evaluation is one dimension of our practice that requires more effort and resources. The reality of operating 24-hour crisis services for clients and families with complex service needs often makes it difficult for us to allocate organizational resources (time, funds, etc.) to identifying goals and outcomes and then measuring and analyzing results. We need more sponsored research and profiling of the work in the YWCA on our program innovations such as this. As the funding climate for some services tightens and mandated accountability functions move toward more evidence-based measures of quality, we need to focus our organization and program efforts to make improvements in this area.

Jennie: At the moment, success and impact are most often identified anecdotally (with the resolution of a particular case being assessed in a team activity that includes reflection and application of trauma-informed principles) or as part of other, often informal, evaluation processes. For example, individual staff may report that they feel more competent as a result of ongoing trauma-related training or the availability of clinical supervision. Teams problem solve issues applying trauma-informed principles and reflection, which often increases compassion in our workers. We have found that by analyzing difficult issues or clients, service providers more readily see women's strengths and focus on shifting their energies in a more effective direction.

Lorraine: How do you transmit this approach to the women and to new (and experienced) staff?

Jennie: The staff members are keen to learn about trauma and trauma-informed work, but women, especially in our VAW shelters, generally are not asking for the kind of support that directly touches the trauma content. We focus on how to connect with women where they are, and we are less didactic than we used to be, preferring instead to create community and connect with the women through the incremental steps involved in building safety and stability, whether this is by securing housing or finding other resources for them and their children.

Trauma creates disconnections, and we try to ameliorate that. In our teams, we may still encounter the idea that the "real" work involves a woman disclosing details of her abuse and having the attending emotional experiences that go with that. However, we try to encourage growth and healing without going to the content of the trauma. In the VAW shelters, this is tricky, because to get emergency housing or other supports, women are often asked to document their trauma, so the discussion happens. This is an example of how the larger system can create conditions that make it difficult to practise strictly within a trauma-informed framework. But we continue to maintain there is no obligation to hear the details or to tell the details. That said, we also want to be responsive in a way that can take advantage of moments with women where aspects of the trauma are present and there might be an opportunity for insight or a more informed choice. We try to bring awareness and compassion to these encounters, neither probing for disclosure nor avoiding the source of the discomfort or distress.

Our homeless shelter is a much larger, busier environment than our VAW shelters. Residents often find it challenging and sometimes triggering to live with so many others. The need continually to problem solve around co-operative living strategies has meant that in that setting we often end up working with women to navigate how their past and current traumas are affecting their here-and-now interactions with others. Here we have tended toward a hybrid between trauma-informed and trauma-specific work. We don't attempt to deconstruct the content of a woman's actual trauma. We have found that the accessibility of the service includes paying attention to the structure of the program and the stance of the staff, but also working with women to widen their own strategies to include ones less defined by trauma. There is a certain amount of trauma recovery work that is useful in such dynamic environments. We are reluctant (and unable) to rely on power-over techniques as the main way of creating safety in such an interactional setting.

There have been significant organizational resources invested in communicating the approach to staff. It has been interesting to observe that although many women who are practising in settings where our trauma-informed model is in place have engaged in extensive team training and group discussion, there is still an elusive quality to the approach. This may be related to the lack of clearly articulated goals and outcomes. It may also be related to the difficulty social workers who are either new to the field or new to traumatology may have in identifying clinical contexts where an analysis of trauma would be useful, and then applying the knowledge in skillful intervention.

Lorraine: Do you transmit these ideas to the women you serve?

Jennie: With the women, yes, we do explicitly communicate—in individual and group programming—about the effects of different forms of trauma (for women and their kids) and we try to support women to build and share a range of skills for mitigating those impacts. Doing this can help lessen shame and anxiety. For example, framing parenting challenges in relation to trauma can ease the extreme fear women in VAW shelters have about being judged for the ways their kids are behaving and their own responses to that behaviour.

Lorraine: Have you let other agencies and services know about your approach?

Jennie: The YWCA has communicated this approach reasonably well to other service providers in our sector in informal settings and to funders (public and private). As public awareness of mental health issues has grown, the ability to frame the work we do with women in terms of trauma can be helpful in mobilizing support and understanding. We have not, however, engaged in much formal knowledge-sharing through conference presentations or publications.

Lorraine: Do you have an example of success with this approach?

Jennie: Yes, we had a client who had come to Canada several years earlier fleeing an extremely violent abuser and an unresponsive police system. She was told by those close to her not to make a refugee claim, and her undocumented status added to her vulnerability, which led to a sequence of abusive relationships here. She and her three children faced a number of issues, the most urgent being that she was in danger of being deported to the unsafe situation in her country of origin. We connected her to a lawyer and worked with them to make a refugee claim using a trauma-informed approach; arguing that her decisions had been survival decisions, and that inconsistencies in her story were related to trauma-related injuries. We identified aspects of her current behaviour that reflected mental health issues and were clearly trauma related. She won her refugee status based on these trauma-related examples. We felt that was a successful application of our philosophy.

Conclusion

What lies ahead? Becoming trauma informed requires a range of adjustments in practice and system designs, supported by research, innovative change and inspired leadership. This is a tall order, and requires complex thinking. Becoming trauma informed benefits from collaboration and co-operation between all levels of service delivery. For the survivor, the support milieu becomes a web of relationships rather than another experience of being overwhelmed. Becoming trauma informed for systems and services is an ongoing process of system change and quality improvement, requiring constant adaptations and ongoing monitoring.

The contributors to this book offer hope and direction for this complex undertaking. Their many approaches and philosophies of practice offer rich ideas for practitioners, policy-makers and program and system developers alike. The challenging theoretical dilemmas posed offer all sectors rich food for thought. Innovative practices in a range of settings offer inspiration. Illustrations of agencies or institutions engaging with the challenges and moving past resistance are reassuring. Issues in improving our collective responses to a range of diverse populations offer clear challenges to "mainstream" practices and policies. And integrating gender and equity lenses into our planning and change processes remains underdeveloped, but critically important.

Across Canada, individuals, agencies and institutions are taking up these challenges. Ultimately, people with lived experiences of trauma can take credit for this shift in thought and practice, by providing their own challenges and teachings to our systems of care. It is those with lived experiences of trauma, as well as service providers, who will benefit. Through trauma-informed services, survivors can feel safe enough to access the help they need, stay with treatment and improve their health: this includes cutting back on problematic substance use; experiencing fewer symptoms of trauma; and gaining a greater sense of agency, self-esteem and capacity for mutuality and authenticity in relationships. This book is a contribution to that change. Becoming trauma informed is indeed a big challenge, but one that is increasingly being embraced by trauma survivors, service providers, substance use and mental health services and other health and social services and systems.

Becoming trauma informed is a process. This process is built on knowledge and a wide range of types of evidence, and requires innovative thinking, leadership, compassion and understanding. Fortunately, interest in becoming trauma informed in both practice and system design is flourishing in Canada. This interest has given us an opportunity to gather and showcase a range of theoretical, clinical and systemic perspectives on trauma-informed work, and to showcase these efforts in this book.

Undoubtedly, there are many other examples of trauma-informed practice in various settings and with more and more diverse groups developing in Canada and beyond. In this book, the contributors provide examples of work at the individual, group, agency and intersectoral levels. These examples are part of a "joined-up" service system approach to becoming trauma informed: the examples are distinct from trauma-specific or integrated system designs, and reinforce the centrality of trauma for people accessing help from various service systems. This increased interest in becoming trauma informed reflects significant efforts in practice and health system design to function as whole systems and to engage meaningfully with transdisciplinarity. The non-linear nature of complex service interventions, the influence of specific contexts and the constant evolution of evidence and practice will continue to make the path to becoming trauma informed a complicated one. As such, there is much more to be done to implement and evaluate "what works" in trauma-informed interventions, across multiple settings and with different populations.

To move forward, there is a dire need to integrate knowledge, practice and experiences in creating trauma-informed responses. Current practitioners and system designers consider how to integrate theories or parts of theories on trauma, anti-oppression, feminist and other approaches into their current practice. Conscious consideration of the theoretical material presented here, along with other current thinking, is a foundation for better practices in this area.

Practices can then be modified or introduced. For example, trauma-informed and harm reduction–oriented screening and intake processes in addiction and mental health services can be developed. In this context, trauma-informed intake and screening processes are important in creating a culture of safety within our interactions and our agencies to more effectively and consciously engage people who have difficulty seeking help and navigating relationships with service providers and with processes.

Creating linkages between trauma-informed and trauma-specific approaches across service tiers is also crucial. For example, trauma-informed work in prevention and outreach-oriented services needs to be, and can be, effectively linked with services that offer trauma-specific treatment in hospitals and other intensive treatment settings for those who want this approach. The roles of practitioners who provide trauma-informed support in community-based programs serving specific populations and those who work in intensive mental health services can be clarified. Such linkages address the recommendations for a tiered system of care as defined in *A Systems Approach to Substance Use in Canada* (National Treatment Strategy Working Group, 2008), where each tier of care understands and is respected for its role in providing support.

Many more services have yet to consider how to integrate trauma-informed practice within intensive treatment settings. In addition to agency-wide policies, narrower examples exist of how to embed trauma-informed practice and system change in intake processes, and treatment planning in mental health services.

An area of integration less often addressed is the physical health impacts of trauma in primary care and mental health and substance use treatment settings. This practice of addressing physical health impacts has often been neglected, although practitioners are increasingly recognizing the links between stress responses and substance use and mental health. Along with these connections, practitioners and systems planners need to promote an understanding of the role of sex and gender in the physical health impacts of trauma, and to respond in gendered and trauma-informed ways in a range of settings. This includes treating chronic pain, gastrointestinal problems, asthma, musculoskeletal difficulties and other health problems that differ in prevalence, expression, disease course and treatment for men and women.

Diversity and equity issues also need to be integrated into systems of care and systems design. The needs of Aboriginal girls and women, for example, are often not responded to adequately. Amnesty International's Stolen Sisters campaign and the Native Women's Association of Canada's Sisters in Spirit initiative are revealing the alarmingly high levels of trauma among and violence against Aboriginal women. Aboriginal women, men, their families and communities have also suffered immeasurably due to historical and ongoing colonization. Culturally safe, holistic support for Aboriginal people is critically needed, with trauma-informed practice as a key component.

Finally, integrating practice with education is critical. Trauma awareness always underpins trauma-informed practice. Given the scope of the adaptations needed across settings and populations, the structures for learning about trauma and its implications need to be innovative and multiple. For example, multi-sectoral communities of practice could be used to build consensus on system-level approaches. Blogs could provide immediate updates on research findings. Websites could be used as a source for collected evidence. Webcasts could broadcast oral presentation of new findings and debate around new approaches. Researchers could use virtual collaboratories (locations for social and other scientists to collaborate) to engage in transdisciplinary research. Listservs could connect people to updates on news, programming and research. And people could meet other innovators at conferences. All of these mediums offer opportunities for integrating new knowledge into training and education. They are tools to accelerate the speed of uptake of trauma-informed knowledge and practice.

There are many reasons to be hopeful about becoming trauma informed. Through mechanisms such as the Grounding Trauma conferences and the Canadian Centre on Substance Abuse online SystemAction web workspace, practitioners across Canada have indicated an overwhelming interest in learning more about trauma, its centrality in the lives of people with substance use and mental health disorders and the broad implications for practice and policy. These efforts and interests underpin many emerging examples of systems of care improvement, such as efforts to reduce traumatization in collaborations between substance use and child welfare systems. While being trauma informed may not be the sole purview of any agent, service or location, it is clearly an important process to be embedded in all systems that aim to serve and support people. We hope that others interested in trauma-informed practice will be inspired by the work of the contributors to this book.

References

National Treatment Strategy Working Group. (2008). *A Systems Approach to Substance Use in Canada: Recommendations for a National Treatment Strategy.* Ottawa: National Framework for Action to Reduce the Harms Associated with Alcohol and Other Drugs and Substances in Canada. Retrieved from www.nts-snt.ca/2010%20Documents/nts-report-eng.pdf

About the Editors

Nancy Poole, MA, PhD candidate, is the director of research and knowledge translation for the British Columbia Centre of Excellence for Women's Health, and the provincial research consultant on women and substance use issues for BC Women's Hospital in Vancouver. Nancy is well known for her collaborative work on research, training and policy initiatives on women's substance use issues with governments and organizations on local, provincial, national and international levels. She is currently doing doctoral studies on virtual knowledge translation, studying the role of virtual communities of practice (vCoPs) to collaboratively examine evidence on women's substance use issues and generate consensus on avenues for improving our response.

Lorraine Greaves, PhD, is senior investigator at the British Columbia Centre of Excellence for Women's Health and its founding executive director. Prior to that, she was the founding director of the Centre for Research on Violence against Women and Children in Ontario. She is the lead mentor of IMPART, a training program for researchers in gender and addiction and their intersections with mental health, violence and trauma issues. As executive director of the Health Systems Strategy Division at the Ministry of Health and Long-Term Care in Ontario, she developed equity and intersectoral strategies for policy development. She is internationally recognized as an expert in women and tobacco use, gender-based analysis and integrating gender and equity into policy and practice.

Nancy Poole and Lorraine Greaves co-edited the book *Highs and Lows: Canadian Perspectives on Women and Substance Use* (2007), also published by the Centre for Addiction and Mental Health.

About the Authors

Janice Abbott has been the CEO of Atira Women's Resource Society since 1992 and of Atira Property Management Inc. since its launch in 2002. In 1995, Janice spearheaded the opening of Shimai Transition House, a specialized transition house for women affected by violence who were struggling with substance use and mental wellness. Janice's understanding of and passion for supporting others to understand the complex relationship between violence and substance use comes from her lived experience. Throughout Atira's herstory, Janice has championed barrier-free and low-barrier access to programs and services for women, ensuring Atira's programs are accessible to all women and their children.

Branka Agic, PhD candidate, is the manager of health equity at the Centre for Addiction and Mental Health and deputy director of the Collaborative Program in Addiction Studies in the School of Graduate Studies at the University of Toronto, where she received a master's degree in health science in health promotion. Branka has a medical degree from the University of Sarajevo in Bosnia and Herzegovina. She is a doctoral candidate in the Dalla Lana School of Public Health at the University of Toronto. Her primary interests include mental health and substance use in immigrant, refugee, ethnocultural and racialized groups.

Donna Akman, PhD, CPsych., is a psychologist with the Women's Program at the Centre for Addiction and Mental Health and an assistant professor in the Department of Psychiatry at the University of Toronto. She has worked extensively as a clinician and researcher in the area of women's mental health. Donna has a long-standing interest in developing, implementing and evaluating feminist-informed approaches to women's mental health care.

Sabrina Baker, MSW, RSW, has worked for more than 30 years in mental health care in various settings, focusing on family-centred care and family therapy. She currently works in private practice, specializing in promoting recovery with families whose relatives have mental health issues by providing support, education and counselling. She is passionate about teaching, training, supervising and consulting students, workers and volunteers in promoting and providing family-centred care. Sabrina co-wrote *Promoting Recovery from First Episode Psychosis: A Family Guide* (Centre for Addiction and Mental Health, 2009) and has contributed chapters to other books on family-centred care.

Richard Bebout, PhD, is chief clinical officer at Community Connections in Washington, D.C., and has been affiliated with the human services agency since he earned his doctorate at the University of North Carolina at Chapel Hill in 1987. Richard has contributed more than 20 articles and book chapters on mental health services and frequently trains and consults in the areas of supportive housing, trauma-informed care and M-TREM, a group approach to addressing the impact of traumatic violence on men's lives. Richard also maintains a private therapy practice in Washington.

Julia Bloomenfeld, MSW, RSW, is the director of clinical services at the Jean Tweed Centre, an agency for women with substance use and gambling concerns in Toronto. Since graduating in 1991, Julia has spent most of her career in women-centred services in the criminal justice and substance use sectors, where she has delivered programs that respond to the distinct needs of women, especially those with a history of trauma. Julia has actively supported a shift toward providing care that is more trauma informed by participating in various community of practice forums, including discussion and trainings, and by writing in the substance use sector.

Vivian B. Brown, PhD, founder and former CEO of PROTOTYPES, a California non-profit agency, has more than 40 years of experience developing innovative mental health, substance use, trauma-informed, trauma-specific, HIV/AIDS and co-occurring disorders services. She has conducted outcome studies, including the Women, Co-occurring Disorders and Violence Study, and has numerous publications. She has sat on many federal, state and local advisory committees, including the Substance Abuse and Mental Health Services Administration's National Advisory Council and Women's Advisory Committee. Vivian provides consultations about integrating mental health, substance use, health and trauma services to organizations and state and local agencies throughout the United States.

Stephanie R. Capyk, M.Ed., RCC, CCC, was the clinical supervisor and manager at the Victoria Women's Sexual Assault Centre in British Columbia until 2012. Since 1997, she has worked for women's safety through doing community-based research, counselling survivors of sexualized and domestic violence and facilitating learning about trauma, healing and reconnecting with one another and the natural world. In recent years, her practice has shifted to supporting counsellors as a trainer and clinical supervisor. Stephanie's current projects include raising a baby and bees with her partner on their farm in northern Alberta.

Gloria Chaim, MSW, RSW, is the deputy clinical director in the Child, Youth and Family Program at the Centre for Addiction and Mental Health. She is assistant professor in the Department of Psychiatry and an adjunct lecturer in the Factor-Inwentash Faculty of Social Work at the University of Toronto. Gloria's main interest is in the development of service capacity for under-served populations, particularly women, children, youth and families where concurrent disorders are a concern. To foster opportunity for innovation, her focus most recently has been on developing cross-sectoral networks and collaborations that provide a forum for knowledge exchange and joint service and research initiatives.

Jennifer Chambers is co-ordinator of the Empowerment Council, a voice for clients at the Centre for Addiction and Mental Health (CAMH). On behalf of the council and its predecessor, the Queen Street Patients Council, Jennifer has worked to have the client voice heard where it was not heard: in interventions in cases before the Supreme Court, through standing at inquests and by training members of the Toronto Police Service. She spent several years negotiating the CAMH Bill of Client Rights. She focuses on connecting the client voice with evidence that supports it and exploding the myth that the client voice (or advocacy) and good science are at odds.

Natalie Clark's work is rooted in more than 15 years of experience with Aboriginal girls as an ally, auntie, sister and group facilitator, and through her own journey. Her work is informed and mobilized through her interconnected identities, including her English, Welsh and Aboriginal ancestry; as a solo parent of three Aboriginal children; and as an academic and a community-based researcher and counsellor. Natalie practises and provides training on trauma-informed girls' groups, including *It's a Girl Thang*, which she co-developed. Her recent work involves developing indigenous girls' groups in partnership with the Interior Indian Friendship Society and School District 73 Aboriginal Programs in Kamloops, B.C.

Stephanie S. Covington, PhD, LCSW, is a clinician, organizational consultant and lecturer who for more than 25 years has focused on creating gender-responsive and trauma-informed services. Her experience includes designing women's services at the Betty Ford Center, as well as developing programs for women in criminal justice settings. She was a consultant to the United Nations Office on Drugs and Crime in Vienna and was selected for the U.S. federal Advisory Council on Women's Services. Her publications include six gender-responsive, trauma-informed treatment curricula. Stephanie is based in La Jolla, California, where she is co-director of the Institute for Relational Development and the Center for Gender and Justice.

Lynda Dechief, MSc., is a researcher and consultant in women's health and social issues, with a focus on the intersections of oppression, violence, substance use and mental health issues. Her company, Equality Consulting, collaborates with non-profit organizations, research centres and government agencies to work toward making the world a safer, healthier place for those most marginalized and stigmatized. This involves community-based research and evaluation, program and policy development and management, workshop creation and facilitation and writing. Lynda has a master's degree in population and public health and feels that she has learned the most important lessons from the women she has directly supported and advocated for.

Colleen Anne Dell, PhD, is a professor at the University of Saskatchewan in the Department of Sociology and the School of Public Health, where she holds a Research Chair in Substance Abuse. She is also a senior research associate with the Canadian Centre on Substance Abuse, Canada's national addictions agency. Colleen's research is grounded in a community-based participatory approach and focuses on Aboriginal populations, criminalized women and substance-using populations. She has worked extensively at the community and national levels, including with the Elizabeth Fry Society and the Senate of Canada.

Amy Druker, BSW, MSW, works with young people and their families at Oolagen Community Services as an individual and family therapist. She values a narrative therapeutic philosophy in her conversations with young people and families. Amy's previous work with substance-using pregnant and parenting women helped grow her understanding of the systemic injustices women face as a result of the stigma against women who use substances, particularly pregnant/parenting women. She remains involved with the Grief and Loss Education and Action Group as a volunteer. She is excited about the social change initiatives that have come from the group's work around systemic change in the child welfare system.

Roger D. Fallot, PhD, is director of research and evaluation at Community Connections, a private, not-for-profit agency that provides a full range of human services in Washington, D.C. He is a contributing author and co-editor (with Maxine Harris) of *Using Trauma Theory to Design Service Systems* (Jossey-Bass, 2001) and consults widely on the development of trauma-informed cultures of care in human services. Roger and a group of clinicians at Community Connections have developed a men's version (M-TREM) of the Trauma Recovery and Empowerment model (TREM), a group intervention for working with survivors of physical and sexual abuse.

Maria Haarmans, MA, PhD candidate, has 20 years of experience in hospital and community settings working with individuals with schizophrenia. She has trained in cognitive-behavioural therapy for psychosis (CBTp) with leading experts in Canada and the United Kingdom. Maria has published on CBTp and gender issues and provides training and supervision/consultation for mental health practitioners. She practises and promotes empowering and depathologizing approaches to psychological distress. Maria has a master's degree in community psychology (feminist stream) from the University of Toronto. She is completing a doctorate in clinical psychology, focusing on gender role socialization and psychosis, at the University of Liverpool.

Mary Harber, MSW, PhD candidate, is an assistant professor in the School of Social Work and Human Service at Thompson Rivers University in Kamloops, British Columbia. She has been a social worker for 24 years and has practiced in a variety of contexts, including child welfare, substance use, youth, sexuality and disability. Her current research and community work focuses on supporting individuals with fetal alcohol spectrum disorder using creative engagement to help them develop social skills that facilitate community inclusion.

Lori Haskell, Ed.D., Cpsych., is a clinical psychologist and author of *First Stage Trauma Treatment: A Guide for Mental Health Professionals Working with Women* (Centre for Addiction and Mental Health, 2003). She has a status appointment as an assistant professor in psychiatry at the University of Toronto and is an academic research associate with the Centre for Research on Violence against Women and Children. Lori lectures and teaches on topics related to complex trauma and its treatment, vicarious trauma and violence prevention.

Joanna Henderson, PhD, CPsych., is a clinician scientist with the Child, Youth and Family Program at the Centre for Addiction and Mental Health and an assistant professor in the Department of Psychiatry at the University of Toronto. Joanna has worked extensively with children and youth with complex behavioural and emotional needs and their families. Currently, she is developing, implementing and evaluating evidence-based practices for addressing the needs of youth, particularly youth with co-occurring mental health and substance use concerns. Joanna's other research interests include trauma, trauma-informed care, youth risk-taking, improving access to care, treatment engagement and collaborative models of service delivery.

Steven Hughes, M.Ed., is the manager of training and development for the Canadian Training Institute in Toronto. He has worked in the social service support system for more than 25 years. As a lifelong learner, Steven is interested in adult education, accelerated learning, dialogue methods, violence prevention in organizations, appreciative inquiry and practices that help individuals cultivate self-awareness and unlock their full potential. Steven is committed to bringing positive energy to organizations so that individuals in the workplace can flourish and make their unique and valued contributions to the world.

Paul Hyman is president of Brain Fitness International. He is an integrative functional specialist combining mind/body approaches and brain research, working in conjunction with other health care and education professionals. During his 10 years as a therapist at the Centre for Addiction and Mental Health (CAMH), he was a member of the design team responsible for creating Ontario's first problem gambling program and also developed a stress management program. Paul is a licensed Brain Gym instructor/consultant and pioneered the use of Brain Gym at CAMH.

Frances Jasiura, BPHE (Hons), BSW, RCC, co-founder of Change Talk Associates, offers practice-based training and virtual coaching across Canada, strengthening people's capacity to guide change conversations and positively influence health outcomes. Her work is informed by decades of experience in motivational interviewing, training and counselling. Empowering women in addiction day treatment programs has inspired her respect for groups as a context for sustainable change. Frances is a member of the international Motivational Interviewing Network of Trainers and a contributing author in the book *Motivational Interviewing in Groups* (Guilford Press, in press). She is also a certified spiritual director.

Yona Lunsky, PhD, CPsych., is an associate professor in the Department of Psychiatry at the University of Toronto; the section head of research in the Dual Diagnosis Program at the Centre for Addiction and Mental Health; and an adjunct scientist at the Institute for Clinical Evaluative Sciences. She is also a clinical psychologist who works primarily with adults with developmental disabilities. Her research focuses on the mental health of adults with developmental disabilities and their caregivers, and she has published more than 100 research papers and book chapters on the topic.

Judy Lyon, MA, MPCP, SFTT, has more than 20 years of experience as an addiction counsellor in health care and corrections settings. She most recently was lead addiction counsellor at the Aurora Centre in Vancouver. Judy now works as a counsellor, consultant and focusing-oriented therapy trainer in private practice in Surrey, British Columbia. She specializes in working with complex trauma and related issues, such as addictions and disordered eating, and is an active advocate for trauma-informed, integrated care.

Tammy MacKenzie, M.Ed, is a manager within the Addictions Program at the Centre for Addiction and Mental Health. Prior to this, she was manager of the Pathways to Healthy Families Program at the Jean Tweed Centre. Given her work with women who have children and substance use concerns, she has taken a particular interest in the grief and loss of these mothers whose children are not in their care.

Peter Menzies, PhD, is a member of Sagamok Anishnawbek First Nation in northern Ontario. He has spent 10 years building culturally congruent mental health and addiction programs in partnership with urban and First Nations communities. Before joining the Centre for Addiction and Mental Health, Peter held front-line and management positions at both Aboriginal and mainstream agencies. He earned a doctorate from the University of Toronto and received the Centre for Equity and Health in Society's Entrepreneurial

Development and Integration of Services Award in 2005 and the Kaiser Foundation's Excellence in Indigenous Programming Award in 2011. His research interests include Aboriginal homelessness, intergenerational trauma, child welfare and suicide prevention.

Anna M. Palucka, PhD, is a clinical psychologist in the Dual Diagnosis Program at the Centre for Addiction and Mental Health and an assistant professor in the Department of Psychiatry at the University of Toronto. Her clinical and research interests include mental health issues in developmental disabilities, pathways to the use of emergency services by people with autism spectrum disorders, the impact of life events and trauma, and forensic issues. Currently, Anna is exploring applications of mindfulness-based interventions in supporting and treating people with developmental disabilities and their caregivers.

Barbara Peck, MA, MSW, works at the Victoria Women's Sexual Assault Centre as a counsellor and as the co-ordinator/trainer for the centre's TIPS (Trauma-Informed Practice and Support) program. She has been involved in the anti-violence movement for many years, and sees both her counselling practice and the TIPS program as a means of effecting social change. She has a background in physiological psychology and social work, and has also worked in the areas of head injury, women's health and career counselling. Currently, Barb is striving to ensure her work is more fully informed by an understanding of anti-oppressive practices.

Athina Perivolaris, RN, MN, is an advanced practice nurse at the Centre for Addiction and Mental Health (CAMH), specializing in mental health and geriatrics. She obtained her degrees from the University of Toronto, where she has a clinical appointment as adjunct lecturer with the Bloomberg Faculty of Nursing. Athina co-led CAMH's prevention of restraint and seclusion initiative, working for three years with stakeholders to develop and implement the restraint prevention strategic plan. She collaborated and consulted with external organizations embarking on their own restraint prevention initiatives. Athina is a team leader for the Registered Nurses' Association of Ontario best practice guideline *Promoting Safety: Alternative Approaches to the Use of Restraints.*

Ann Pottinger, RN, MN, graduated from the University of Toronto, where she has a clinical appointment as adjunct lecturer at the Bloomberg Faculty of Nursing. She is an assistant lecturer at the School of Nursing at York University and an advanced practice nurse at the Centre for Addiction and Mental Health (CAMH). Her areas of focus include geriatrics, mental health and health equity. She co-led the CAMH Restraint Minimization Taskforce and partnered with stakeholders to help shape CAMH's restraint prevention journey. Ann is co-author of "The End of Life" and "Mental Health Practice" in *The Health Care Professional's Guide to Clinical Cultural Competence* (Elsevier Canada, 2007).

Tammy Rasmussen, MSW, RSW, is a trauma therapist at the Jean Tweed Centre in Toronto. With more than 15 years of clinical experience, Tammy specializes in providing therapy to women whose lives have been affected by trauma and substance use and/or gambling. Tammy offers individual and group counselling to women, as well as consultation and training to service providers working concurrently with trauma and substance use and gambling issues. For the past four years, Tammy has been integrating sensorimotor psychotherapy into her practice, in addition to using other approaches, such as eye movement desensitization and reprocessing (EMDR), mindfulness, cognitive-behavioural therapy and energy psychology.

Cheryl Rolin-Gilman, RN, MN, CPMHN(C), is the advanced practice nurse with the Women's Program at the Centre for Addiction and Mental Health (CAMH). She is adjunct lecturer for the Lawrence S. Bloomberg Faculty of Nursing and the Department of Psychiatry at the University of Toronto. Her particular interest is in working with people with trauma histories. She has specialized training in dialectical behaviour therapy. In 2008, Cheryl co-authored *Clinical Supervision Handbook: A Guide for Clinical Supervisors for Addiction and Mental Health* with members of the professional practice group at CAMH and the Faculty of Social Work at the University of Toronto.

Susan Rosenkranz, MA, is a PhD candidate in the Department of Psychology at York University in Toronto. Her primary clinical and research interests are in the field of childhood traumatic stress. Her current research explores factors accounting for the connection between exposure to potentially traumatic events in childhood and the development of substance use problems during adolescence.

Diane Smylie, MSW, RSW, is working on the Connections Project (knowledge exchange for agencies serving women with substance use problems) with McMaster University in Hamilton, Ontario. She also works with the BC Centre of Excellence for Women's Health, supporting a provincial project to strengthen trauma-informed care in mental health and substance use services. Previously, Diane worked at the Jean Tweed Centre in Toronto, which provides programming for women with substance use problems and their families. She has more than 17 years of clinical and management experience in substance use services, including methadone maintenance and services for pregnant and parenting women.

Roberta K. Timothy, PhD, has used anti-oppression approaches for more than 20 years as a therapist, trainer, group facilitator, researcher, community organizer, professor and clinical supervisor in community and educational settings and in private practice. Her interests include critical expressive arts therapy, trauma and transgenerational violence, work culture and organizational change, resistance education and creative resistance. Roberta holds a bachelor's degree in political sciences, sociology and international justice and human rights, two master's degrees in political sciences and counselling psychology and a doctorate in adult education, community development and gender studies. She is doing a Social Sciences and Humanities Research Council of Canada post-doctoral fellowship in the Counselling Psychology Department at the University of Toronto.

Brenda Toner, PhD, completed her degree at the University of Toronto, followed by a post-doctoral fellowship in eating disorders. Brenda is a full professor in the Department of Psychiatry at the University of Toronto and graduate co-ordinator at the Institute of Medical Science in the university's Faculty of Medicine. She worked at CAMH for more than 25 years, more recently as a senior scientist and head of Women's Mental Health Research. Brenda has expertise in eating disorders, anxiety, depression, chronic pelvic pain, chronic fatigue, and irritable bowel syndrome, as well as psychosocial factors that affect women, such as violence, body dissatisfaction, discrimination and gender role socialization.

Mercedes Umaña, PhD candidate, has more than 20 years of experience facilitating personal, community and organizational development and healing processes locally and internationally as an educator, therapist, researcher and consultant. Her areas of interest include anti-oppression practice, community mental health, health psychology, trauma, post-traumatic growth, bereavement, HIV, intersectional analysis and research methodologies and knowledge translation. Mercedes holds a bachelor's degree and a master's degree in psychology and is a doctoral student in the Counselling Psychology Program at the University of Toronto. Mercedes has worked as a therapist at Women's Health and Women's Hands Community Health Centre for more than 10 years.

Cristine Urquhart, MSW, RSW, co-founder of Change Talk Associates, offers training and coaching across Canada in evidence-based communication practices that increase engagement and build motivation for health-related change. Passionate about improving the health of women, Cristine translates research to practice, integrating women-centred, motivational interviewing and trauma-informed approaches. She has worked with the BC Centre of Excellence for Women's Health as a trainer and program designer for various projects since 2005. Cristine is a member of the international Motivational Interviewing Network of Trainers, an instructor at the University of British Columbia and a contributing author to *Motivational Interviewing in Social Work Practice* (Guilford, 2011).

Carolyn Ussher, MSW, is the manager of client services at the Children's Aid Society of Toronto, where she has worked since 1994 in various roles, including front-line intake worker and supervisor for both intake and ongoing family services. Carolyn has a particular interest in improving child welfare service provision and co-ordination for children and families where substance use is a concern.

Linde Zingaro, PhD, completed her doctorate in educational studies at the University of British Columbia, where she won the IIQR Dissertation Award. Her thesis, "Speaking Out: Storytelling for Social Change," was published in 2008. Linde's academic efforts reflect her lifelong work in activist and advocacy roles: as administrator, educator and counsellor working with individuals and groups struggling with trauma and marginalization. After a decade of front-line work with street youth, she has maintained a private counselling practice in Vancouver for 26 years. Since 1992, she travels every year to Japan to work with women's groups and service providers dealing with child abuse and violence against women.

Milton Keynes UK
Ingram Content Group UK Ltd.
UKHW050720010724
444982UK00014B/977